1984 Yearbook of Agriculture
Animal Health

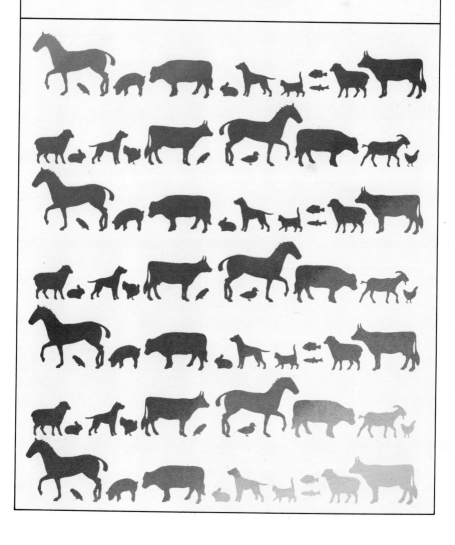

Animal Health
Livestock and Pets

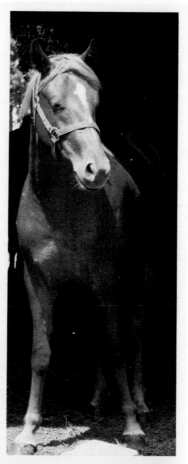

Animals receive nature's first protection through the antibodies in their mother's first milk. This is nature's way of protecting the young.

Before and after birth, owners must give nature a hand in developing and maintaining the health of domesticated animals. You as the owner are the key to your animal's health and welfare. Your personal commitment and knowledge of the basics— good housing, nutrition, sanitation and preventive medicine—are the most important first steps toward years of companionship or high profit margins.

Regardless of the number of animals you keep or your purpose in raising them, the basics of good health remain the same.

Housing is important to provide animals protection from the elements and predators as well as easy access to or a home base for your animals. Depending on your location, this can be as simple as shade, a small yard for a pet, or as expensive as a large confinement facility or a barn.

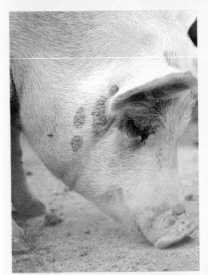

Although types of feed vary from open pasture to packaged commercial feed, basic nutritional needs remain the same for all animals—energy foods, protein, vitamins, minerals and lots of clean fresh water.

Clean cages, barns, aquariums and other animal facilities dramatically lessen the chance of disease or parasites in your animals. Preventing the entry of diseases from other locations through vehicles, equipment and clothing is also essential. Sanitation spells prevention.

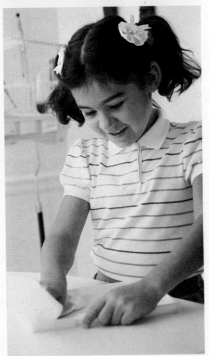

Grooming is a good preventive tool—to keep animals clean and free of external parasites. It's also a good way to observe the condition of your animals.

Preventive medicine is the final link in the circle of good animal health and includes vaccinations and internal and external parasite control.

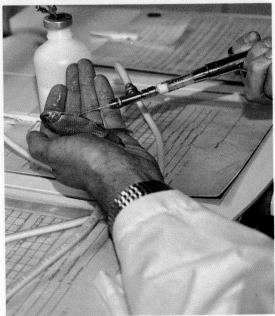

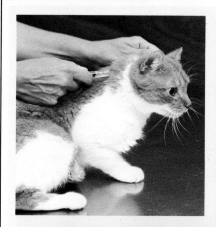

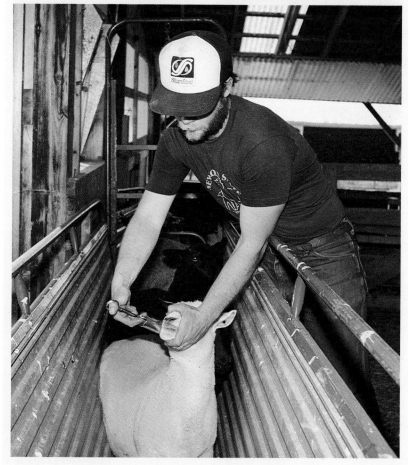

When you pick a veterinarian is up to you, but an early and continuing relationship is best. The veterinarian is not there just to help when your animal is sick or injured. He or she can help make sure things don't "go wrong."

Most practicing veterinarians are not only licensed by State veterinary medical boards, they are also accredited by Federal and State governments to participate in animal health programs. This is where government responsibility comes in. Government regulations are aimed at preventing the spread of diseases domestically or internationally. Your veterinarian will know what health certifications are required before you transport livestock or pets.

Poultry and Pet Birds . . .

Dairy and Beef Cattle . . .

Sheep and Goats . . .

Swine . . .

Fish . . .

Dogs and Cats . . .

Rabbits and Other Small Animals . . .

Horses . . .

You are the Key to their health.

Foreword

None of us takes animal health for granted, whether that health involves the livestock which represent a livelihood or the pets that have been entrusted to our care.

We can be proud that animals in the United States are among the healthiest in the world.

This book was written to provide helpful information on animal health to both pet owners and those who have livestock in their charge. There is something of interest here for nearly everyone.

It is appropriate that such a book should be published this year, the centennial of the creation of the Bureau of Animal Industry (BAI) in the U.S. Department of Agriculture. Congress created the bureau in 1884 in response to the petitions of frustrated farmers and ranchers whose livestock were so plagued with disease that overseas markets were refusing to buy from this country.

Today, the work of the original BAI is divided among several USDA agencies.

This book is an extension of that work and an expression of our continuing concern.

John R. Block
Secretary of Agriculture

Preface

This Yearbook should be of great value to livestock and pet owners, serving as a handy guide for their animals' health.

Americans spent $4.6 billion in 1982-83 for veterinary services, according to the American Veterinary Medical Association.

Expenditures for dogs, cats, other household pets, and horses accounted for 82 percent of that amount. In these categories dogs and cats had the biggest share.

Outlays for agricultural animal veterinary services totaled 18 percent, with the largest amounts going to cattle and poultry.

These figures reflect the deep concerns of owners for the health of their animals. Sharing those concerns are U.S. Department of Agriculture and other Federal agencies, land-grant universities and colleges, and other organizations both State and private. Wide-scale cooperation in the 1984 Yearbook of Agriculture came from all areas of concern.

Deep appreciation is expressed to the Committee that planned the book, and contributed much time and great expertise. The Committee consisted of:

Chairman—**Norvan L. Meyer,** *Animal and Plant Health Inspection Service (APHIS)*

David Batson, *Food and Drug Administration*

Irving Cashell, *former veterinary practitioner*

Dixon Hubbard, *Extension Service*

Jack Hyde, *Agricultural Research Service (ARS)*

Charles A. Kiddy, *ARS*

Dyarl King, *ARS*

Larry D. Mark, *APHIS*

Edward L. Menning, *National Association of Federal Veterinarians*

H. Graham Purchase, *ARS*

Dale Schwindaman, *APHIS*

Floyd Smith, *APHIS*

Jim A. Stunkard, *Director, Bowie Animal Hospital*

Marty Vanier, *Animal Health Institute*

Photo Coordinator—**Marie T. Sebrechts,** *APHIS*

Jack Hayes
Yearbook Editor

CONTENTS

I. INTRODUCTION

USDA

Marie T. Sebrechts   Kevin Shields

USDA   USDA-APHIS

Animal Health: Our Roles in Achieving It

By John K. Atwell

If you are reading this book, it is more than likely that you own one or more animals. It may be a single dog, cat or parakeet . . . or you may raise a thousand head of cattle. Regardless of the number of animals or your purpose in raising them, you are concerned with their health and welfare.

I can appreciate the concern of animal owners "officially" from my position as deputy administrator for veterinary services, Animal and Plant Health Inspection Service. Or I can evaluate the importance of animal health "professionally" as a veterinarian trained in the prevention and treatment of animal diseases.

But those "official" or "professional" approaches

John K. Atwell is Deputy Administrator for Veterinary Services, Animal and Plant Health Inspection Service.

don't count nearly as much as a person's own *personal* commitment, when the health of his or her animal is concerned. Services and programs provided by animal health officials and veterinarians respond to the fact that people care.

That fact comes through loud and clear whenever a rancher and a veterinarian work a herd side by side, or when a veterinary practitioner examines a pet in the presence of its owner. My own 10-year-old miniature poodle gives me a daily reminder of the personal importance of animal health.

This Yearbook of Agriculture is offered to people like you because you care about animal health. I hope it will serve you well as a useful reference on the diseases and pests of animals.

But before you put this book on your reference shelf, think for a moment about who

Introduction

is really responsible for animal health, and how those responsibilities are met.

Three Key Areas

Animal health means more than taking the necessary care, and calling the veterinarian when an animal is sick or injured. There are three important areas of responsibility: First, your responsibility, as owner or caretaker. Second, the responsibility of the veterinarian. And finally, the Government has a distinct and important role in assuring the health of animals.

You, as the owner or caretaker, have the most immediate responsibility. There's an old saying, "The eye of the master fattens the calf," which is to say that you are the one who best can provide the feed, water, shelter, sanitation and health care for your animal or animals. You are in the best position to know when "something goes wrong."

There is no substitute for personal commitment, and with it you can do a great deal. The fact that you are reading this book shows your awareness.

And there are other sources of information. Your cooperative extension service, through your county agent,

can provide helpful advice and a variety of publications. The State university and the State experiment station are also excellent sources. Beyond these institutions and agencies, there are feed suppliers and manufacturers of pharmaceuticals and veterinary biologics who publish information on the care of pets, livestock and poultry. Livestock and poultry associations can also help.

Armed with this information, you can handle most day-to-day needs. And you can learn about the need for preventive health care, such as vaccination and treatment against parasites.

But at some point, you need to call in the expert—your veterinarian. The veterinary practitioner is the animal health professional. His or her education has been long and rigorous, demanding a high commitment to scientific and professional discipline.

Good Ties Help

When you call the veterinarian is up to you, but an early and continuing relationship is best. This expert is able to diagnose and treat diseases that threaten your animals. More importantly, he or she can recommend and take preventive measures against dis-

Animal Health: Our Roles

eases, parasites and pests. The practitioner also can develop overall herd (or flock) health management plans; these deal with the total environment of livestock- or poultry-growing operations.

Veterinarians are not there just to help when things go wrong. They can help make sure that things don't go wrong.

They also have another responsibility of which most people are unaware: Reporting certain diseases to the Government, either because they are of public health significance, or because they are regulated under Government animal health programs. In addition, they may examine animals, conduct tests, and sign vaccination and health certificates under these programs.

Most practicing veterinarians not only are licensed by veterinary medical boards of the various States, they are accredited by Federal and State Governments to participate in these animal health programs.

This is where Government responsibility comes in.

The Government is mandated to prevent, control and eradicate several types of diseases. These include animal diseases that can be transmit-

ted to man, such as rabies, brucellosis (undulant fever), psitticosis (parrot fever), and tuberculosis.

Some diseases are of economic importance to the livestock and poultry industries, and cannot be controlled solely by practicing veterinarians. And finally, there are potentially catastrophic foreign diseases that could wreck our domestic livestock and poultry industries if they were to become established in this country.

Control Capabilities

To appreciate the role of the Government, we need to look at the disease control capabilities, respectively, of owners, the veterinary practitioner, and the animal health official.

Owners can do a great deal to keep pets and livestock free of disease, especially through good preventive measures. They can limit contacts with potential sources of infection. But such measures provide no complete guarantee, especially when new animals are added to a herd or flock, pets or livestock travel to and from shows, or neighboring herds and flocks become infected.

The veterinarian can treat individual animals, or all the animals in a herd, and may succeed in eliminating individual cases of a particular disease, or through vaccination may provide protection against exposure to some diseases.

But the practitioner may have little power, as one individual, to stop some highly contagious diseases that spread from herd to herd, or wherever animals are bought or sold. Practitioners can advise farmers on sanitation and disease precautions, but some disease organisms still may move to new sites in dirt or manure on vehicles, equipment, boots and clothing. Practitioners can prescribe treatments against disease-causing ticks and mites, but may have little power to stop their overall spread.

Gene Alexander

So it falls to the Government to stop the spread of highly contagious diseases, and to eliminate them where practical means exist. It's the Government's job because these diseases can be controlled only when animal movements are regulated, and the Government alone has the authority to impose such regulations. And it's not until such regulations are in force that the owner and practitioner can feel secure in the care and treatment of individual animals and herds.

The Government's primary job is to stop or severely restrict movement of infected and exposed animals. Examinations are required and specific tests prescribed to locate infected flocks. Health tests and certification assure that animals are free of those diseases when they are sold or shipped. The Government also can specify conditions and limits for vaccinations, and may require identification of animals moving in marketing channels.

Regulations specify the proper disposal or slaughter of infected and exposed animals. Inspection and testing of animals at slaughter further support Government disease eradication programs—as well as assuring consumers that the meat they buy is safe, wholesome and accurately labeled.

Foreign Diseases

This kind of protection also must include foreign animal diseases. This means strictly regulating the importation of livestock, poultry and their products.

Some foreign diseases are so contagious and so destructive that all susceptible livestock from affected countries are barred from entry into the United States. For virtually all other livestock and poultry, foreign government veterinarians must inspect, test and certify that they are free of communicable diseases. Our own animal health officials check the animals again at our ports of entry. Most shipments also must pass port-of-entry quarantines, except at Canadian and Mexican border crossings.

Then too the Government regulates manufacture and distribution of veterinary pharmaceuticals and biologics, and the use of some feed additives. This assures users that products do what they are supposed to do, have no harmful side effects or residues, and are free of contamination. It is added protection for livestock and poultry, and pets as well.

Introduction

Humane Care

And beyond disease-preventing activities, there has evolved Government responsibility for the humane care of certain animals that are marketed wholesale, used for research, exhibited in shows and zoos, or transported on common carriers.

The three levels of responsibility—owner, veterinarian and Government official—effectively complement one another. Without each of these, we would not enjoy the outstanding animal health that we do today.

Thanks to owners across the country, our livestock and poultry industries are among the most productive in the world.

Trained Corps

We are served by a corps of highly educated veterinarians, who are equipped with the most modern facilities, and backed up by a highly reliable network of diagnostic laboratories.

And thanks to Government animal health programs, we have eradicated 12 major diseases of livestock and poultry within the past century. Beyond that, we have kept devastating foreign diseases away from our shores.

Animal health is no accident.

We can look back to positive acts that led to the animal health conditions we can enjoy today. We can look back to establishment of the U.S. Department of Agriculture (USDA) in 1862, to formation of the American Veterinary Medical Association in 1863, to the Nation's first graduate Veterinary Medical School at Iowa State University in 1879, and to establishment of the Bureau of Animal Industry within USDA in 1884.

Supportive organizations have been established over the years, such as the U.S. Livestock Sanitary Association in 1897 (now the U.S. Animal Health Association) and many livestock and poultry associations.

Events such as these marked the way to better animal health. But most of all it was, and still is, the concern of countless animal owners such as you that assure better care for all types of animals.

"The eye of the master fattens the calf." That eye has seen the need for trained veterinarians, for scientific research, and for coordinated animal health programs— with government, veterinarians and owners acting together.

Animal Health: Our Roles

Barring the Door to Foreign Disease

By Edwin I. Pilchard

Preventing foreign disease outbreaks in cattle, other livestock, and poultry requires cooperation by all who import animals or unsterilized animal products from affected countries. Prevention also requires that no one brings or sends prohibited animal products or prohibited souvenirs into the United States.

Failure to comply with Federal animal import laws could have devastating consequences for producers and consumers. Violators may be prosecuted, fined, and even imprisoned.

Information on animal import regulations may be obtained from the U.S. Department of Agriculture's veterinarian-in-charge for each

State, or by contacting the USDA Import-Export Staff in Hyattsville, Md.

Traveler's Tips

Travelers planning to enter or re-enter the United States from foreign countries should familiarize themselves with the information in a valuable little booklet titled "Traveler's Tips." This booklet can be obtained free by writing to APHIS Information, 732 Federal Building, Hyattsville, Md. 20782.

Federal laws aimed at foreign animal disease prevention are enforced through an inspection network that includes the U.S. Customs Service and USDA.

Working around the clock at ports, airports and border crossings, USDA inspectors examined 306,000 airplanes, 51,000 oceangoing vessels, 60 million motor vehicles from Mexico, 128 million pieces of passenger luggage, and

---

Edwin I. Pilchard is a Principal Staff Officer, Veterinary Services, Animal and Plant Health Inspection Service.

Introduction

178,000 mailed packages of agricultural interest in 1983. From this, they seized and destroyed 274,000 unauthorized animal products.

Despite these and other preventive actions, foreign animal diseases sometimes have reached the United States.

For example, exotic Newcastle disease has entered by way of smuggled pet birds each year since 1971, except 1976. Each entry was followed by prompt diagnosis and eradication, without reaching domestic poultry. However, a 1971 outbreak of exotic New-

castle disease in Southern California poultry cost $56 million to eradicate.

More recently, in 1983, type 2 bluetongue disease was discovered in some Florida cattle.

What should the animal owner do when a foreign disease is suspected?
First, promptly call a qualified, licensed veterinarian or, if one is not available, call the State or Federal Veterinarian, and request a diagnosis.

Since many serious foreign diseases resemble less

Fred S. Witte

Barring Foreign Diseases

serious domestic ones, a final diagnosis often requires laboratory testing of appropriate specimens.

Specially trained foreign animal disease diagnosticians are available throughout the country to make followup examinations and collect the proper specimens, as soon as the State or Federal veterinarian decides that the suspected disease may be foreign. As one can readily appreciate, the animal owner, veterinarian, and diagnostic laboratory are our first line of defense against a foreign disease that has entered the country.

Some Precautions

— Avoid moving any animals, animal products, feed, or bedding from the premises when a contagious disease is present

— If a foreign disease is suspected, do not move sick or dead animals to a laboratory

— Instead, have the proper specimens collected and submitted by a qualified, trained veterinarian

— Do not permit service representatives, friends, neighbors, or others to visit the suspected animals, and avoid any other activity whereby the disease agent might be accidentally carried away to infect additional herds.

The National emergency 24-hour telephone number for reporting suspected foreign animal diseases is area code 301, 436-8092.

What happens when a foreign animal disease is confirmed by a Federal laboratory?

The Secretary of Agriculture is promptly advised of the situation by the chief veterinary officer of the United States. The Secretary may then declare a National animal disease emergency if the seriousness of the situation justifies such action.

With an official emergency declaration, special funds and personnel can be made available immediately to combat the disease outbreak. Disease eradication operations include industry and State representatives in federally operated Regional Emergency Animal Disease Eradication Organizations (READEO's).

In years when there are no actual outbreaks of emergency animal diseases, the READEO managers and technical specialists maintain emergency preparedness by simulating outbreaks in national test exercises.

II. BACKYARD POULTRY AND PET BIRDS

Planning Helps Avoid Problems

By Edward T. Mallinson

A variety of official rules exist to control the movement of birds. You should know what regulations might affect your bird or flock when transporting them nationally or internationally.

USDA-APHIS

To have the most fun and obtain the most profit from keeping backyard poultry or pet birds, you need to do some planning. But first, it is important to be aware that poultry and other birds (avian species) are subject to the

Edward T. Mallinson is Associate Professor, Virginia-Maryland Regional College of Veterinary Medicine, University of Maryland campus, College Park. He is chief editor/writer for this section.

same general sorts of laws and regulations that affect other types of pets and livestock. Second, bear in mind that sound economic principles apply to avian operations as they do to other business ventures. Third, plan to manage poultry and birds with care and skill to protect both their health and yours.

The following serves as an introduction to the planning needed to ensure that your avian experience is as safe and enjoyable as possible.

Laws, Regulations

Backyard poultry, including game birds and waterfowl, and most of the various assortments of pet or hobby birds need to comply with a variety of official rules. These may be local ordinances, state regulations, or laws developed by Congress. Various departments of agriculture, interior, wildlife, commerce, and health may be involved. Rulings frequently deal with health certifications and tests for poultry or birds transported within a state (intrastate rules), between states (interstate), and into or away from the United States (international).

Your State Veterinarian knows the rulings that would affect your bird or flock. Contact your State Department of Agriculture for the address and telephone number. Your local librarian also may be of considerable assistance.

Know the rules before you start, especially if you are involved in buying, selling, dealing, trading, showing, shipping, breeding or hatching. Watch for zoning ordinances.

Economic Aspects

– Home-produced eggs and poultry meat generally are more expensive than those available at food stores. Personal enjoyment and other values may, however, be more important to you.

– Know your market before you start. Have a good idea of who will buy, sell, or process what you produce.

– Identify sources for specialty and medicated feeds needed for your flock or aviary. Locate one and preferably two dependable suppliers.

– Consider annual purchase of started pullets for egg production. This may save you complexities and problems common to rearing your flock from 1 day of age on up.

– Obtain details on the proper processing, storage and refrigeration of poultry and eggs if you intend to have sufficient production for retail sales. Your county Cooperative Extension agent can supply excellent guidance.

Veterinary Help

Before beginning, locate a source of competent veterinary help. With or without a disease outbreak, professional guidance can help in many ways.

State veterinary medical associations (address and phone number often available from State Veterinarians or local librarians) can fre-

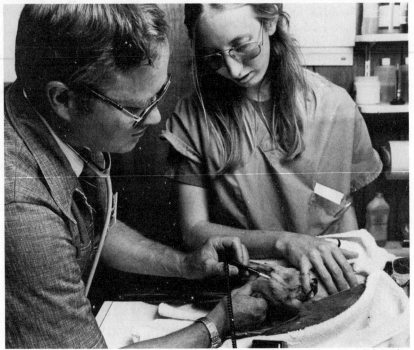

Marie T. Sebrechts

Proper avian health care should include regularly scheduled visits to the veterinarian, so be sure to locate a source of competent veterinary help in your area.

quently help pet bird owners and backyard poultry producers locate a veterinary practitioner specializing in avian medicine.

Most States operate several diagnostic laboratories handling poultry and other birds. These laboratories often provide their services free of charge. Many operate under auspices of your State university or college of veterinary medicine. Your State department of agriculture or State Veterinarian will guide you to those diagnostic laboratories closest to you.

Most states operate several diagnostic laboratories handling poultry and other birds.

USDA-APHIS

Your Health Risks

Be aware that, as with most other similar activities, there are some health risks.

– People can become exposed to avian tuberculosis from poultry, including game birds, kept over 2 years of age.

– Humans working with Newcastle disease infected poultry birds may develop an eye and eyelid inflammation (conjunctivitis) that should be treated by a physician.

– Turkeys and other poultry or birds may be the source of erysipeloid skin infections in people slaughtering or otherwise handling infected stock.

– Psittacosis can be transmitted from the avian species to humans. The risks can be minimized by purchasing quality stock and avoiding dirty or dusty environmental conditions which allow fecal material to become suspended in the air.

– Control dustiness when cleaning old poultry buildings or bird roosts. Use respirators and lightly wet litter to help prevent human histoplasmosis, a serious respiratory infec-

Barry Fitzgerald

Backyard poultry and pet bird owners close to commercial flocks have a responsibility to their neighbors whose entire livelihood depends on poultry production, since so many avian diseases are readily transmissible from one species to the other.

tion originating from certain molds that like to grow in the soil and in old avian droppings.

Neighborliness
Remember that disease can affect all types of birds, and all types of people keep birds. Disease outbreaks never discriminate. They directly or indirectly hurt everybody. The disease prevention steps outlined in the following chapter serve as your guide to protecting not only your flock but the flocks of others near and far who care about avian health and depend on poultry and other birds for family income and companionship. Good neighbors are good soldiers in disease prevention.

Preventing Disease

By Edward T. Mallinson

No other consideration is more central than disease prevention for a healthy, satisfying flock of commercial, semi-commercial, hobby or pet birds of any type.

Disease prevention focuses primarily on dedicated planning and sound management practices that keep infectious diseases out in the first place and stops noninfectious diseases before they start. With this approach, you place a higher priority on planning and expenditures for disease prevention than on short-term savings and stop-gap treatments.

It is more than a list of long- and short-range health protection and preservation practices. It is essentially a

Edward T. Mallinson is Associate Professor, Virginia-Maryland Regional College of Veterinary Medicine, University of Maryland campus, College Park.

mental attitude that recognizes the ever-present risk of disease and the fact that disease prevention doesn't cost; it pays—and many times over.

Failure to concentrate first on planned disease prevention often leads to personal disappointment and sometimes disastrous financial loss. In contrast, a flock with good health security management is a delight, and a source of both pride and profit.

Basic Areas

This type of management encompasses seven basic considerations: Confinement, proper nutrition, top quality replacements, isolation and segregation, cleanout and cleanup, stress management, and well-reasoned medication.

Confinement. Regardless of the size of a flock, its health is most secure when it is confined to a fenced-in pen at least, and preferably to a fully enclosed shelter. Poultry al-

Regardless of the size of a flock, its health is most secure when it is confined to a fenced-in pen at least, and preferably confined to a fully enclosed shelter.

USDA-APHIS
Kevin Shields

Clean fresh water and feed should be readily available as a key part of proper nutrition to keep your birds healthy. Allow sufficient space to enable birds to tilt head to swallow naturally.

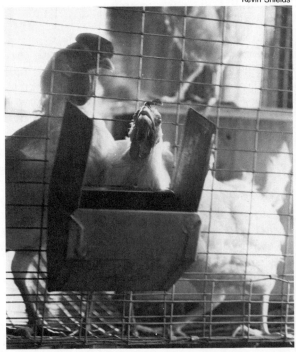

lowed to run loose as scavengers often have a diet insufficient to maintain peak growth and performance. Far fewer eggs are produced and they frequently may be lost, stolen or broken. Stray poultry become exposed to diseases in wild birds and neighboring flocks, bringing disease back home and to other farms.

Confinement further protects poultry and other birds from weather extremes, dogs, cats and many other predators. But most importantly it puts you in control of what your flock eats, the second priority in disease prevention.

Nutrition. A commercial poultry ration is a miracle of modern research and manufacturing. Today's poultry mashes and pellets are nutritionally complete with proper balances of essential proteins, grains, vitamins and minerals for outstanding growth, health and productivity. Similar excellent commercially produced feeds are gradually becoming available to keepers of caged or other exotic birds. Commercial feeds should always be fed according to manufacturers' instructions.

Do not be misled by the cheapness or attractiveness of grains or old-time practices, or throwing birds some "scratch feed" and letting them fend for themselves. Commercial feeds provide your birds with their best opportunity to build a constitution that will resist infection and achieve inherited capacities for extraordinary performance. But if you must feed grains, be sure to provide grit.

Water, Vitamins

An ample, cool, clean, regularly available supply of drinking water also is a key part of proper nutrition, protecting the sensitive function of the avian kidney and its water-balance mechanisms. Scant, dirty or warm water often leads to low water consumption, poor feed utilization, metabolic stress and kidney failure.

Generally, 1- to 21-day-old fowl benefit from vitamins added to their drinking water. Commercial vitamin supplements that can be added to the drinking water are available from most feed suppliers.

Quality Replacements. Birds with inherited capacities for top growth and productivity are available to the owners of small poultry flocks from hatcheries, dealers and pullet suppliers participating in the National Poultry Improvement Plan (NPIP).

Enormous progress has been made by participating

Chuck Herron

Know your source! Does this seller know about the disease, genetic, husbandry and sanitation backgrounds of these birds? If you're not sure, don't buy.

Emblems used to identify breeders, hatcheries and dealers participating in the National Poultry Improvement Plan.

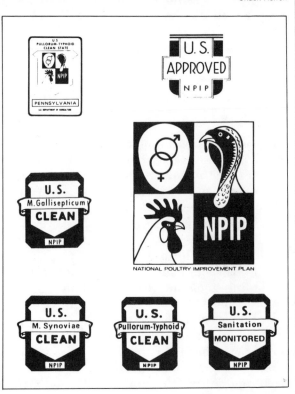

chicken, turkey, game bird and waterfowl breeders and university and U.S. Department of Agriculture researchers over the past 50 years. The result is the ready availability of stock with amazing durability and outstanding growth and egg production rates. Modern broilers weigh 4.3 pounds in only 8 weeks and today's layers annually produce 260 or more eggs per hen housed.

High-producing commercial strains of chickens often are available from local hatcheries. Specify whether you want egg-type, meat-type or dual-purpose type chicks or pullets. Each type has been scientifically developed for each production purpose.

Pet Bird Progress

Breeding and health improvement progress is becoming more evident among breeders and dealers of pet birds (finches, parakeets, cockatoos, etc.). Programs such as the proposed National Cage and Aviary Bird Improvement Plan (NCABIP), which is similar in concept to the NPIP for poultry types, are anticipated in the near future for pet bird types.

Poultry available from NPIP classified sources have been free for many years from pullorum disease and fowl typhoid, diseases very destructive to baby chicks and growing fowl. The same cannot be said for unclassified stock you may be tempted to buy from nonparticipating auctions, dealers, hucksters, or untested custom or neighborhood hatcheries. Further, NPIP hatcheries and dealers often supply stock free of various avian mycoplasma infections, and other diseases responsible for death losses in broilers and turkeys, poor egg production in laying chickens, and chronic colds in all types.

Poultry sold under NPIP and pet-type birds under hopefully forthcoming NCABIP emblems must comply with State-Federal verification programs that assure that health standards cooperatively developed by breeders, scientists and the government are being met.

So, ensure your flock or collection's health security. Watch for poultry and other birds advertised and sold bearing nationally recognized emblems of NPIP or NCABIP special attainment. Do not lose your advantageous disease prevention position by restocking with unclassified, unrecognized, possibly diseased or smuggled stock. Their disease, genetic, hus-

Preventing Disease

bandry and sanitation backgrounds may be questionable.

Names, Addresses

The names and addresses of NPIP or equivalent sources are available from your State Department of Agriculture, the U.S. Department of Agriculture, Room 828, FCB #1, Hyattsville, MD 20782, or your local Cooperative Extension Service agent. The latter can be found in your telephone directory under "county government" or your county's name.

Isolation, Segregation.

When people, equipment and poultry or other birds circulate or travel from one farm or location to another, the stage is set for obvious or hidden but always costly introduction of disease. The same is true when birds of one type are kept close to others of a different type or allowed to intermingle or mix.

If you do not practice flock isolation, you give bacteria, viruses, and other disease-producing agents repeated opportunities to spread from other premises to yours.

Fowl or bird pox, Newcastle disease, coryza, mycoplasmosis, laryngotracheitis, fowl cholera and salmonellosis are examples of a few diseases that may spread to your oper-

ations if your flock is not isolated from outside visitors, borrowed equipment and poultry or other birds from other locations. This can best be done by severely reducing human traffic (visitors and servicemen, etc.) between other poultry or pet bird operations and yours.

Visitors should wear freshly cleaned coveralls and hats and disinfected boots. Borrowed or used equipment needs to be thoroughly cleaned and disinfected, not missing reasonably accessible interior parts.

Mixture Problems

If you raise a mixture of types of poultry or birds or allow wild birds to mingle with your flock you are inviting disease. This is because disease agents that ordinarily are mild in or infect only one type obtain an opportunity to become more contagious to the type(s) you are keeping.

For example this happens when Pacheco's disease, a hidden infection in conures (medium-sized South or Central American hook-bills), makes contact with susceptible cockatoos or parrots and produces devastating outbreaks of psittacine herpes virus infection.

It may also happen when wild waterfowl mingle with or

22

Visitors to your flocks should wear freshly cleaned coveralls and disinfected boots, so that they don't carry any disease problems in from other flocks which they have visited.

Marie T. Sebrechts

get close to domestic waterfowl, game birds, turkeys or chickens. Then, strains of avian influenza virus, ordinarily very mild in wild waterfowl, are given the opportunity to modify and become so damaging to their new host that they may produce plague-like disease.

Types of Newcastle disease virus that may be mild in cage pet birds can be devastating when they infect poultry. Histomonas parasites spread from chickens, where it is an almost hidden disease, to turkeys where severe losses occur.

These are only a few of numerous examples of how mixing species is bad disease prevention. As scientists learn more about the viruses and bacteria afflicting cage pet and wild birds, the list of infections that spread when species or types mix or are raised too close undoubtedly will increase.

At a minimum, keep different types or species totally separated in distant pens or buildings or different farms. Ordinarily you are wise to specialize in raising only one type. Along with increasing your skill with the type selected from specialization, you will limit contact with other types and their diseases.

Preventing Disease

You are wise to specialize in raising only one type or species of bird. Along with increasing your skill with the type selected, you will limit potentially dangerous contact with other types and their diseases.

Chuck Herron

Marie T. Sebrechts

When restocking your operation, use healthy day-old or started stock from a single source.

Cleanout and Cleanup.

This key disease prevention practice is also known as all in, all-out management.

Pet bird breeders, dealers, and shop owners also can benefit from this approach.

To gain the benefits of this procedure, if you are a backyard poultry owner, you need to sell, process or otherwise depopulate your entire flock or operation every 12 to 18 months. No birds should be left over as favorites or pets as this defeats the purpose of a complete cleanout. Meat from processing a flock can be frozen or canned for later consumption.

The entire house, pens or runs and all equipment in or near this area then should be carefully cleaned and disinfected. Details are provided under sanitation procedures in the chapter on general management requirements in this section.

These steps are brought to their successful conclusion by restocking your operation with healthy day-old or started stock from a single source. New additions should not be made until the next cleanout.

The total cleanout aspect of this recommendation is not ordinarily practical for keepers of fancy or show poultry

Chuck Herron

Cleanout and cleanup stop disease cycles that can persist and magnify from year to year.

breeding stock or a few pet birds. Nonetheless, it could be done, in part, by moving prized breeders or pets to a temporary location for later return after cleaning and disinfection have been completed.

Cleanup and cleanout stops disease cycles which persist and magnify from year to year when an entire flock is not entirely depopulated. Failure to practice this disease prevention step soon leads to progressively severe exposure of chicks, baby or immature fowl, or pet birds to an ever

Preventing Disease

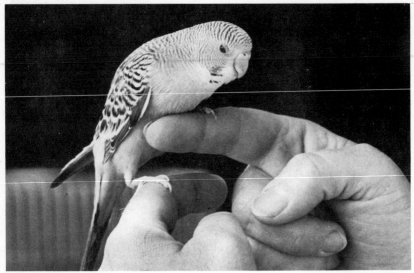

Kevin Shields

Scientists are proving that gentle handling, "talking to" and hand-feeding pets provide a life climate that is supportive to health, increasing an animal's ability to adjust to change and resist disease. Excessive babying can, however, be detrimental to avian health.

increasing assortment of harmful viruses, bacteria, mycoplasmas, molds, and parasites which build up in older birds and their surroundings.

Stress Management. Extreme or sudden changes from normal conditions produce a strain or stress on poultry and bird health. On the other hand, less severe change can be beneficial.

Consequently, variations in room temperatures, feeds,

new pen mates, and caretakers may be made safely and often to advantage, provided they are modest and gradual.

Gentle Handling

Good managers plan their changes well ahead to avoid the disadvantages of excess stress and to capitalize on well-managed change. They also know, as scientists are proving, that gentle handling, "talking to" and hand-feeding their stock or pets provide a life climate that is supportive to health, increasing an animal's ability to adjust to change and resist disease. However, excessive babying or absence of any stress or change can be detrimental to avian health.

Vitamin supplementation and low-level antibiotics are often given in the feed or drinking water at times of unavoidable stress, such as moving time, breeding season, and when the weather becomes especially uncomfortable.

Medication and Vaccination. Because of their extra ability to persist in poultry and pet bird surroundings and populations, certain diseases require use of low level, highly refined and tested drugs for their control. Consequently, limited, well-reasoned medication should be considered in most disease prevention plans. Vaccination—a common poultry production technique which stimulates poultry or birds to develop their own natural, active immunity to disease— also has a place in these plans.

In growing chickens, for example, a disease prevention plan ordinarily includes the use of feeds containing medications (coccidiostats) to pre-

vent coccidiosis, a growth-retarding and occasionally fatal intestinal disease, and day-old vaccination against Marek's disease, an often fatal tumorous disease usually occurring between 8 to 24 weeks of age.

In turkeys, dietary medication for histomoniasis (blackhead), an ever-threatening liver and intestinal disease on turkey farms, is a basic part of turkey health security management when used along with other preventive practices that will be described later in this section.

Reports from aviary operations and veterinarians indicate that well-reasoned, planned preventive antibiotic medication programs may be used for control of respiratory diseases in selected pet bird distribution and breeding operations.

Current research soon may make vaccination against Pacheco's parrot disease a valuable practical procedure for many hook-billed birds (psittacines).

Casual Use Risky

It is important to distinguish between casual use of medications and their careful use as part of a well-reasoned health management program. Too often owners, by habit, curiosity or force of attractive ad-

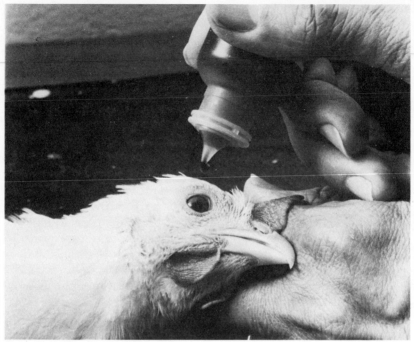

Norman Pruitt, University of Maryland

Vaccination is an important and relatively easy method of preventing a variety of poultry diseases, but should be well-planned and used in moderation.

vertisements, begin to rely more and more on antibiotics and other drugs to control all flock problems. The result can be an unfortunate rearrangement of basic priorities, increased operating costs, and the loss of advantages gained when basic disease prevention practices are the true foundation of a flock's health.

In contrast, use of well-recognized programs of medication and vaccination serve as a final link in the circle of health management practices that keep disease either completely out or at very low and easily managed levels.

Nutritional Diseases

By Edward T. Mallinson

This chapter applies to nutritional diseases affecting both backyard poultry and pet birds. Nutritional problems are being given special attention here because of their common occurrence in small flocks and pet birds.

Some of the more commonly recognized deficiency diseases are: Rickets, starvation, vitamin A deficiency (nutritional roup), perosis, gout, vitamin E deficiency, obesity, nutritional myopathy (white muscle disease) and an assortment of skin, reproductive, feathering and eggshell abnormalities.

In a majority of cases, these diseases can be prevented with the regular use of freshly manufactured, com-

Edward T. Mallinson is Associate Professor, Virginia-Maryland Regional College of Veterinary Medicine, University of Maryland campus, College Park.

mercial feed. Do not feed such commercial feeds skimpily, with table scraps or along with appreciable amounts of corn or other grains. Those practices put the commercial mix out of balance and start problems that would have been avoided if you had relied primarily on the commercially balanced feed.

Occasional treats, as with people, are all right, but you are better off to base 95 percent of your poultry diet on commercially produced complete rations.

Fruit, vegetables, and dairy products may need to be considered for hook-bills and songbirds because certain common seed preparations may be deficient in several essential nutrients.

Rickets. One scientific term for rickets is osteomalacia, which means bone softening. It is caused by a lack or imbalance of calcium or phosphorus or a deficiency or dete-

Nutrition is extremely important for your pet's health. Hook-bills and songbirds can benefit from supplemental vegetables, fruits and dairy products.

Kevin Shields

rioration of vitamin D_3.

Affected poultry or birds, especially the young, develop a lame, stiff-legged gait or may rest excessively in a squatting position. There is also decreased growth. Beaks may be easily bent from side to side. Leg and wing bones may become softened, bowed or twisted.

Rickets, one of the commonest nutritional deficiencies in small flocks and birds of prey (raptors), usually responds well to extra oyster shell or coarse limestone in the diet and additional vita-

min D_3. Vitamin D_2, a form of vitamin D that may be given to children, dogs, cats, and livestock, is not effective with poultry and birds.

Starvation. Death losses from severe shortages of sufficient feed to provide the protein and energy necessary to support life processes still occur. It most frequently is encountered when stock is allowed to free-range in areas with scant vegetation, and during winter months when feed intake must be especially high to maintain normal body temperature.

Hatchling Problems

Starvation or starve-outs also is found in 1- to 2-week-old stock when they fail to start eating very soon after hatching and then lose sufficient energy to be active enough subsequently to find food.

Extremes of brooding temperatures may drive hatchlings away from their feed and lead to starvation. Incorrect size and misplacement of feeders also can make feed inaccessible and lead to the same end.

Low-grade marginal starvation and poor performance have been linked to diets containing excess fiber. This may occur under free-range conditions or when bargain, high fiber feeds are used.

"Stress lines" may be seen in wing feathers of pet birds that have missed feedings. Attention to detail and "watching your birds" are the best ways to prevent starve-outs.

Vitamin A Deficiency. Another term for vitamin A deficiency is nutritional roup, which basically means a chronic cold-like or respiratory condition of nutritional origin.

Affected poultry or pet birds—usually but not always the relatively young—first become droopy and soon develop swollen, sore eyelids that may be sticky with thick or cheesy discharges from the inside eyelid surfaces (conjunctiva). Similar heavy discharges may be found in and around the nostrils or may accumulate in facial sinuses, producing a swollen face.

Whitish-yellow mouth sores may be seen in severe cases.

Guidance on Roup

Seek professional guidance if you suspect nutritional roup in poultry or other birds. Several important infectious diseases which may look like this disease will require special treatment and attention.

Vitamin A deficiency may require vitamin A injections. Less severe cases are treated with addition of multiple-vitamin water-dispersible supplements to the drinking water.

Your risk can be reduced by purchasing or preparing feed in relatively small quantities. Extended storage of feed *before* or *after* you make a purchase can lead to a breakdown of vitamin A and other essential vitamins.

Perosis. Also known as slipped tendon or manganese deficiency, perosis is a leg deformity involving the hocks. This problem often results from the interplay of inherited, management, and nutri-

Nutritional Diseases

USDA-APHIS

It is important to maintain correct size and placement of feeders so that feed is readily accessible and none of your birds starve.

Kevin Shields

tional factors. It is mainly seen in small flocks fed non-commercial feeds or unsupplemented diets based mainly on corn.

Crowding or other conditions, such as brooding on newspapers, other slippery surfaces or rearing on unnatural walking surfaces, brings out any tendencies for slipped tendon. Heavy, fast-growing chickens and turkeys are apt

Generally it is much safer to oversupply than undersupply waterer space. Extra water in locations where your birds tend to congregate most heavily during different times of the day or night can pay big health and productivity dividends.

to develop perosis if nutritional and management precautions are not taken.

Acute Gout. Water deficiency is one of the major causes of acute gout and kidney failure in poultry. A similar disease sometimes is seen in parakeets.

Kidney Failure

The disease usually is characterized by sudden losses, darkening of the head and shanks, dry and somewhat shrunken breast muscles, and speckling of the surfaces of many internal organs with chalky, white, extremely tiny needle-like urate crystals. Kidney failure is at the base of the development of these crystals in most instances and although many other infectious and noninfectious or toxic conditions may lead to this failure, none is more common or potentially damaging than a lack of drinking water.

Provision of extra water fountains on warm days in the summer or in cold weather, when overall feed intake is high, will go a long way to protect the kidneys of poultry and birds. Water intake will be suppressed if the water offered is dirty, too hot or too cold.

Vitamin E Deficiency. This disease is also known as encephalomalacia, which means brain softening or degeneration. Usually it is seen in the young as a nervous disorder characterized by loss of balance, falling over backwards while flapping the wings and other disturbances of head, neck or leg control.

Stale or rancid feed with deterioration in vitamin E is the usual cause. Most commercial mixes contain antioxidants to prevent this deterioration, so it generally is not a problem if poultry or bird feed is fed within 4 to 6 weeks of manufacture. Always store your feed in a cool, dry place (a refrigerator, if convenient) to reduce vitamin E or other quality losses.

Nutritional Myopathy. This disease is also known as white muscle disease because of the yellow-to-grayish-white color that can be observed in degenerated breast muscles in chickens and gizzard muscles of turkeys. It is suspected that large hook-bills, cranes, and other birds may experience the disorder.

Inadequate Selenium

Nutritional myopathy is often the result of a combined deficiency of vitamin E and inadequate levels of the trace mineral selenium.

Corn or other grains raised east of the Mississippi River reportedly are low in selenium and appear to be associated with the occurrence of nutritional myopathy. Feed manufacturers generally take special precautions to assure that their feeds supply adequate levels of selenium.

Obesity. This occurs in pet birds and some strains of table egg layers when maintained in cages. It is most prevalent in caged layers during summer months when they tend to consume more energy-rich feed than they really need.

Birds on a sunflower seed diet frequently become obese. Birds or poultry so affected usually do not perform to their maximum potential and may be more prone to heatstroke or reproductive problems.

Most layer feeds manufactured for summer feeding take into account the need to lower the energy level. Wheat bran sometimes is substituted for part of the corn. This must be done with care as an excess may reduce egg production.

Abnormalities. Nutritional deficiencies in poultry or other birds, besides causing the disorders just described, also may produce serious skin, reproductive, feathering, or eggshell abnormalities.

Pantothenic acid and biotin vitamin deficiencies may result in skin inflammation,

crusty accumulations around the eyes and mouth, and cracked skin between the toes and on the bottom of the feet.

Nearly any deficiency may alter reproductive fertility or egg hatchability, and a number of dietary problems such as starvation and certain amino acid deficiencies may cause feather loss or loss of normal feather color patterns. Soft-shelled or thin-shelled eggs are not uncommonly the result of deficiencies of calcium or vitamin D_3.

Confusing Symptoms

Unfortunately, symptoms of these deficiencies resemble certain parasitic, bacterial, or viral diseases or poisonings common to backyard poultry and pet birds. As a result, whenever you observe these symptoms you should obtain a professional diagnosis to get on track for treatment and future prevention.

In general, it is best to avoid home compounded do-it-yourself type rations. Most well-known, commercially prepared feeds are superior in quality to unplanned, self-mixed feeds. The home operator rarely has the experience, the selection of ingredients, or the necessary quality control resources available to today's feed manufacturers.

Infectious Diseases

By Edward T. Mallinson

Infectious diseases ordinarily are produced by protozoa, bacteria, viruses, parasites, or fungi. Their accurate diagnosis frequently requires expert laboratory analysis.

Protozoan diseases are produced by single-celled animals that can be seen as small and usually rounded creatures when magnified 40 times their size in a common light microscope. They frequently attack the digestive tract of most types of poultry and pet birds. They are involved also in producing malaria-like infections of the blood of pigeons, cockatoos, and other pet birds.

Digestive protozoan infections such as coccidiosis, trichomoniasis, histomoniasis, hexamitiasis, and giardiasis

ordinarily are prevented by keeping poultry or birds off the ground and on dry deep fresh litter or in cages where exposure to droppings is almost totally prevented.

Keeping waterers clean and as free of fecal droppings as possible is another important step in preventing digestive protozoan infections.

Protozoan infections of the blood stream—such as plasmodium, leucocytozoan and hemaproteus infections—generally are prevented by confinement to prevent exposure to bloodsucking insects. Numerous species of mosquitoes, blackflies, biting midges, and certain flies transmit these infections.

When it is impossible to confine your flock or collection to preclude exposure to these flying insects, they must be controlled with insecticide sprays and by the removal, at a distance as large as you can, of weeds and trash from the

Edward T. Mallinson is Associate Professor, Virginia-Maryland Regional College of Veterinary Medicine, University of Maryland campus, College Park.

Kevin Shields

Preventing digestive diseases and maintaining healthy birds is easier when you keep them caged off the ground, because they are less likely to come in contact with fecal droppings.

perimeter around your operation.

Mowing May Help

High insect populations are fostered by any place where water can accumulate, from ditches to streams or lakes, especially when bordered by heavy vegetation. Such border areas sometimes can be improved by mowing.

Specific protozoan infections of chickens, turkeys, and other birds will be discussed separately in the special diseases chapters of this section.

Preventive and outbreak treatments are included in the preventive medicine tables in this chapter.

Bacteria Infections. Bacteria are very small forms of life visible only as small dots or short rods when magnified 1,000 times their size in a microscope. In bacterial infections the causative bacteria travel to various locations of the body via the bloodstream. Chronic infections occur when the bacteria localize in one or more organs or tissues.

Disease-producing bacteria generally are capable of not only invading many different parts of the body, but also many different species of birds and animals.

Disease Features

The following outlines some of the more distinguishing features of these infectious agents that not uncommonly are found in both backyard poultry and a variety of other birds.

Chlamydiosis. Infections with the causative bacteria, *Chlamydia psittaci*, in man and birds are called psittacosis. In poultry and other avian types, such as turkeys, the disease is called ornithosis.

Chronic lung infections and persistent intestinal infection and diarrhea are the main effects. They may be severe, mild or almost undetectable. In pigeons, the eyelids may become crusty and swollen.

This disease is detailed further in the *Special Diseases of Pet Birds* chapter.

Colibacillosis. Caused by *Escherichia coli*, this bacteria may act as a primary invader or secondary infection following another disease.

The young are more frequently affected, particularly when sanitation is below standard.

Air Sac Disease

A major problem can be encountered when the infection produces severe, cheesy-like inflammations over the heart, liver and air sacs of growing birds. This form of colibacillosis is often called "air sac disease." It is a common complication of chilling or poor ventilation combined with acute viral and mycoplasma infections.

Colibacillosis of the navel or omphalitis, which produces reddening, swelling, mushiness or wetness around a poorly healing navel, can result in the loss of many hatchlings during the first 7 to 10 days of life. Shipment of day-old stock over long distances tends to increase these losses, which usually have their origin at the hatchery or breeder flock level.

Chronic infections of the oviduct (salpingitis), the liver (coligranuloma), and leg or wing joints also occur.

Erysipelas infections are especially destructive to turkeys. They may be found also in chickens, game birds, and waterfowl. Wild birds may be infected along with swine, sheep, and humans. The infection in birds usually starts from breaks in the skin due to fighting or cannibalism.

People handling poultry or birds sick with this disease can develop painful infections of the hand or fingers. Professional medical assistance should be obtained immediately to prevent deeper, more serious infection.

Fortunately, prompt administration of penicillin or other antibiotics is highly effective in controlling this disease. The causative bacteria tends to resist disinfectants and survives well in alkaline soils for months to years.

Hemophilus Infection. Infections produced by *Hemophilus gallinarum* typically produce "colds" where discharges from the eyes and nose and swelling of the face are prominent symptoms. The disease is discussed in further detail under fowl coryza in the chapter on *Special Poultry Diseases*. Pheasants and guineas also may be infected, and possibly other avian species.

Mycoplasmosis. An assortment of small, relatively delicate bacterial agents called mycoplasma afflict the respiratory and reproductive organs of many avian species.

The list of affected types now includes chickens, turkeys, partridges, pheasants, peafowl, quail, guineas, ducks, and pigeons. As research in pet bird diseases expands, the list will lengthen.

Prolonged Course

Mycoplasma infections have a prolonged course in a flock or colony, frequently setting the stage for more serious respiratory disease should shipping stress or ventilation problems develop.

Mycoplasma characteristically worsen and extend the effects of virus or other bacterial infections. They often are "behind the scenes" in outbreaks of fowl coryza and air sac disease, and in lowered egg production.

These infections may also occur in joint tissues, producing swelling and lameness (synovitis).

Fowl Cholera

Pasteurellosis. Under the right conditions, poultry, game birds, waterfowl, wild birds, and many pet birds can suffer heavy losses following acute infections with *Pasteurella multocida*.

Chronic infections subsequent to an acute outbreak may result in joint, wattle, sinus, nasal, and middle ear or skull bone infections. The latter often results in twisting of the neck similar to that in Newcastle disease.

The disease is not egg-transmitted. It is, however, readily spread by recovered wild or domesticated carrier birds or animals and contaminated crates, feedbags, shoes, and equipment.

Salmonellosis. There are more than 2,200 different species of *Salmonella* (S.) bacteria. Most are capable of infecting many different types of pets, poultry and livestock. Some, like pullorum disease (*S. pullorum*) and fowl typhoid (*S. gallinarum*) are particularly infectious to poultry. They are discussed at the beginning of the poultry disease chapter. Both readily spread to day-old stock by infected breeders via the hatching egg.

Paratyphoid Types

Diseases caused by the remaining salmonella species are termed paratyphoid infections. Losses from these infections can range from negligible to severe. The young are usually but not always the most prone to infection.

Shipping stress, lack of drinking water soon after hatching, parasitism and generally poor sanitation foster more severe outbreaks.

Paratyphoid bacteria have three main modes of spread—a contaminated environment, contaminated feed, and breeders where fecal and nest box dust contamination allow bacteria to enter hatching eggs through natural pores in the eggshell.

Severe outbreaks with sudden deaths have been reported in game birds, waterfowl, canaries, wild and other birds. Suspected cases should be referred to your diagnostic laboratory. Avian salmonellosis sometimes is transmitted to people.

Staphylococcosis. Some types of *Staphylococcus aureus* are capable of producing both acute and chronic infections in all types of fowl. Turkeys, chickens, and pheasants are susceptible, especially turkeys. Although staphylococcal infections spread slowly, they can, over a period of time, produce considerable contamination of a flock's general surroundings. Without cleaning out and cleaning up, poultry or birds in the affected house are at risk of serious skin or generalized infections.

Bumblefoot Problem

Staph infections frequently result in formation of hard swollen cores or abscesses. A rather common problem called bumblefoot is actually a form of skin staphylococcosis. It is discussed in more detail in the *Miscellaneous Diseases* chapter.

Staph infections of the hock and other joints of the leg also occur. Leg joints frequently become hot and swollen with thick grayish-white fluid. Affected birds are slow

Infectious Diseases

to walk and prefer to rest on their hocks.

Streptococcosis. This infectious bacterial disease, caused by *Streptococcus zooepidemicus*, has been reported in chickens, turkeys, waterfowl, pigeons, and other wild or pet birds. Losses can be sudden, resembling a fowl cholera outbreak.

Tuberculosis. Also known as TB, this slow spreading, usually chronic *Mycobacterium avium* infection is found worldwide. It is mainly a disease of birds or poultry greater than 2 years of age, especially those that have had some contact with the soil.

Infections have been reported in poultry, game birds, large parrot-type pet birds, hunting birds (raptors), and other types of birds in zoos. Although rarely infecting people, avian tuberculosis also can be found in swine, sheep, mink, and cattle.

Affected birds generally continue to eat despite their gradual and eventually severe loss of weight. Many internal organs contain hard rounded gray to yellow pea-sized nodules which increase in number and size as the disease progresses.

The causative bacteria of avian TB resists many of the drugs used for treating tuberculosis. Major points in control of this disease are housing designs that keep poultry and birds away from their droppings; rotation ranges or removal of upper soil layers from small lots; and most importantly the marketing of poultry after their first laying season and game birds after their second.

Bacterial Control

The characteristic of many bacterial infections to produce carriers, hatching egg transmission, or long-lasting contamination of buildings is one of the main reasons why it is so important to:

1) Depopulate premises periodically; 2) Clean and disinfect all areas used; and 3) Replace the flock with quality NPIP classified fowl that participate in officially verified programs for detection, control, and eradication of several bacterial diseases transmitted by hatching eggs.

Your care in avoiding casual purchase of poultry or pet birds at shows, roadside sales, or the use of undisinfected hauling crates or boxes always is important. A so-called bargain or shortcut could easily introduce infections into your operation that will be far more difficult and costly to remove than they would have been to prevent in the first place.

Poor control of rats, mice, or raccoons, and the entrance of wild birds, also contribute to the introduction and persistence of bacterial diseases.

Although vaccinations are available for some bacterial diseases (for example, erysipelas, fowl cholera, mycoplasmo-sis), various antibiotics and other chemotherapeutic agents are the main medications used against bacteria.

Excessive exposure to bacteria, or weakened immunity from poor housing, malnutrition, and the effects of various virus infections interfere with effective antibiotic treatment and vaccination.

Drugs Used in Feeds

The following information is provided as a guide to the wide assortment of drugs that may be available for use in poultry feeds. The authors and publishers assume no liability for errors or omissions. Official clearances on drugs and other chemicals are constantly changing. More information on these FDA, USDA and EPA changes appear in the *Code of Federal Regulations, The Federal Register* and the *Feed Additives Compendium*.

Listings and clearances do not apply to all avian species. Read all drug label directions. Follow dosage and withdrawal instructions carefully. Do not mix or administer one drug along with another, unless labels indicate such combinations are approved.

Key to Uses:
C = Chickens   D = Ducks   P = Parrot-types   T = Turkeys
Pheasants: Approvals are expected, but not final, for two medications for pheasants. One is for a coccidiosis preventive (coccidiostat) and the other for gapeworms (thiabendazole). Check with your veterinarian or feed supplier to determine current clearances.

Bacterial Enteritis: Neomycin (C,D,T).

Blackhead: Furazolidone, Nitarsone (C,T); Carbasone, Dimetridazole, Ipronidazole (T).

Chlamydiosis (Psittacosis): Chlortetracycline (P).

Chronic Respiratory Disease (CRD): Erythromycin, Furazolidone, (C,T); Chlortetracycline, Oxytetracycline, Tylosin (C).

Coccidiosis: Amprolium, Nitrofurazone, Sulfadimethoxine and Ormetoprim, Sulfaquinoxaline,

Infectious Diseases

Zoalene (C,T); Buqinolate, Chlortetracycline, Clopidol, Decoquinate, Furazolidone, Lasalocid, Monensin, Nicarbazin, Nitromide + Sulfanitran + Roxasone, Oxytetracycline, Robenidine Hydrochloride, Salinomycin (C); Butynorate (T).

Colibacillosis: Sulfadimethoxine and Ormetoprim (C).

Coryza: Erythromycin, Sulfadimethoxine and Ormetoprim (C).

Crop Mycosis: Nystatin (C,T).

Enteritis, Non-Specific: Chlortetracycline, Furazolidone, Neomycin, Oxytetracycline, Penicillin (C,T).

Fowl Cholera: Sulfaquinoxaline, Sulfadimethoxine and Ormetoprim (C,T). Oxytetracycline (C); Novobiocin (D,T), Chlortetracycline (D).

Hexamitiasis: Butynorate, Chlortetracycline, Furazolidone, Oxytetracycline (T).

Necrotic/Ulcerative Enteritis: Furazolidone (C,T); Bacitracin Methylene Disalicylate, Lincomycin (C).

Salmonellosis: (Paratyphoid, Paracolon—*Arizona, Pullorum and Fowl Typhoid):* Furazolidone (C,T), Sulfaquinoxaline (Typhoid) (C); Chlortetracycline (Paratyphoid) (T).

Serositis, Infectious: Novobiocin (D).

Sinusitis, Infectious: Chlortetracycline, Furazolidone, Oxytetracycline (T).

Staphylococcosis: Novobiocin (C,T).

Synovitis: Chlortetracycline, Erythromycin, Furazolidone, Oxytetracycline (C,T).

Worms:
Capillary Worms—Coumaphos, Hygromycin B (C).
Cecal Worms—Butynorate + Piperazine + Phenothiazine, Phenothiazine (C,T); Coumaphos, Hygromycin B (C).
Common Roundworms—Coumaphos (C).
Large Roundworms (Ascarids)—Butynorate + Piperazine + Phenothiazine, Piperazine (C,T); Hygromycin B (C).
Tapeworms—Butynorate + Piperazine + Phenothiazine (T).

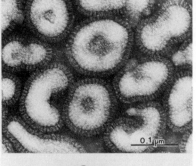

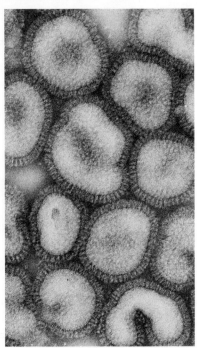

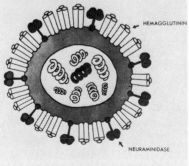

Dr. Gopal Murti, St. Jude Children's Research Hospital

illustrations provided by Dr. Robert G. Webster, St. Jude Children's Research Hospital

Virus Diseases

Viruses are the smallest of the infectious agents. They can be seen only by the most specialized techniques which magnify their size over 100,000 times.

They usually focus their attacks on only one or two organs or parts of the avian anatomy and only on certain types of poultry or birds. In some instances, however, they do produce generalized plague-like infections of almost all parts of a bird's body and of many different types of birds.

H5N2 avian influenza virus magnified 270,000 times.

Diagram of an influenza virus showing the two kinds of surface spikes and eight separate pieces of RNA as coils in center of particle.

The latter occurs in outbreaks of viscerotropic velogenic Newcastle disease (VVND, exotic Newcastle disease) and highly lethal forms of avian influenza.

The main signs of either VVND or lethal avian influenza are severe depression, almost total cessation of egg production, and rapidly in-

Infectious Diseases

creasing and spreading death losses reaching levels of 50 to 90 percent or higher. Heads of affected birds usually are darkened and sometimes enlarged with watery fluid accumulations in the wattle, around the eyes and in the comb. Severe diarrhea is common. Survivors may develop twisted necks, paralysis of the legs or wings, or other forms of incoordination.

Internally, large and small hemorrhages are found in many different parts of the

Water Medication and Injectables

Water medications and injectables can provide an especially convenient way to prevent or treat disease in small or hobby operations. The following is a guide to preparations that may be available from local veterinarians or distributors. Drugs constantly are under review; consequently, current approvals may differ from this list. No endorsements or discriminations are intended or implied.

Some preparations may be used in the drinking water and others by injection, some in both chickens and turkeys and others in one type only. Therefore, read and follow label instructions and withdrawal times very carefully.

Blackhead (Histomoniasis): Dimetridazole, Ipronidazole.

Chronic Respiratory Disease: *Mycoplasmosis*—Chlortetracycline, Erythromycin, Oxytetracycline, Spectinomycin, Streptomycin, Tylosin.
Colibacillosis—Gentamicin, Lincomycin + Spectinomycin, Spectinomycin.

Coccidiosis: Amprolium, Sulfadimethoxine, Sulfamethazine sodium, Sulfaquinoxaline.

Coryza: Erythromycin, Sulfadimethoxine, Streptomycin.

Erysipelas: Erythromycin, Penicillin.

Fowl cholera: Erythromycin, Oxytetracycline, Streptomycin, Sulfadimethoxine, Sulfamethazine sodium.

Hexamitiasis: Chlortetracycline, Oxytetracycline.

Salmonellosis:
Paracolon—Gentamicin, Spectinomycin.
Paratyphoid—Gentamicin.
Pullorum—Sulfamethazine sodium.
Typhoid Fowl—Sulfaquinoxaline.

Exotic Newcastle disease frequently leaves birds or poultry uncoordinated and depressed.

USDA-APHIS

Dr. Kay Wheeler, USDA-APHIS

Heads of avian influenza-affected birds usually are darkened and sometimes enlarged, with watery fluid accumulations in the wattle, around the eyes and in the comb.

Infectious Diseases

body. They are seen most often as reddish-brown spots or blotches along the interior of the upper and lower digestive tract, on the ovaries and over the fat of the abdomen.

The extraordinarily severe disease produced by either of these generalized virus infections is one of the main reasons extraordinary steps are taken for their control and eradication.

Fortunately, as already mentioned, most viruses of poultry and pet birds do not produce such extensive damage. Nevertheless, the damage they do produce, wherever they concentrate their activities, is generally severe and a serious problem.

Respiratory Disease. Many viruses produce acute respiratory infections, characterized by watery eyes, clicking or gurgling sounds, cough-like sounds, nasal discharges, open-mouthed breathing or stretching the neck to gasp for air.

Such respiratory symptoms are observed in either mild or lethal forms of avian influenza, Newcastle disease or other paramyxovirus infections in a broad variety of poultry and pet bird types. They also are seen with laryngotracheitis and bronchitis virus infections in chickens, and in quail bronchitis.

Brain Damage. Other avian disease viruses tend to concentrate their effects on the brain and other parts of the nervous system, producing incoordination, paralysis or partial paralysis of leg or wing muscles.

Convulsions

Peculiar positioning of the neck or head, convulsions or trembling also are commonly seen during or long after certain attacks of such viruses as avian encephalomyelitis (epidemic tremor) virus of young chicks, pigeon encephalitis virus, and various strains of mosquito- and blackfly-carried forms of encephalitis in pheasants, other game birds, turkeys, and waterfowl.

Newcastle disease frequently leaves birds or poultry uncoordinated. Some head and neck twisting has been observed in turkeys and other types afflicted with avian influenza.

Skin Disease. Bird and fowl pox viruses are found in many avian types. They tend to be specific for certain species, but apparent overlapping pox infections between different poultry and bird species are being reported.

Raised, reddish brown to

black scabs singly, in clusters or widely spread occur usually on the unfeathered skin of the head and neck. They may also occur around the vent or on the feet or legs. Cage birds and wild birds often have pox damage to their feet or legs and this effect may appear as horny growths. Pox may also involve the eyes, mouth, and upper digestive tract.

Mosquitoes, biting unfeathered parts of the bird's body, are involved in the introduction of most fowl or bird pox infections.

Damage to Immunity. Virus infections are notorious for their ability to increase the susceptibility of poultry and other birds to invasion of bacteria. They interfere also with the development of immunity following vaccination.

Noteworthy among the virus diseases producing these effects are bursal disease of chickens, and adenovirus infections in turkeys (turkey hemorrhagic enteritis) and possibly in pheasants (marble spleen pulmonary edema syndrome).

Leg Weakness

Reovirus infections have been recognized recently as a threat to good digestion and growth in chickens and a significant factor in the production of broiler leg weaknesses and ruptured hock tendons in older heavier meat-types.

As more is learned, you can expect to see more viruses identified in all sorts of poultry and birds for their roles in producing increased susceptibility to secondary bacterial diseases, vaccination failures, poor growth ("runting"), leg weakness and, as some researchers have suspected in cage pet birds, even in feathering abnormalities.

New Viruses. A host of newly recognized virus infections now are being reported in many of the parrot-type birds (papovaviruses), and in finch-type birds (paramyxoviruses). With increased research funding, the role of these and other new viruses in producing illness in all sorts of birds will be much better understood in the future.

Transmission. All the precautions given for preventing protozoan and bacterial infections need to be doubled for virus diseases. The reason is the extraordinary ability of viruses to survive in nature and to break through the normal defenses of the healthiest or weakest members of a flock, aviary or other bird collection.

Their extremely small

Barry Fitzgerald

*When serious exotic diseases
do occur, scenes like this are
common. State and/or federal
quarantines are placed in effect
to protect the Nation's poultry
industry and export markets. The
1983–1984 avian influenza outbreak in the mid-Atlantic States,
which cost over $59 million to
eradicate, was reportedly fed by
movement between farms.*

size further contributes significantly to the ease by which
viruses are transmitted from
one location to another. This
is because literally millions of
fully infectious virus particles
can become easily suspended
in and on a speck of dust, dander, or other debris.

Riding the Wind
Viruses then are transported
easily to new locations riding
on the wind with loose feathers flying from place to place;
on the tiny hairs of flies; on
the fur of dogs, cats, and mice;
on the feathers of wild birds;

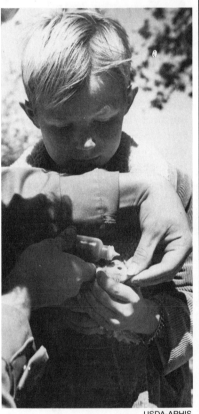

USDA-APHIS

*Vaccines can often be adminis-
tered as simply as putting a drop
in the eye or nostril.*

in the hair and on the shoes and clothing of children, relatives, neighbors, friends, servicemen, and deliverymen; on and in boxes and equipment; and on anything else living or dead that can move or be transported.

The over $59 million outbreak of lethal avian influenza in the mid-Atlantic States during 1983 and 1984, where over 350 poultry farms became infected, reportedly was fed by the movement of dusty used egg flats, unsanitized feed delivery trucks, and most importantly, the movement of people between farms.

Spread of viruses by the movement of people, products, and equipment is suspected in transmission of nearly all avian viral diseases, regardless of bird type or flock size.

Virus Disease Control. Your first line of defense is flock or aviary isolation and segregation. Only you can really prevent viral diseases from entering your operation. Exercise your property rights to control and set security and sanitation standards for all people, stock, products, and equipment you use or buy.

If a Virus Hits

Although antibiotics and sulfonamides are effective in killing bacteria, they have no such effect on viruses. The main things you can do to treat virus infection are: Maintain feed and water consumption, avoid chilling, provide vitamin and mineral supplements, and keep an extra high level of cleanliness and hygiene.

Extra cleanliness is needed because viruses reduce your birds' resistance.

Antibiotics, although ineffective against viruses, may help suppress potential secondary bacterial invaders, while vitamins boost natural barriers to infection.

Using Vaccines. In the experience of the author, the most appropriate vaccines for backyard chicken flocks are laryngotracheitis, Newcastle, bronchitis, bursal disease and pox vaccinations. The first three often can be administered as simply as putting a drop in the eye or nostril.

Although packaged in 500 to 1,000 bird-dose bottles, these vaccines are extremely low in cost when compared to the expense of vaccines for a similar number of dogs, cats, or other animals. To be effective, they must be stored under refrigeration.

Follow manufacturer's directions. Virus vaccines can be delicate and will decay rapidly if not handled as directed.

Vaccines

The following is a guide to vaccines or other biologicals that generally may be available for the prevention of numerous avian diseases. Always use as directed on the manufacturer's label. Vaccine often can be obtained through your local veterinarian or feed supplier.
Vaccines are listed below according to appropriate species.

Chickens

Avian encephalomyelitis (epidemic tremors)
Bronchitis*
Bursal disease
Coccidiosis
Colibacilloisis
Coryza (Hemophilus)
Fowl cholera (P. multocida)
Laryngotracheitis*
Marek's disease
Mycoplasmosis**
Newcastle disease*
Pox (fowl and pigeon strains)
Reovirus (malabsorption)
Tenosynovitis (ruptured tendon)

*Eye or nose drop vaccines are produced and easily applied, thus making them very practical for backyard flocks.
**A nonspreading (injectable) vaccine has been licensed. It can be used to protect the respiratory health and endurance of backyard or other types of hobby chickens.

Turkeys

Avian encephalomyelitis
Coccidiosis
Colibacillosis
Erysipelas
Fowl cholera
Mycoplasmosis
Newcastle disease
Pox

Ducks*

Duck virus enteritis (DVE)
Infectious serositis (P. antipestifer)
Virus hepatitis
Virus hepatitis yolk antibody

*Vaccines for DVE and infectious serositis are sometimes used in geese. Check with manufacturer or your veterinarian for species or state clearances.

Pigeons

Pigeon pox

Restricted Vaccines

Some vaccines may be available in certain States and not others. This is because some vaccines may be experimental or for limited, controlled use only under the specific approval of your State Veterinarian. Examples of a few such vaccines are:

Canaries—Canary pox vaccine

Pheasants—Marble spleen vaccine

Turkeys—Hemorrhagic enteritis or avian influenza vaccines.

Enteritis Vaccines

Vaccines against hemorrhagic enteritis of turkeys and marble spleen disease of pheasants may be available to you on an experimental basis. Contact your Cooperative Extension Agent or your State Veterinarian for details and any special clearances. Duck and goose producers are advised to do the same with respect to vaccines for preventing duck virus enteritis.

Avian Medicine Departments at several State universities and colleges of veterinary medicine are conducting research on development of vaccines for pet bird virus diseases. Local veterinarians, breeder and trade associations can keep you informed on the progress and possible local availability of these newer products.

Although vaccines can provide substantial resistance to many viral diseases, it is important to recognize that vaccine protection is rarely 100 percent and further that it is essentially impossible to vaccinate against all known and some yet to be discovered virus diseases. So, along with some selected, well reasoned use of vaccines, your main safeguard remains dedication to basic disease prevention practices.

Parasite Problems. The term parasites as used here refers to multi-celled disease-producing agents that, despite their frequently very small size, ordinarily are visible with the naked eye.

Some of these parasites exist on the outside of the body, others on the inside. They chiefly fall into four main groups—nematodes (such as roundworms, gapeworms, capillaria worms, cropworms, tetrameres, and cecal worms), trematodes (tapeworms), small insects (lice, fleas, and various types of flies), and ticks and mites.

Infectious Diseases

A great number of different species of parasites exist within each group, and all types of birds and poultry can be afflicted. Their complete discussion is beyond this chapter's scope.

Affect Skin, Weight

Parasites rarely cause widespread, obvious, rapidly spreading symptoms nor do they usually cause sudden high death losses. Rather, they primarily cause birds or poultry general skin irritations, anemia, or gradual—but sometimes very severe—weight loss.

Weight loss frequently is the result of a parasite's interference with the digestion and absorption of food; anemia is the result of their blood-sapping activities.

Some parasites interfere with normal breathing.

Most spend part of their time in or on the bird parasitized and other portions of their life somewhere else in their host's surroundings. The need for most parasites to complete part of their life cycle off the host gives you an advantage in their prevention and control.

Nematodes, Tapeworms.

You can control most of these parasites by keeping chickens, turkeys, game birds, and most other types of birds either on wire or on impervious (such as concrete) well drained surfaces with deep, dry, fresh litter.

By so doing, you will prevent or reduce significantly your flock's exposure to mature worm eggs that otherwise would have been eaten if your birds had access to dirt or soil or fecal droppings.

Failure to do so encourages the consumption of feces (droppings), insects, earthworms, slugs or snails, all of which may carry various nematode and tapework life stages in their tissue or organs.

Fighting Insects

Many parasitic insects, (bedbugs, blackflies, pigeon flies, and mosquitoes), also spend part of their life cycles off their host. Others such as biting lice and sticktight fleas spend their entire life cycle on their avian host, completing all life stages in and on the skin and feathers.

In the first situation, you need to eliminate off-host breeding grounds and hiding areas outside or inside your operation. When this is not possible, your attention must be given to either applying insecticides directly to these breeding/hiding areas or to

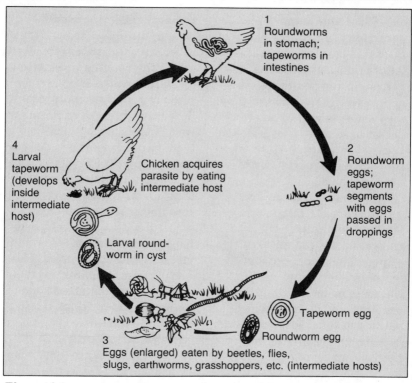

1 Roundworms in stomach; tapeworms in intestines

4 Larval tapeworm (develops inside intermediate host)

Chicken acquires parasite by eating intermediate host

Larval roundworm in cyst

2 Roundworm eggs; tapeworm segments with eggs passed in droppings

Tapeworm egg

Roundworm egg

3 Eggs (enlarged) eaten by beetles, flies, slugs, earthworms, grasshoppers, etc. (intermediate hosts)

The need for most parasites to complete part of their life cycle off the host gives you an advantage in their prevention and control. This diagram illustrates the various stages of a tapeworm and a roundworm of poultry—both parasites with an indirect life history.

screening off access to your buildings or pens.

Loose boards and cracks and crevices are ideal hiding places. So also are wood and junkpiles. Allowing chickens, turkeys, game birds, waterfowl, and other birds to run loose or roost at night outdoors in trees or in poorly repaired buildings seriously reduces your chances for effective control.

Where the insect spends its life entirely on poultry or birds, direct application of insecticide sprays or dusts to the skin and feathers usually corrects the situation. It generally is necessary to reapply insecticides two or three times at 10- to 14-day intervals to kill new lice or fleas that emerge from insecticide-resistant parasite eggs nestled in the feathers.

Infectious Diseases

Ticks and Mites. This parasite group shares many of the same life cycle characteristics of parasitic insects. Some chicken red mites, chiggers, and ticks, although they may cause anemia and skin irritations, may be overlooked because in many instances they spend relatively little time on their hosts.

Others—northern fowl mites, scaly leg mites, and feather, depluming, subcutaneous and air sac mites—either hide in less obvious feathered parts, burrow under the skin, or locate themselves deep within the body. Once again you must focus on eliminating or treating hiding places or applying parasite-killing sprays directly onto your birds.

Survive for Months. Pesticide applications for off-host mites and ticks should always be made with forceful spraying into cracks and crevices in and around buildings where mites and ticks survive for many months between meals.

Vigorous cleanup, including scraping away old caked litter and manure, and other good housekeeping procedures are essential to a successful control program. The off-host mite or tick must be exposed to be killed. If hiding places

remain, infestations will return.

Control of mites which spend their entire lives within or on the bodies of poultry or birds requires special procedures that bring treatments into direct contact with the body part where the mites exist.

Other parasite-carrying flock members, commonly wild free-flying birds, and old structures that have not been depopulated to allow thorough cleanup and application of insecticides and disinfectants are the main culprits in perpetuating infestations of all types of parasites.

Diseases Due to Fungi. Aspergillosis, candidiasis, dactylariosis, and favus are all avian diseases produced by different species of fungi or molds. Each has its own set of key features. They will be discussed separately, but as in all other poultry and bird health cases, hygiene and sanitation are your best defense.

Aspergillosis may be found in most bird species. In most instances, it results from massive exposure to airborne *Aspergillus* mold spores.

Lungs Prime Site

The spores usually originate from grossly contaminated litter (moldy straw or woodshav-

Common Pesticides[1]

Many different pesticides (insecticides and miticides) are used against external parasites of poultry and livestock. Those most frequently used for poultry and their more common methods of application are listed below. Read labels before purchase. Not all brands are for poultry or pets.

LICE AND MITES
Pesticides:

Carbaryl (Sevin)
Coumaphos (Co-Ral)
Malathion
Permethrin (Ectiban, Permectin, Atroban and Others)

Ronnel (Korlan)
Stirofos (Rabon)
Stirofos plus Dichlorvos (Ravap)

General Methods of Application[2]: Always follow label directions and precautions carefully.

Lice—Spray or dust birds. Repeat monthly as needed or directed. Stirofos and dichlorvos may be labeled for use as a premises or litter spray for louse control.

Mites (Common Red Mites and Northern Fowl Mites)
Apply to birds according to label. Add dusts to litter and/or dusting boxes. Spray premises. Give emphasis to roost and premises treatment for red mites, and to direct bird treatment for fowl mites.

Note: Scaly leg mite treatment may not require use of a pesticide. *Repeated* applications of mineral oil will loosen the crusts, relieve the inflammation, and suffocate the mite.

FOWL TICKS
Apply malathion, carbaryl or stirofos sprays to roosts, the house interior and coops. Repeat treatments may be necessary.

---

[1]Check with your county Cooperative Extension agent for any changes in this information. Pesticide approvals frequently are reviewed and modified.

[2]Approved methods of application vary between products. *Always* follow label directions.

ings), feed, or dusty surroundings. The lungs are the prime site where these spores collect. Their sporulation and further web-like growth leads to development of numerous small tightly adherent yellowish nodules or button-like specks in the lungs.

More advanced infections result in invasion of the air sacs, trachea (windpipes), liver, brain, and other locations. Valuable individual birds sometimes can be successfully treated with specialized drugs.

Candidiasis is a poultry or pet bird disease that produces patchy, grayish-white, raised, slightly rough thickenings in the mouth, esophagus, crop, sometimes the proventriculus and only rarely the intestine. It often is secondary to some other debilitating condition.

It also is a complication of prolonged treatment with antibiotics or other medications. This is not uncommon in imported birds originating from quarantine stations or in turkeys subjected to lengthy antibiotic treatments for chlamydiosis.

Affected poultry or birds may exhibit few symptoms other than retarded growth, listlessness, ruffled feathers, or diarrhea.

Preventive Steps
Proper control of primary disease conditions, being certain that waterers are regularly cleaned of accumulating feed particles or slime, and use of antibiotics for only as long as necessary are your main considerations for preventing candidiasis in any type fowl.

Preventive drugs and chemicals are secondary in importance to basic sanitation and sound nutrition.

Dactylariosis, a disease mainly of young chickens and turkeys, is similar in cause and prevention to aspergillosis. But unlike aspergillosis, the principal symptoms are nervous disorders (tremors, circling, and incoordination) rather than respiratory difficulty. The causative fungus grows naturally in old sawdust.

Favus is a term sometimes used to describe a number of relatively uncommon fungal diseases of the skin of poultry and other birds. Such infections usually produce gray-white crusts on the unfeathered skin (usually of the head and neck). Good nutrition and inherited vigor may well account for the rarity of this disorder in the vast majority of commercial poultry flocks.

Poisoning

By Edward T. Mallinson

Poisoning is not a particularly common cause of poultry or pet bird illness. In the experience of most, some other disorder or problem more likely is the source of the trouble.

So when you are suspicious of poisoning, be cautious about accusations. Look first for other possibilities and contact your nearest veterinarian, cooperative extension service agent, or State diagnostic laboratory for assistance.

Feed often is falsely incriminated. Nevertheless, to be on the safe side always secure and save a 10- to 25-pound quantity of the feed or any other toxic material you suspect for laboratory analysis. Skimpy samples can be

Edward T. Mallinson is Associate Professor, Virginia-Maryland Regional College of Veterinary Medicine, University of Maryland campus, College Park.

misleading and often useless to your testing laboratory.

Botulism and mycotoxicosis are two of the most common intoxications in backyard flocks. They are not manmade toxins. Instead, both are naturally occurring, essentially "organic" poisons.

Botulinum toxin develops as a natural, exceedingly toxic substance when any type of plant or animal material decays. Mycotoxins are the by-product of the natural growth of molds on grain or other feed ingredients. This growth can occur in the field, after harvest, during storage, and right up to the time of feeding.

Botulism. This poisoning is more likely found in chickens, captive game birds (such as pheasants, quail), waterfowl, and raptors (owls, hawks, falcons and kestrels). Vultures appear to be the only resistant birds. Pheasants seem extremely susceptible.

Poisoning

Always patrol your indoor and outdoor bird pens on a daily basis to pick up and remove dead birds or other animals, in order to avoid consumption of decaying carcasses by your flock which can lead to severe botulism intoxication (poisoning).

Marie T. Sebrechts

Affected stock, regardless of type, develop severe drowsiness, weakness, and progressive loss of control of the legs, wings, and neck. Death soon follows the onset of total paralysis and deep coma.

Because of the extraordinary potency of botulinum toxin, many types of birds—penned pheasants particularly—need only to consume small amounts of a decaying carcass, such as pieces of tissue or maggots from a single dead mouse or a small dead bird, to develop severe poisoning. Muddy alkaline shallow ponds or lakes, rich in decaying vegetation, can contribute to extensive waterfowl deaths from botulism.

Need to Patrol Pens

As a consequence you should always patrol your indoor and outdoor bird pens on a daily basis to pick up and remove dead birds or other animals. During summer months, outdoor game fowl pens should receive even more frequent inspection. Waterfowl should be fenced and fed away from lakes and ponds when low water levels cannot be corrected.

A variety of treatments are possible to reduce botulism losses. Your local veterinarian often can be of assistance. Fertilizers containing ammonium sulfate have been used to acidify the ground where botulism has been a problem in the hope that soil acidification will reduce the probability of toxin buildup.

Occasional paralysis of the neck, wings or legs of a few scattered growing chickens is not uncommon. The condition is not botulism and affected chickens almost always recover overnight. This condition, known as pseudo- or false-botulism, is generally believed to be a less typical form of Marek's disease.

Mycotoxicosis (aflatoxicosis). In contrast to aspergillosis and other fungal diseases caused by mold spores actually invading the body tissues of poultry or birds, mycotoxicosis is the result of eating feed contaminated with the poisonous byproducts of fungus growth on feed ingredients. In some instances, losses—especially of the young—may be very high.

In turkey poults or ducklings, incoordination and convulsions may occur. In the more common, less well-defined situation, the presence of low levels of mycotoxins may induce growth depression and unthriftiness.

All species of birds may be susceptible in varying degrees. Chronic liver and kidney damage is sometimes encountered. Some mycotoxins produce sores in the mouth, others skin inflammation.

Treatment of mycotoxicosis is based primarily on removal of the offending feed, and brief supplementation of the ration with antibiotics, vitamins, and some additional dietary fat and protein.

Use Fresh Feed. Your best prevention hinges mainly on the use of freshly manufactured feed that is fed out promptly so as to reduce the time available for further toxin development during storage.

Commercially produced feeds and grains used for home-produced feed should be free of visible mold growth and kept cool and dry. Do not allow insides of storage bins to sweat.

Mold inhibitors often are added to commercially produced feeds to retard or prevent fungal growth. Pelleted or crumbled rations are considered advantagous because less surface area is available for mold growth. Furthermore, many ingredients are protected from air-exposure damage.

Poisoning

Miscellaneous Diseases

By Edward T. Mallinson

Bumblefoot, cannibalism, egg binding, feather picking, leg weakness, and various reproductive or anatomic disorders are common to many avian types. Their origins usually stem from a combination of factors, both infectious and noninfectious.

Management (poultry or bird densities, feeding practices, etc.), marginal nutritional deficiencies, recognized and unrecognized infectious agents, and inherited (genetic) weaknesses or predispositions may all be involved. Because of the complexities, control procedures may be only partially effective.

Bumblefoot. Large swellings or hard cores developing

in the foot or foot pad are believed usually to be the result of repeated bruising or injury to the foot and/or bacterial invasion of the foot through bruised areas or via penetrating wires, splinters, or other sharp wires or objects.

The likelihood of bumblefoot is increased by insufficient deep, cushioning litter; sharp edged roosting boards; caked litter or other damp unsanitary walking surfaces; and allowing heavier birds to rest on and jump from excessively high perches.

A lack of vitamin A or other vitamins may heighten the chances of some birds developing bumblefoot.

Cannibalism. As used here, cannibalism refers to harmful picking and clawing activities performed by certain members of a bird or poultry flock against others. Weaker or smaller stock usually are the victims of cannibalism.

Overcrowding and high

Edward T. Mallinson is Associate Professor, Virginia-Maryland Regional College of Veterinary Medicine, University of Maryland campus, College Park.

Marie T. Sebrechts

Metal or plastic clip-on eyeshields or "specs" have been used to make it difficult for birds to peck accurately at each other.

Miscellaneous Diseases   61

temperatures have been associated with the increased occurrence of cannibalism, along with a lack of enough fiber in the ration. An insufficient number of feeders seems to increase cannibalism.

Boredom a Factor

Lack of exercise, and boredom from being able to consume all daily feed requirements too quickly, also are suspected in relation to cannibalism.

This problem sometimes has been overcome by providing poultry and other birds with treats of greens, chunks of leafy hay, whey blocks, rolled newspaper, or other items with which they may exercise and satisfy some of their natural clawing and pecking instincts.

Providing less feed but at more frequent intervals may also help to avoid cannibalism both in poultry and in cage pet birds.

When cannibalism becomes a problem, ordinarily you should begin your first efforts at correcting overcrowding. In some instances, this may require moving a portion of the flock to other quarters; separating larger, faster growing birds from smaller, possibly less aggressive but still valuable, slower-growing birds; or identifying and removing the main troublemakers. Beaks and face feathers of the most cannibalistic birds may be obviously blood-stained, helping in identification.

Debeaking (removing part of the beak) is practiced widely to control cannibalism in commercial poultry. Metal or plastic clip-on eyeshields or "specs" also have been used to make it difficult for birds to peck accurately. Decreasing the temperature and brightness of pens may be a further help in reducing cannibalism.

In many instances feather picking is an early form of cannibalism. The same causative factors apply. Feeding changes, reduction of boredom, control of external parasites, and reduced lighting may prevent poultry, game birds and pet cage birds from developing feather picking into the worse habit of cannibalism.

Egg Problems

Unlaid eggs sometimes accumulate in the oviduct, the tubular organ where the egg-white and shell are formed. The abdomen of affected birds can become severely distended from this condition, called egg binding. The problem is discussed further in the chapter on pet bird diseases.

A similar disorder that also can cause abdominal enlargement results when egg yolks released from the ovary fail to pass into the oviduct, thus accumulating in the abdominal cavity. The causes of these problems are ill-defined, but may be related in part to conditions that produce obesity, flightiness or nervousness.

Other reproductive ailments perplex flock owners and scientists. Some of these disorders—such as salpingitis (distension of the oviduct with whitish curdy material or yellow cheesy cores)—may be due to viral, bacterial, or mycoplasmal infections prior to maturity.

Abnormal soft or misshapen eggs, ruptured egg yolks, and prolapse or "blowout" of the oviduct frequently are associated with management and feeding problems. Infections with such respiratory viruses as Newcastle or bronchitis virus frequently result in weak or misshapen eggshells or watery whites.

Lameness. Leg weakness in birds or poultry has such a vast number of potential causes that their adequate discussion is beyond the scope of this chapter. A combination of inherited, nutritional, and infectious factors may be involved.

The most useful tips for keepers of small flocks and aviaries are: 1) Keep hatchlings and young growing birds off slippery surfaces and, 2) Provide these young birds, and their breeder parents, with the most nutritionally complete ration possible.

A common cause of one-legged lameness in pet birds, especially parakeets, is kidney tumors.

Deformities. Malformations often draw considerable attention, but they generally—unless very extensive in a flock or aviary—are only of passing interest.

One disorder, sometimes called "wind puffs," causes a bird's body to rapidly become unusually large and rounded. When examined, affected birds are found to be very puffy and light.

Wind puffs usually are due to accumulations of air under the skin after a tear or rupture occurs in one of a bird's natural internal air sacs following a flying injury, castration surgery done to produce fatter heavier males (capons), or possibly the heavy breathing and coughing that may accompany severe respiratory infection. Valuable birds can be treated surgically.

Special Poultry Diseases

By Edward T. Mallinson and
Jim A. Stunkard

This chapter provides brief descriptions of diseases that 1) more commonly are found in small, backyard poultry flocks, or 2) are more significant economically or personally when they do occur. Further reading on these and many other diseases is recommended.

All Poultry Types. Two important diseases shared by chickens, turkeys, guinea fowl, partridges, pheasants, quail, and domestic waterfowl (ducks and geese) are pullorum disease and fowl typhoid.

These salmonella infections, transmitted via breeder flocks and hatching eggs, are capable of producing severe, rapidly spreading disease— especially in young chickens and turkeys. They also can cause havoc in guinea fowl and upland game birds. Infection and losses have been reported as well in waterfowl and occasionally other avian and mammalian species.

In most states, testing of breeder flocks now is mandatory for detecting and controlling pullorum-typhoid. However, some untested flocks do exist. To be sure you avoid the risk of these diseases, always insist on purchasing U.S. (NPIP) Pullorum-Typhoid Clean stock.

Small, local dealers and custom or home-type hatcheries—because of their small size or more remote location— may escape detection and testing by State poultry health agencies. It is to the benefit of all concerned that such operations participate in NPIP programs and become tested.

Edward T. Mallinson is Associate Professor, Virginia-Maryland Regional College of Veterinary Medicine, University of Maryland campus, College Park. Jim A. Stunkard is Director of the Bowie Animal Hospital, Bowie, Md.

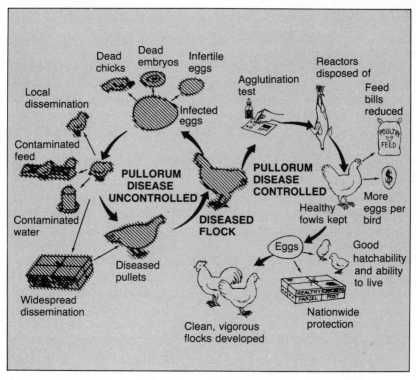

A comparison of the serious effects of uncontrolled pullorum disease and the results of detection and disposal of reactors.

Chicken Diseases

Coccidiosis. At least five distinctly different species of intestinal coccidial protozoans infect chickens. All can produce considerable inflammation in different sections of the digestive tract below the gizzard.

Two of these coccidial species, *Eimeria (E.) necatrix* and *E. tenella,* cause massive and often fatal hemorrhages. With *E. necatrix* these hemorrhages result in severe distention of the middle of the intestine. With *E. tenella,* the two, blind cecal pouches become swollen with dark blood-filled debris. Numerous preventive and therapeutic anticoccidials are available from feed stores and livestock suppliers.

Fowl Coryza. This disease, caused by the bacteria *Hemophilus gallinarum,* often is involved in respiratory diseases of multiple-age flocks where periodic cleanout and cleanup is not practiced.

Affected chickens generally develop very watery eyes, and severe reddening and swelling of the sinuses surrounding one or both eyes. Discharges coming from the eyes and nostrils of affected birds typically have a very offensive odor—much more so than in other respiratory infections of chickens.

Several antibiotics and other chemotherapeutic agents are effective in suppressing the infection. Dramatic improvements have been reported with the use of erythromycin preparations via the drinking water.

Laryngotracheitis, a respiratory virus infection of chickens and occasionally other species of fowl, often results from failure to maintain tight flock security and isolation.

The disease typically produces marked hemorrhage of the windpipe (trachea) of chickens, and flock death losses of 5 to 20 percent. It is readily introduced through purchase of recovered virus carriers at auctions, fairs, or poultry shows.

Poultry catching crates and hauling trucks that are not cleaned and disinfected between hauls have frequently been associated with outbreaks in new flocks or new distant locations.

The movement of people and animals between farms also is involved. Clothing and fur easily can be contaminated with virus-laden dust particles.

If you own a flock of show chickens, are located in an area where this disease is prevalent, or make replacement purchases at live poultry auctions, you should seriously consider vaccination against laryngotracheitis. Excellent, easily administered products are available at very modest cost.

Liver Ailments

Lymphoid Leukosis, a virus-caused disease, also is called "big liver disease." It causes large tumors in many internal organs, especially the liver, and needs to be distinguished from avian tuberculosis and Marek's disease. Unlike Marek's disease, which also produces liver and other internal tumors, lymphoid leukosis is breeder flock transmitted, whereas Marek's is not.

Infected females usually transmit the infection through the egg to some or all of their offspring. There is no preventive medication or vaccination.

As an aid in preventing lymphoid leukosis, which can kill 25 percent or more of a flock of mature chickens in 12 months' time, you should obtain all chicks at one time from the same parent stock and place them in fully-depopulated clean and disinfected quarters. Avoid further additions until the next cleanout.

Marek's Disease is a very common liver tumor and paralysis-producing virus disease of chickens, now fortunately under reasonable control through vaccination. Novice poultrymen failing to obtain chicks vaccinated at one day of age with one of several types of Marek's vaccine will often be severely disappointed when high Marek's death losses begin at about 8 to 10 weeks of age and persist to 20 to 25 weeks of age or longer.

Day-old vaccination almost is a must for preventing this disease. Excellent protection is obtained from vaccination, especially if vaccinated chicks are placed in dust-free clean and disinfected pens.

Small hatcheries usually can get veterinary assistance locally or from vaccine suppliers on a good day-old Marek's disease vaccination program for their customers. Marek's disease and vaccina-

tion for this disease are not considered hazardous to human health.

Mites and Ticks

Scaly leg mites, caused by the mite *Knemidocoptes mutans,* produce slow-spreading but eventually very severe thickening of the skin of the shank, and raising and discoloration of the shank scales. It usually is encountered on old poultry premises and on aged chickens.

Direct miticide treatment of affected shanks and eventual flock depopulation and cleanup generally eliminates scaly leg mite problems.

Fowl ticks, *Argas persicus,* are sometimes called blue-bugs. Besides causing anemia, they may cause tick paralysis in growing or adult hens. They also transmit spirochetosis, a serious bacterial disease not only of chickens but also of turkeys, game birds, waterfowl, and other birds.

Tick control requires removal of breeding and hiding areas in and around the chicken house as already discussed and application of sprays specifically labeled effective against ticks.

Turkey Problems

Aortic Rupture. When pushed for rapid weight gain, 8- to 20-week-old turkeys—often the nicest toms—may succumb rapidly to massive internal hemorrhage. This occurs when a weakening and then a tear develops in either the heart wall or the aorta, the largest blood vessel exiting from the heart.

Limiting feed intake during the most critical period, 16 to 20 weeks, helps prevent this condition.

Blackhead. More correctly termed histomoniasis after the name of the causative protozoan, *Histomonas meleagridis,* this disease is troublesome particularly to turkeys. Outbreaks also occur in chickens and captive game birds. Affected turkeys are found to have large cheesy laminated cores in the cecal pouches and large and small irregularly-round, slightly sunken yellowish-gray, greenish or red areas of degeneration on the surface of the liver.

Three of the most important preventive considerations are 1) routine use of antihistomonal drugs in feed, 2) separating turkeys from chickens, and 3) pen designs that keep turkeys from finding and eating earthworms. Routine worming for cecal worms also is advisable in the total control of the blackhead.

Types of Enteritis

Coronaviral Enteritis. Death losses in young poults can reach levels of 50 percent or more when they are stricken with this persistent intestinal virus disease. Good nursing care (supplemental heat, antibiotics, vitamins, and hygiene) can help cut losses.

Prevention is accomplished best by all in, all-out management systems and thorough cleaning and disinfection after complete depopulation. There are no vaccines for turkey coronaviral enteritis.

Due to a distinct group of avian adenoviruses, *hemorrhagic enteritis* can produce fatal bloody diarrhea in 15 percent or more of a flock of young turkeys. Typically occurring around 10 to 12 weeks of age, the main symptoms are sudden onset, depression, bloody droppings and a concurrent drop in feed and water consumption.

The intestine is filled with bloody material. The spleen, as in marble spleen disease of pheasants, may be swollen and mottled.

There is no particularly satisfactory treatment; in fact, avoid sudden changes in feed or management during an outbreak. Antibiotics reportedly may increase severity of this disease.

Preventive vaccines and emergency antisera preparations are available in some States. Contact your nearest State diagnostic laboratory for guidance.

Other turkey problems include erysipleas, fowl cholera, roundworms, ticks, avian influenza, hexamitiasis, paratyphoid infection, arizonosis, colibacillosis, and aspergillosis.

Game Bird Ills

Cecal Worms. Although the causative nematode, *Heterakis gallinae*, is known to live in the ceca of chickens, turkeys, guinea fowl, quail, and waterfowl, it is particularly damaging to the ceca of pheasants. To prevent cecal worms, game birds should be managed to keep them from eating earthworms or eating off the floor. When this is not possible through rearing on wire, new ground or on an impervious surface, the flock should be treated periodically with a commercially available wormer.

Keep in mind that the cecal worm egg often carries along in its interior the histomonal protozoan that causes blackhead in peafowl, grouse,

quail, wild turkeys, and possibly other types and game birds.

Gapeworms. This unique Y-shaped reddish parasite, *Syngamus trachea*, lives in the windpipes of pheasants, peafowl, guinea fowl, partridges, quail, waterfowl, turkeys, chickens, and other fowl. Affected birds show openmouth breathing, head shaking, grunting or other signs of labored breathing. Severe infestations can cause suffocation, particularly in the young whose windpipes are narrower.

Pen-raised pheasants may soon be able to benefit from preventive levels of thiabendazole in their feed.

As with numerous other parasitic worms, it is important to give attention to management details that prevent or at least minimize a flock's exposure to fecal droppings, and such intermediate hosts as earthworms, slugs and snails.

Marble Spleen Disease. The adenovirus causing this disease of pheasants is closely related, but not identical, to that causing hemorrhagic enteritis of turkeys.

Severe lung congestion with bloody watery fluid is a prominent finding in pheasants found dead with this disease. Fatally afflicted pheasants usually die very suddenly. Mortality is highest as a rule from 10 weeks of age to maturity, and ranges from 5 to 15 percent.

There are no treatments. Outbreaks generally run their course and subside within a month. Marble spleen vaccine may be available in some States on an experimental basis. Contact your nearest diagnostic laboratory or State veterinarian for guidance.

Quail Disorders
Quail Bronchitis. This highly acute, frequently fatal respiratory disease of quail is believed to be caused by an adenovirus. The first outbreak in a flock can be very severe with sneezing, coughing, and loss of appetite spreading to all members. It is very damaging to young quail. Mortality may approach 40 percent. Some survivors develop twisting or bending of the neck.

The disease is produced by a completely different virus than that causing infectious bronchitis in chickens. Consequently, bronchitis vaccines for chickens are of no value in preventing quail bronchitis.

Isolation from other quail flocks and the use of two-year-old breeders have helped prevent serious outbreaks.

Ulcerative Enteritis. This acute infection of the intestinal tract is caused by the spore-forming bacteria, *Clostridium colinum*. Although originally called quail disease because of its devastating effect on quail, ulcerative enteritis is being recognized with increasing frequency in other species of young captive upland game birds and on some occasions in turkeys and chickens.

The disease, which can be mistaken for coccidiosis, mainly produces marked droopiness and severe diarrhea. Small, deep ulcers are scattered along the intestine, while the liver often is found to be covered with large bright yellow- or buff-colored patches.

Up to 100 percent of a young quail flock may be killed by this disease within a few days. Lower, but costly, losses may occur in other game birds.

Having a supply of antibiotics for water administration on hand ahead of time may be the only way to save a flock. One day's delay in proper treatment can be disastrous, but timely administration of bacitracin via the drinking water can produce pronounced improvement.

Water or feed use of streptomycin or tetracyclines also are effective. Water medication may, however, be preferable when as often occurs the flock may be so ill that feed consumption has ceased, and the only way to assure that antibiotics are consumed would be medication via the drinking water.

Flock isolation, segregation, and regular cleanout and cleanup are essential steps in preventing ulcerative enteritis. Always separate old birds from young birds. Keep them on separate premises if you can.

Other game bird diseases are arthropod-borne encephalitis, staphylococcosis, botulism, tuberculosis, coccidiosis, hexamitiasis, erysipelas and fowl cholera.

Waterfowl Diseases
One of the major diseases of the duck-raising industry in the United States, *duck virus hepatitis* must be a primary health consideration for those keeping ducks, especially Pekins.

The disease occurs almost exclusively in ducklings less than 4 weeks of age. It is an extremely acute, rapidly spreading infection with 50 to 95 percent mortality rates.

Affected ducklings soon lose their ability to stand. In a short time they fall on their sides, with death occurring within an hour of the onset of symptoms. The head and neck often are drawn backwards (opisthotonus). Internally, livers are swollen and spotted with hemorrhages.

Antibiotic treatments are of no value. Immediate administration of duck viral hepatitis antiserum preparations, if potent, can significantly alter the disease's course when used in time.

In most instances, the disease is controlled by vaccinating ducklings, or vaccinating their breeder parents who transmit temporary immunity to their offspring—thus protecting them during their early critical weeks of life.

Federally licensed vaccines and antisera are produced at the Duck Research Laboratory, P.O. Box 217, Eastport, N.Y. 11941.

Duck Virus Enteritis, also known as duck plague, is caused by an avian herpes virus capable of producing diarrhea, dehydration and high mortality in all ages of wild or domestic ducks, geese or swans. In many outbreaks Muscovy ducks suffer far heavier mortality rates than other waterfowl on the same premises.

Typical of plague-like maladies, the internal organs of

Special Poultry Diseases

waterfowl with duck virus enteritis are found to contain numerous hemorrhages. The reddened areas of hemorrhage are especially prominent on the liver, the interior and exterior of the intestine and other areas of the digestive tract, throughout the heart and in the ovary. State authorities should be notified of suspected outbreaks.

Vaccine May Help

There is no effective treatment other than possibly vaccinating unaffected waterfowl as soon as possible. Although such vaccination may not prevent all the losses, some vaccinated waterfowl will survive.

State authorities may be able to help you obtain the approvals you will need to use a federally licensed duck virus enteritis vaccine. Contact the aforementioned Duck Research Laboratory in New York where this vaccine is produced.

Vaccine may be authorized also for use in preventing future outbreaks on those farms and locales where duck virus enteritis has been confirmed previously.

The main point in preventing this disease is to keep your waterfowl from mingling or mixing with wild waterfowl because the causative virus is not uncommon in these birds. Their presence in or near your operation should be prevented, and doubly so if you happen to keep Muscovies.

Infectious Serositis. The bacteria, *Pasteurella anatipestifer*, generally is regarded as the cause of infectious serositis in both ducks and geese. In ducks, it may be known also as new duck disease or duck septicemia, and in geese as "goose influenza". It is not to be confused with the viral disease, avian influenza.

Affected ducks or geese often have a mucous discharge from the eyes or nostrils, coughing and sneezing. Diarrhea, incoordination, and emaciation also may accompany this disease.The hearts and livers of infected ducks or geese often are covered with a thin grayish-white slightly adherent film. This or similar changes also may be seen in waterfowl infected with other bacterial infections such as fowl cholera or colibacillosis.

Antibiotics and sulfonamides have been reported as useful in treatment. A federally licensed vaccine also is available.

Other waterfowl diseases are botulism, fowl cholera, colibacillosis, paratyphoid infection, coccidiosis, and aspergillosis.

Special Diseases of Pet Birds

By Jim A. Stunkard and
Edward T. Mallinson

The main characteristics and basic prevention and control strategies for many of the disorders and diseases that will be discussed here have been covered in a previous chapter on *Infectious Diseases*. The chapter you now are reading provides additional features that will apply first to all types of pet birds, and then to selected diseases found mainly in only one or two types.

All Bird Types

Noninfectious and miscellaneous disorders have been listed first because they generally are the types of problems most people face keeping pet birds.

Jim A. Stunkard is Director of the Bowie Animal Hospital, Bowie, Md. Edward T. Mallinson is Associate Professor, Virginia-Maryland Regional College of Veterinary Medicine, University of Maryland campus, College Park.

Beak Deformities. Abnormally overgrown upper beaks may occur. Parakeets frequently need the upper beak trimmed, filed or ground back until it overlaps the lower beak only slightly. This often applies to large parrot types and raptors as well. In some cases, beak deformity is the result of mites, inherited defects, poor nutrition, injury or tumors.

Bumblefoot. Predisposing causes in pet birds, besides those discussed under general diseases, include vitamin A deficiency and confinement to hard potentially abrasive cement floors. Padding of perches, vitamin A injections and surgical treatment may be required to correct this condition in raptors and other valuable birds.

Claw Deformities. Small perching birds, especially canaries and other finches, may be prone to fractured bones if claw deformities are not corrected. This usually requires trimming away claw overgrowth and the control of any concurrent leg mite infestations.

Egg Binding. This life-threatening condition is the result of a bird's inability to complete laying an egg. Found in nearly all pet bird types, it is most often seen in parakeets, cockatiels, finches, and canaries.

Lack of exercise, allowing poorly conditioned hens to breed, infections of the oviduct, and obesity have all been implicated in predisposing birds to this problem. Low calcium intake when seeds or grains are overfed also may play a role.

A generally helpful home remedy has been to place the affected bird in a steaming bathroom (85° to 90° F and 70 percent humidity) for 1 or 2 hours. Consult your veterinarian when additional treatment is required.

Excessive Egg Laying

Birds in high egg production risk egg binding and general exhaustion if their diet is not complete in all essential vitamins and minerals and formulated to supply an increased supply of protein, calcium and energy (calories).

Feathering Ills. Abnormal molting or feather loss can occur in all avian species. Such problems may be related closely to malnutrition, hormonal imbalances, parasites, tumors, obesity, and boredom. A veterinarian should be consulted to fully evaluate the situation. The stress of fright or overheating also may be involved.

Light daily misting of birds with water from an atomizer stimulates many birds to preen their feathers more actively, with significant improvement in the appearance of their plumage.

Hernias. Weakened abdominal muscles in any type of bird and especially in parakeets leads to abdominal ruptures that can be mistaken for tumors. Treatment may not be required. Surgical correction sometimes is indicated.

Injuries. Many veterinarians are skillful and innovative in treating avian injuries. Broken beaks, wings and legs, punctured crops and severe lacerations (cuts or tears) are frequently treated successfully by prompt surgical attention.

Lameness. Refer to earlier chapter on *Miscellaneous Diseases* for a brief discussion.

Dieting Can Help

Malnutrition. Deficiencies are prevalent in all pet birds causing beak, skeletal, nervous, muscular, feathering and reproductive problems. In parakeets, lipidosis, a serious problem taxing vital internal organs, is treated by gradually increasing a bird's exercise routine while decreasing feed consumption, especially seeds. Veterinarians can prescribe a reducing diet.

Poisoning. Homes often contain many items toxic to pet birds. The list includes several house plants, aerosol can propellants, natural gas when a pilot light fails, rodenticides, mothballs, cigarette butts, and denture cleaners.

Overheated non-stick frying pans or fumes of burned meat or fat have been reported to cause sudden widespread avian deaths in some home aviaries. Lead poisoning can result from pecking and eating curtain weights, lead shot and some paints and wine bottle foils.

Tumors. Pet birds, especially parakeets, appear susceptible to a wide range of benign and malignant tumors. Fatty skin tumors often may be treated by dietary changes. Skin or superficial tumors frequently can be removed sur-

gically, but large internal tumors usually are inoperable.

Protozoan Diseases

Coccidiosis. Various *Eimeria* and *Isospora* species of coccidia have been found in various types of birds. Although the number of recognized infections is rather low, the disease does produce loss of appetite and watery stools.

Accurate diagnosis is made by examining fecal specimens microscopically to demonstrate the causative coccidial oocysts.

Giardiasis. This disease is caused by a protozoan that moves about in intestinal secretions by whip-like action of its tail (flagella). Giardiasis can result in very persistent diarrhea, depressed appetite and weight loss.

Cockatiels, cockatoos, and parakeets are the most susceptible, especially the young fledglings. Microscopic examination of fecal specimens leads to accurate diagnosis and appropriate treatment.

Malaria of Birds. Several different forms of avian malaria affect pet birds of all types. All are transmitted by bloodsucking flies and mosquitoes. Very briefly, the major forms are blood infections with *Hemaproteus, Leucocytozoon,* and *Plasmodium* species.

Special Diseases of Pet Birds

Hemaproteus, while producing mild and often unnoticed infections in raptors, canaries, and other finch types, has been found to produce fatal illness in pigeons, doves, and cockatoos.

Leucocytozoan infections can be a serious problem in young parakeets, canaries, pigeons and raptors. Anemia and droopiness, soon followed by death, may be seen. Older birds may exhibit few, if any, signs of illness. Internally, the major changes are swelling of the liver and spleen and damage to the heart (myocarditis).

Infection with *Plasmodium* species occurs less frequently than the other avian malarias. It usually is found in canaries, finches, pigeons, and doves. Symptoms can include ruffled feathers, swollen eyelids, pale watery blood, general weakness, and in severe cases, death. Livers and spleens of affected birds often are darkened and enlarged.

Trichomoniasis. This protozoan infection, which also is caused by a flagellated motile (swimming) protozoan, is a problem principally in canaries, finches, pigeons, doves and raptors. The mouth is the chief site of involvement.

Advanced infections result in severe accumulations of yellow cheesy debris on the tongue and in the back of the mouth (pharynx). Infections should be professionally confirmed and treated with appropriate drugs.

Bacterial Diseases
Chlamydiosis (psittacosis or ornithosis). As already discussed, the disease is not limited to pet birds. It also is found in turkeys and waterfowl.

This can be an especially serious problem not only in imported parrots and related psittacines, but also in long-established domestic aviaries where prolonged, high death losses can occur. The disease has been called parrot fever.

Imported birds are treated routinely with chlamydiostatic antibiotics to control this infection. Sometimes, however, poor consumption of antibiotic-treated feed means that a portion of imported birds may continue to remain infected. Such birds may become fatally sick soon after purchase.

Chlamydiosis occurs mostly in imported birds, but also can make gradual inroads into a domestic breeding operation when an undetected carrier sheds infection throughout an aviary. Periodic cycles of antibiotic medication are being recommended to avert this problem.

Research supported by the pet industry, private sources, and various agencies is being aimed at developing better methods to detect carriers and consistently get rid of infections. Your veterinarian can keep you informed on this progress.

Outside aviaries or pet bird collections are at risk of chlamydiosis from infected wild free-flying birds.

Other Bacteria

Colibacillosis, pasteurellosis, salmonellosis (paratyphoid) and tuberculosis—were previously discussed. These also are pet bird diseases and—with the exception of tuberculosis—usually respond to antibiotic treatment. They are largely preventable through practice of the good management recommendations emphasized in later chapters on *General Management* and *Management: Pet Birds.*

For example, poor sanitation or excessive stress increases the likelihood and severity of paratyphoid infection in many types of pet birds. Pasteurellosis can be fatally introduced in small birds or pigeons by cat bites and into raptors by consumption of pasteurella-infected waterfowl.

Pseudomonas and *Proteus* infections appear more common in pet birds than poultry. These infections, like colibacillosis, often begin as a complication of a virus infection, poor ventilation (too drafty or too stuffy), malnutrition, or any other weakening conditions.

Tuberculosis, not only a problem in old chickens or game birds, is one of the most common bacterial diseases of hawks and several other types of pet or hobby raptors. Large, adult parrots and macaws also are susceptible.

Hemophilus infection (coryza) is discussed later in this chapter under special diseases of pigeons.

Viral Diseases

Pox Virus. This infection in pet birds appears differently from one type of bird to another. In canaries, pox produces severe breathing difficulties and rough thickened areas around the eyes and beak. Parrots, such as Blue Front and Yellow Head or Yellow Nape Parrots, develop cheesy thickenings in the mouth and throat. Pox involvement of the head and eye may occur also in these and other parrots.

Pigeons develop raised pox scabs around the eyes and

face. In raptors, pox produces lumpy (nodular) thickenings of the feet, shanks, and face. The upper digestive tract also may be affected.

Vaccines have been used for pigeon and canary pox. Others may be available in the future for parrot types and raptors. Each type basically requires its own pox vaccine. In other words, a vaccine that is effective for one type of bird often is ineffective in another bird type.

Herpes Virus. Several different herpes virus infections are found in pet birds. They generally are limited to specific types such as parrot types, pigeons and raptors and will be discussed or mentioned under special diseases of these birds. They are different from livestock and human herpes viruses.

Newcastle Disease. Includes Exotic Newcastle Disease (Velogenic Viscerotropic Newcastle Disease). This is a highly contagious disease capable of infecting most birds. The disease may be characterized by respiratory, digestive, or nervous system involvement.

Signs of the disease and expected mortality rates vary depending on the strain of the virus and susceptibility of the host.

The infection may be transient or inapparent in pet birds, with carriers serving as a threat to the poultry industry—where the disease can cause nearly 100 percent death losses.

Even large psittacines (parrots, conures, and cockatoos) generally suffer more severe infections with higher mortality rates than the smaller types of birds like parakeets, canaries, and finches.

Pet bird survivors of Newcastle disease may develop chronic nervous disorders such as tremors, wing droop, partial or complete leg paralysis, or twisted necks.

Avoid "bargain" pet birds. Pet bird smuggling is not uncommon, and such birds escaping tests for Newcastle disease at licensed bird import stations pose a hazard to individual bird owners, pet dealers, and the nation's food supply. Anonymous reports of bird smuggling can be made by calling a special Department of Agriculture office at 301-436-8065, or your official State Veterinarian.

Parasitic Diseases
Scaly Face or Leg Mites. *Knemidocoptes pilae* and similar mites are responsible for a variety of common disorders

in parakeets, lovebirds, and other psittacines. Finches and canaries are affected less frequently.

In parakeets, infestations by this burrowing mite produce crusty proliferations at the cere or corners of the mouth. The tunneling of this parasite can deform the beak eventually. Scaly accumulations sometimes also develop under the beak, around the eyes, on the legs, and near the vent.

In large hook-bills (psittacines), the damage produced by scaly mites is less obvious and less common. Thickening around the nostrils (nares) may be the only sign of infestation.

Canaries and finches, when infested, usually develop "coat of armor" like scabs of the shank of the leg, similar to those described earlier in older backyard-type chickens. Pigeons with this parasite exhibit both facial and leg involvement. An injectable treatment and effective ointments are available.

Tracheal and Air Sac Mites. The trachea (windpipe) and air sacs of finches, canaries, and occasionally parakeets and dwarf parrots can become the home for tiny internal mites *(Sternostoma* and *Cytodites).*

These parasites cause birds to make characteristic "clicking" or "smacking" sounds. Canaries and other birds may cease singing, lose weight, develop open-mouthed breathing and make repeated attempts at throat-clearings.

Various techniques are available for diagnosing, treating and preventing these mites. Obtain professional guidance promptly if you suspect this condition.

Worms. Ascarids (roundworms) may produce weight loss, depressed appetite and diarrhea in young or breeding pigeons or hook-bills, especially Australian parakeets. Examination of stools microscopically provides the diagnosis.

Capillaria worms are a serious problem in raptors. They also parasitize canaries, parakeets and other pet birds.

Cecal Worms *(Heterakis gallinae)* and gapeworms *(Syngamus trachea)* have been reported in pet birds of various types. They can be introduced through the feeding of earthworms which are intermediate hosts of these parasitic worms.

Fungal (mycotic) Diseases. Refer to descriptions in earlier chapter on *Infectious Diseases.*

Psittaciformes (Parrots, Hook-bills) Brown Hypertrophy of the Cere occurs in female parakeets. It may be influenced by the hormone estrogen. Ordinarily this change does not require treatment.

Overlaying and Exhaustion: Repetitive laying of eggs, leading eventually to exhaustion and frequently life-threatening egg binding, is not uncommon in highly productive psittacines, such as parakeets, cockatoos and especially cockatiels. Several treatments include reducing the daily ration to halt laying, injections of hormones, and in some instances, surgery.

Pacheco's Parrot Disease: Also known as psittacine herpes virus infection, this acute, frequently fatal virus infection appears limited to hook-bills.

Outbreaks of this disease often occur when a recently recovered or infected psittacine or virus carrier conure (a medium-sized South or Central American hook-bill) is added to a group of susceptible birds. Psittacines most susceptible appear to be parrots, cockatoos and macaws.

Devastating infections have occurred in some aviaries. Special microscopic changes in the livers of dead birds enable diagnostic laboratories to provide your veterinarian with diagnostic confirmation in suspected cases.

Severity of outbreaks can be reduced by 1) keeping collections in small, well-separated groups, 2) keeping cages on one level so droppings from infected birds do not contaminate the feed and water of others, and 3) isolating new birds from others for a minimum of 6 weeks. Development of a licensed Pacheco's vaccine, which presently is experimental, may eventually prevent the disease.

Parakeet Fledgling Disease: This newly recognized disease in parakeets and some other hook-bills is caused by a papovavirus apparently transmitted from older fledglings to younger ones grown close by. Mortality rates can be up to 30 to 70 percent before birds reach 1 to 3 weeks of age. Crops are full and abdomens enlarged and reddened.

Moving breeders to another locale to enable cleanout and cleanup of the growing facility can break the cycle of continued and worsening passage of this disease from older fledglings to younger ones.

A suggested approach has been to depopulate the rearing-breeding facility so there are no newborn birds for 3 months, along with disposal of all old nests. Previously removed breeders can then be returned and reused after the premises, cages, and equipment have been thoroughly washed, scrubbed and disinfected.

Hand-feeding can help the spread of this disease. Psittacine papovavirus vaccines are currrently only experimental.

Other Important Diseases of Psittacines: Beak deformity, candidiasis, cannibalism of fledglings by cockatoos, chlamidiosis, colibacillosis, giardiasis, gout, mites, Newcastle disease, paratyphoid, pox, tuberculosis and tumors.

Canaries and Finches
Alopecia or Baldness of Canaries: Dull, dirty feathering, head baldness, feather pulling and lack of singing often appear metabolic or glandular (endocrine) in origin. Professional consultation is advisable.

Toe Necrosis: This problem can result in rotting (gangrene) of a toe or even a leg when blood circulation is blocked from strings unraveling from cloth used for cage

Special Diseases of Pet Birds

bedding or other sources.

Other important diseases of canaries and finches are: Claw deformity, coccidiosis, egg binding, feather picking, giardiasis, mites, pox, trichomoniasis, and worms.

Pigeons and Doves

Coryza: Caused by *Hemophilus gallinarum*, this bacterial disease is also common in backyard chickens. Its main signs in pigeons are sneezing, nasal discharge, and swelling of the face, especially around the eyes. The disease responds well to proper antibiotic therapy.

Pigeon Flies: Dark brown flies with single wings *(Pseudolynchia canariensis)* can sometimes be found moving rapidly among the feathers of pigeons. They live on pigeon blood and may cause heavy losses to squabs. They probably contribute to the spread of pigeon malaria.

Their control depends on thorough cleaning and sanitizing of lofts every three weeks and dusting of squabs with insecticide powders.

Other Important Diseases of Pigeons and Doves: Lice, malaria, mites, pigeon encephalitis, pigeon herpes virus infection, pox, and trichomoniasis.

Raptors (Falcons, Hawks, and Other Birds of Prey): Most important in maintaining the health of raptors is preventing vitamin and mineral deficiencies (rickets), aspergillosis, botulism, trichomoniasis, and very importantly, avian tuberculosis. All of these have been previously discussed in earlier disease chapters.

Tuberculosis is a particularly common and serious malady of raptors. Owls, however, may be less prone to this problem.

A herpes virus infection, known as owl hepatosplenitis or inclusion body disease of raptors, is also of concern. A disease worthy of greater research, it causes listlessness, appetite loss, reduced disease resistance and severe degenerative changes in the liver, spleen and bone marrow.

Foreign Diseases

By Edwin I. Pilchard

A significant part of the $9.6 billion poultry industry would be lost if any of several different foreign diseases were to enter and spread in the United States.

Exotic Newcastle disease (velogenic viscerotropic Newcastle disease) is considered the most dangerous of the foreign poultry diseases because of the ease with which it can spread among chickens, turkeys, pet birds, and other avian species, and its ability to stop egg laying or kill most affected birds.

It appears in a variety of different forms, often seen in chickens as a fatal disease with difficult breathing, swelling of the face around the eyes, and sometimes diarrhea. Pet birds also may exhibit

these signs, and some may show abnormal motions or positions of a leg, wing or the head, caused by nerve damage. The first birds to die in a new outbreak may give no warning they are sick.

Chickens that have been properly vaccinated for Newcastle disease and then become infected with the exotic virus may harbor and shed exotic Newcastle disease virus without showing signs of sickness. These can become potential sources for new outbreaks in unvaccinated chickens and other susceptible birds.

It is sobering to know that an outbreak of exotic Newcastle disease in Southern California in 1972 took 2 years and $56 million to eradicate. It would cost an estimated $280 million in production losses each year if this disease were to become established in U.S. poultry flocks.

Avian influenza is another virus-caused disease that var-

Edwin I. Pilchard is a Principal Staff Officer, Veterinary Services, Animal and Plant Health Inspection Service.

ies widely in the kinds of changes it can produce in infected chickens and turkeys. Humans are not susceptible to avian influenza.

The most lethal form of avian influenza has not been reported in the U.S. since it was eradicated in 1929. However, in 1983 a highly lethal form suddenly appeared in Southeastern Pennsylvania and spread to small areas of Virginia, Maryland, and New Jersey. Experts believe the source of this outbreak was wild waterfowl.

Lethal avian influenza causes deaths in a high proportion of the chickens or turkeys in affected flocks, while ducks and other waterfowl can harbor and shed the virus without becoming sick. Some strains of avian influenza are mild, causing little or no sickness, even though they continue to spread and have the potential to change suddenly and become killers.

Chickens with lethal avian influenza may show swelling of the face around the eyes, dark purplish discoloration of the comb and wattles, skin hemorrhages, and sometimes swollen hock joints and purplish discoloration of the shanks. In laying hens, the first sign is often a sudden drop in egg production, with many eggs laid with no shells or soft shells.

Pet birds are considered susceptible to avian influenza virus, but few of those with the virus show any sign of sickness. Sudden death of pet birds that have been recently bought should prompt their owners to consider either avian influenza, exotic Newcastle disease, or chlamydiosis (parrot fever) as the possible cause—and obtain the services of a qualified veterinarian.

Egg drop syndrome is caused by an adenovirus of ducks that can sometimes affect chickens, causing a decrease in the number of eggs laid each day by the infected flock, or as a failure of layers to come into full production. Both effects can make egg production unprofitable.

The disease has been reported in Ireland, England, the Netherlands, Japan, and Australia. The virus also has been isolated from normal domestic ducks in the United States.

Goose Hepatitis
Wild and domestic geese and Muscovy ducklings are susceptible to the virus of goose hepatitis, which causes a watery, white diarrhea, discharge of fluids from the eyes and nasal openings, and death of many

Prevention of foreign diseases in poultry and other avian species requires cooperation by all who import poultry, eggs and other poultry products or pet birds. Regulations requiring isolation and testing of birds entering the United States are designed to keep out diseases.

goslings. Goslings that survive may not grow, but remain as runts.

Chlamydiosis

Psittacosis or chlamydiosis may not be foreign to the United States. However, the U.S. Public Health Service and USDA recommend giving specially medicated feed to all imported hook-billed birds to rid them of possible psittacosis infection immediately after arrival in this country.

Affected parrots and turkeys may have diarrhea and other signs similar to those described for exotic Newcastle disease and avian influenza. Humans are susceptible to the psittacosis organism. The dis-

ease in turkeys and other non-psittacine birds is called ornithosis.

Prevention of foreign animal diseases in poultry and other avian species requires cooperation by all who import poultry, poultry eggs, and other poultry products, or pet birds, including persons who bring these items with them when entering the United States from abroad. A more detailed discussion of prevention, and an outline of the way this country is prepared to respond to introduction of a foreign animal disease, are given in a chapter titled *Barring the Door to Foreign Diseases* in the first section of this book.

Foreign Diseases

General Management

By Edward T. Mallinson

Regardless of the specific type of poultry or other kinds of birds you may keep for profit, pleasure, or companionship, certain general management requirements always must be met. They are proper feeding, appropriate housing, effective sanitation, and a dedication to disease prevention.

Varying body sizes, behaviors, dietary needs and environmental preferences make special modifications or additional considerations necessary.

Separate chapters follow with descriptions of many of these special management and nutritional needs for poultry and for pet birds.

As you become more in-

formed concerning the many details of poultry and pet bird care, do not lose sight of the basics. Your constancy in always giving the basic considerations of management and disease prevention top priority still reaps the greatest rewards.

Nutrition. General nutritional recommendations were discussed in the chapter on *Nutritional Diseases.*

Housing. Facilities for poultry, cage or aviary birds always should be structurally sound and kept in good repair. This is essential to protect your poultry or birds from injury and to contain them from escape or from visiting other premises.

As much as is practical for the type kept, housing must be designed and maintained to sharply restrict the entrance of other birds or animals. Flock owners and aviary operators should place locks on doors to control and reduce

Edward T. Mallinson is Associate Professor, Virginia-Maryland Regional College of Veterinary Medicine, University of Maryland campus, College Park.

markedly the number of human visitors. People commonly carry diseases from flock to flock on their feet, clothing, or in their hair.

Fencing used for confinement should be of a size and construction sturdy enough to keep wild animals out. Do not underestimate the strength, persistence and cunning of most predators.

Regardless of whether indoor or outdoor housing facilities are used, poultry or birds should be protected from temperature extremes, severe wind, or drafts. Providing extra warmth is always essential for the young.

Cooling Needed

Natural or mechanical means of good ventilation for cooling during hot months of the year are key considerations in proper housing. This is true whether you keep a single pet bird or a flock of 500 or more chickens or parakeets.

Spacing should permit freedom of movement and postural adjustments for each occupant. With perching birds, this includes sufficient perches and other roosting areas for the number confined.

All the birds should be able to get ample clean water and feed at will, without undo or unnatural waiting or competition from pen or cage mates. Note: With certain bird species, fruits or juice may be used as a water substitute or supplement.

Feeders and waterers should be located and of such design as to minimize fecal contamination. These receptacles should be cleaned often. Slime should not be allowed to accumulate in waterers. Feed should not be allowed to build up in the corners or in feeders or other locations. Remove caked or moldy feed immediately.

Enclosures for poultry and other birds should be designed to make cleaning, disinfection, and servicing a relatively convenient task. Cracks and crevices should be avoided or corrected. Mechanical devices that are easy to clean should be used in preference to those where thorough cleaning may be cumbersome.

Flooring Needs

Whenever possible, particullarly where high populations are kept within a relatively small confined area, the housing floor should be of an impervious nature, usually concrete; or made of wire that allows droppings to fall out of reach of cage or pen occupants.

This is a major require-

Kevin Shields

Litter material used over either earth or concrete flooring should be kept deep and dry for the control of most parasitic diseases. Add clean, mold-free litter periodically.

ment for control of most parasitic diseases.

Litter material used over either earth or concrete flooring should be kept deep and dry. It should be stirred frequently and wet spots promptly removed. Add clean, mold-free litter periodically. Allowing poultry or birds repeated contact with dirt or ground contaminated with increasing amounts of fecal

droppings never pays.

Often the only way many diseases have been effectively controlled has been with either wooden-slatted or wire floors. When this is not possible, the frequently cumbersome procedure of annual range or ground rotation has been used—but only with partial success.

Currently there is no truly effective way to disinfect the ground or earth floors. All disinfectants are inactivated by large amounts of dirt or debris.

Cleanout, Cleanup

Sanitation. As already mentioned, proper sanitation is a must for poultry or bird health. For the single caged pet bird in a home, cleaning and disinfection frequently is part of a daily or weekly routine. For the larger collections of either poultry or birds, periodic total cleanout and cleanup is equally or even more essential—although not necessarily done as frequently.

Ponds for waterfowl should not be overcrowded and ideally should be drained periodically.

Very basically, proper sanitation includes those measures you take to expose the total surroundings of your poultry or birds to the action of properly diluted, mixed, and applied disinfectants, insecticides, and miticides.

With poultry, it begins in most instances with annual removal of the entire flock of chickens, turkeys, game birds, and waterfowl for processing. The same approach also may be feasible and certainly a desirable disease prevention practice in retail and bird dealerships when used on a periodic basis at times of the year when business volume may permit.

Of course total depopulation is not advocated for a few home pets, nor is it necessarily practical or advisable for *breeding* colonies or flocks of pet birds or poultry. Here, valuable stock must be retained from year to year.

Nevertheless, some strategic advance planning could allow temporary removal of breeders to other locations, so their cages, pens, and equipment could be cleaned and disinfected. They can be returned later when sanitation has been completed.

The number of birds retained for breeding can be reduced by careful selection. Old breeders, young breeders, and stock for sale can be kept in separate pens or rooms, or better on different premises. It

all comes down to the principle that "disease prevention pays."

Disease prevention management was described in detail in the chapter on *Preventing Disease*.

All Out Clean

Once your poultry or bird removal or relocation step has been completed, the rest of sanitation is straightforward. The key is absolutely thorough cleaning. In other words, remove as much dust, feathers, fecal, and other debris as possible. Litter always must be removed. Old feed and other disposable items should be discarded.

Do not expect disinfectants to penetrate very far. If you can see that a piece of equipment or a board or section of concrete is stained or still has fecal or other debris clinging to it, scrape it, soak it, and scrub it away. Would you rather eat from a clean plate or a dirty plate that had been disinfected?

Proper application of an approved licensed spray, fumigant or fogged disinfectant and similarly applied insecticide represents the capstone of a good sanitation program. It will only be as effective as your prior preparation of the surface to be contacted.

General Management

Follow the manufacturer's instructions exactly. Do not skimp on dilutions. Apply all sprays forcefully and liberally into any existing crack, crevices, and joints—places where insect eggs, mites, bacteria, and viruses frequently are hidden.

A waiting period or "downtime" of 1 to 4 weeks is often advisable following sanititation to allow for die-off of any remaining infectious agents.

Rats, Mice, Flies

Although rat and mouse control has not been discussed in great detail here, it is another significant part of good sanitation.

Cleanout and cleanup time is an excellent chance to attack these pests. They are hungry and looking for feed when your flock, and the feed you've been providing, have been removed. At this time,

they will be much more vulnerable to poison-baited feeds. Contact an exterminator for best results.

Routine, regular baiting or trapping programs are considered the most effective way to keep rats and mice in check. County Cooperative Extension agents and State universities often have active educational programs and materials on the control of these and other pests.

Fly control techniques are available from the same locations. Flies have been documented in the spread of many avian diseases and parasitic infestations. Proper removal of manure is the key to fly control. It can be spread on fields, buried, or incinerated.

When using sanitation products, avoid outdated preparations, store the products at proper temperatures, and most important of all, *Read the Labels.*

Basic Cleaning and Disinfection[1]

Preparation
1. Spray house with an approved agricultural insecticide, then clean out litter.
2. Remove debris and dust from ceiling joist and walls.
3. Brush and blow dust from fans, motors, louvers and electrical equipment.
4. Cover motors and electrical equipment with plastic, and seal watertight.

Cleaning

1. Scrape and brush all equipment—cages, feeders, brooders, waterers, nest boxes, etc.

2. Scrape and sweep floor to remove packed litter and any dust or debris from ceilings and walls.

3. Clean up all debris outside of building—especially around entry room and any other entrances to building.

4. Wet down entire house inside with plenty of water to soak loose any caked material.

5. Thoroughly wash ceiling, walls and floors using water, a cleansing agent (detergent), and a sprayer with at least 400 psi nozzle pressure.

6. Check entire house; "touch up" any areas not absolutely clean.

Disinfection

1. Sanitize entire house inside, and 8 to 10 feet around outside of house, with plenty of registered approved disinfectant at label-approved strength using pressure sprayer.

2. Allow to dry, then place new litter, disinfected equipment, etc.

3. Remove covers from electrical equipment.

4. Obtain the advice of a qualified electrician before attempting to disinfect any electrical equipment. With appropriate safety precautions, surfaces of such equipment reportedly have been treated either by wiping with a disinfectant or by exposure to a disinfectant fog or mist from an aerosol can or mechanical fogger. Never disinfect equipment if power is on! Always consult with an electrician first.

Fumigation

Fumigation gases such as formaldehyde penetrate and help disinfect cracks, crevices and equipment interiors that may be hard to reach by sprays. Their safe use requires skill and experience. Fumigation is practiced mainly in hatcheries, after a severe disease outbreak, or as a periodic extra disinfecting procedure after two or three routine disinfections. Details may be obtained from Vineland Laboratories[2], Vineland, N.J. 08360.

[1]Modified from Committee Reports of the American Association of Avian Pathologists. Although oriented to poultry houses, these basic suggestions could, *with some changes,* be adapted readily for aviaries or other facilities housing pet birds.
[2]Mention of company name does not constitute endorsement or an intended or implied discrimination against other organizations.

Management: Poultry

By Edward T. Mallinson and
Jim A. Stunkard

Numerous excellent texts are available to the backyard poultry keeper. They provide useful, easily understood pointers on all sorts of domesticated fowl. Cooperative Extension agents and university poultry or veterinary specialists often can provide instructional literature on the care of game birds, waterfowl, chickens, and turkeys.

If for example you are keeping laying chickens, you may want to learn more about proper light management because the number of total hours of natural and artificial light your pullets and layers receive every day affects the number of eggs they will lay.

Edward T. Mallinson is Associate Professor, Virginia-Maryland Regional College of Veterinary Medicine, University of Maryland campus, College Park. Jim A. Stunkard is Director of the Bowie Animal Hospital, Bowie, Md.

Daily day length affects the glandular secretion of hormones needed to make birds start and keep laying eggs.

In general, the hours of daily light for growing pullets should be less than for layers. The total hours of daily light for layers should be over 12 and near 14 hours for maximum egg production. The hours of daily light supplied by either sunlight or artificial lighting for layers may be *increased* up to 16 hours, *but should never be reduced.* The light hours must always be as great as the length of the longest day of the year during which you expect to harvest eggs.

Many backyard poultry producers have found it advantageous to consult with persons keeping or supplying large commercial flocks for timely tips on poultry management.

Nutrition

Whenever possible, provide complete commercial all mash, crumbled, or pelleted rations specifically formulated for the type raised. Do not feed the above with grains unless your ration has been designed with the intended need for grain supplementation. Avoid heavy reliance on grains despite their attractiveness.

The dietary data provided is only a guide. Follow the company feeding program of your feed supplier. Never feed a layer egg production ration to any type of young growing poultry. The high calcium levels normally present in layer rations may cause permanent serious injury to the kidney.

Maintain clean water at a temperature between 50° to 70° F. Drinking is reduced if water temperature goes above 70° or below 50°. Day-old chicks can be affected adversely by cold water.

Chickens

Meat-type (broilers): 1 day to 5 weeks—starter feed; 5 weeks to 7 weeks—finisher. Finisher and corn is fed longer for roasters and capons. Withdrawal feed often is fed briefly during the last several days before processing or marketing. The length of time depends on type(s) of medication that may have been used in the finisher.

Egg-type (layers): 1 day to 6 weeks—starter feed; 6 weeks to 13 weeks—grower or pullet developer; 13 to 20 weeks—developer; 20 weeks—layer feed plus oyster shell or limestone grit free-choice.

Note: Anti-coccidial preventive medications (coccidiostats) in most instances should be added to the feed of growing meat- or egg-type chickens.

Turkeys

Turkeys require a significantly higher percentage of protein in their feed than chickens. A coccidiostat in the feed usually suffices until 8 weeks of age, at which time it may be more advantageous to switch to a dietary blackhead preventive medication.

Basically, a turkey starter feed is provided for the first 8 weeks followed by a grower feed until processing or marketing time. Read feed labels for any withdrawal feed recommendations.

Game Birds

(Grouse, Guineas, Partridges, Pheasants, Quail). When available, provide a game bird ration formulated for the specific type raised. A 25 to 30

Management: Poultry

percent protein turkey ration usually provides for well-balanced game bird nutrition. Studies are in process to obtain official clearances for the use of coccidiostats in pheasant rations.

Growing Stock. From 1 day to 5 or 6 weeks during the period of most rapid growth, provide a high protein starter feed—being careful not to supply any supplemental corn or other grains.

Generally after about 6 weeks, game birds raised for meat production should be fed game bird grower and supplemental grain to maturity. Supplemental whole grain is provided only in the evenings from 6 to 9 weeks, and in both mornings and evenings from 10 weeks to maturity.

Don't overfeed grain or your game birds may not get a proper balance of essential nutrients contained in the starter/grower. Some feed companies may provide various grower-type feeds that require no added grain.

When whole grain feeding is begun, be sure to provide grit. Separate grit hoppers usually are preferred.

Breeding Stock. Game birds selected for retention as breeders should be kept from gaining excess weight by feeding a maintenance diet from

maturity to 1 month before the egg production season.

A breeder ration should be fed, without added grain, throughout the breeding season. This often can be either a chicken, turkey or game breeder feed. Breeders should be returned to a maintenance feed after the hens are through laying.

The transitions between maintenance and breeder rations can be eased to reduce stress on birds by partial mixing of these feeds for 5 to 7 days.

Hunting Release Stock. The nutrition and housing arrangements for release stock often require modifications to allow for conditioning to the wild. Consult with local authorities and check game bird literature for important details.

Ducks and Geese

Ducks can be raised in confinement whereas geese prefer to range when there is an abundant supply of tender, succulent weeds and grasses. In either case, both must have ample supplies of water, day and night, whenever lights would be on or feed available. Waterfowl can choke on dry feed. Pelleted feeds are preferred for waterfowl, but are not essential. Provide grower-

USDA

size insoluble grit throughout the growing period.

Growing Ducks. 1 day to 2 weeks—starter feed (22 percent protein); 2 weeks to market or processing—grower feed.

Growing Geese. 1 day to 6 weeks feed goslings 22 percent protein goose starter or high protein chick starter. Avoid feeding any grain during the first 3 to 4 weeks.

After 6 weeks of age, geese can go on pasture with supplemental 15 percent grower pellets. Depending on the quantity and quality of the pasture, or amount of growth desired, adjust the

Geese, such as these African geese, prefer to range where there is an abundant supply of tender, succulent weeds and grasses.

amount of grower up or down. High growth or sparse pasture necessitates increased portions of commercial feeds.

Breeding Ducks or Geese. Males and females selected as potential breeders should be kept from becoming too fat by maintaining them on a breeder-developer diet. Switch the breeders to a duck or goose breeder ration at least 1 month before antici-

Management: Poultry

USDA

pated egg production. Be sure to supply oyster shell free-choice.

Floor Space Needs

Recommendations that follow are minimal standards. As a general rule the more space the better.

Chickens

Meat-type: From 1 day to 11 weeks, 1.25 square feet per bird and from 11 weeks to market or processing, 2 to 2.25 square feet. No roosts.

Egg-type: From 1 day to 11 weeks, 1 square foot per bird, and from 12 to 20 or 22 weeks, 1.5 to 2 square feet. Small farm layers on all litter floor, 2 to 3 square feet per bird. Caged leghorn layers have performed well at about 70 to 80 square inches per bird.

Numerous factors affect the best cage density for any particular group of layers. A few are the number of layers

Geese or ducks selected as potential breeders should be kept from becoming too fat by maintaining them on a breeder-developer diet. Breeding flock of Buff geese.

per cage, and the amount of feeder trough space available to each bird.

Roosts for egg-type chickens raised and maintained on the floor can be constructed of $2'' \times 2''$ or $2'' \times 4''$ wooden boards with rounded or beveled upper edges to protect feet from injuries and infections. They are best located over the dropping pits. Allow 7 to 10 inches of roost space per bird.

Turkeys

From 1 day to 8 weeks, 1 to 1.5 square feet per bird, and from 8 weeks to marketing, 5 square feet per bird (if debeaked) or 7 square feet per bird if not debeaked.

Game Birds

Floor space requirements for game birds on small farms

A Home-Made Cage for Chickens

Step 1: Cut Cage Section A of 1″ × 1″ or 1″ × 2″ welded wire to length indicated in table.

Step 2: Bend as shown in sketch. Use a hammer and edge of a 2″ × 4″ board to help bend even, square corners. Make the 2″ corner bend overlap first.

Step 3: Connect the one loose corner to the 2″ overlap using cage clips and appropriate clip pliers.

Step 4: Cut Cage Section B to length indicated in table. Bend as shown in sketch. Using cage clips, secure both overlaps to cage top, all four side corners, and the double-bottom floor. Even if 1″ × 2″ wire is used, a 1″ × 1″ floor mesh pattern will be achieved. Be sure to secure double-bottom wires at several scattered locations to prevent toe injuries.

Step 5: Cut a 10″ × 10″ door opening on one side. Make a 14″ × 14″ wire door and hinge to cage with standard cage clips. Make opening larger for larger cages. IMPORTANT: Cut all wire ends so they can be bent backwards to prevent forming sharp edges. Split tubing can be slipped over the bottom edge of the door opening to protect caretaker's hands and arms.

Step 6: To prevent crowding, improve sanitation and make feeding and watering easier, cut appropriate openings and attach feeders and waterers to the outside of the cage. Two 12″ × 12″ × 6″ deep nesting boxes should be placed and secured inside the cage. Replace nest straw periodically to maintain freshness and cleanliness.

The finished cage should be located at a convenient height from the floor. A cage stand (see sketch) may be used for this purpose. The cage may also be suspended from the ceiling by small chains or wires.

The cage can be built and furnished with materials and equipment (welded wire, cage clips, clip pliers, feeders and waterers) available from many hardware and feed stores. A catalog of the equipment needed may be obtained from Marsh Farms, P.O. Box 7, Garden Grove, CA 92642.

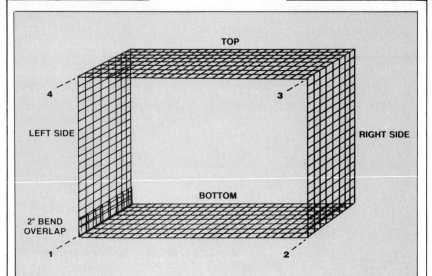

Step 2 bends. Bends needed to form first section of cage. Numbers indicate order of sequence of corner forming bends.

Lengths of Welded Wire Needed for Steps 2 and 4.

Cage Section	Cage Dimensions[a]			
	Floor and top length	Side height	Cage width	Total dimensions of wire sections
A (step 1)	27″ or 45″ (2 hens) (4 hens)	24″[b]	32″	104″[c] × 32″ (2 hens) 140″[c] × 32″ (4 hens)
B (step 4)	27″ or 45″ (2 hens) (4 hens)	24″[b]	32″	84″[d] × 27″ (2 hens) 84″[d] × 45″ (4 hens)

[a] Measurements can be increased to accommodate a maximum of 8 laying hens.
[b] Height should be increased by 6″ if roosts (optional) are planned.
[c] 2 × (length + height) + 2″.
[d] (2 × height) + width + 4″.

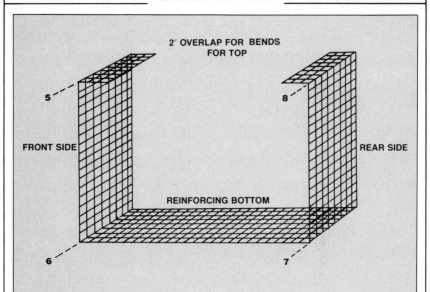

2″ OVERLAP FOR BENDS
FOR TOP

5

8

FRONT SIDE

REAR SIDE

REINFORCING BOTTOM

6

7

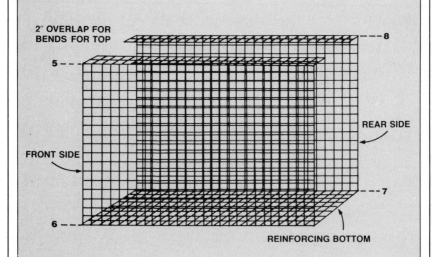

2″ OVERLAP FOR
BENDS FOR TOP

8

5

REAR SIDE

FRONT SIDE

7

6

REINFORCING BOTTOM

Step 4 bends. Bends needed to form second part of cage.
This part reinforces bottom and completes the last 2 sides (front
and rear).

Management: Poultry   99

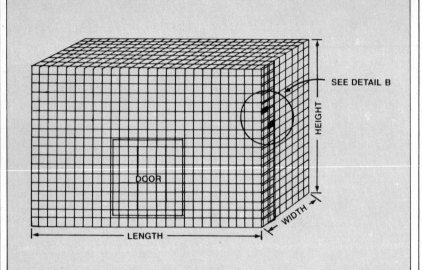

Cage outline

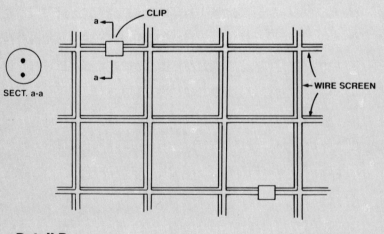

Detail B

University of Maryland
Agri-Engineering Dept.
College Park, MD '84

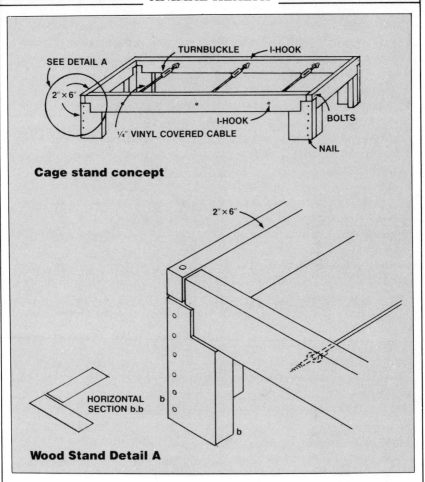

Cage stand concept

Wood Stand Detail A

are similar to those for chickens or turkeys. Breeder pheasants in a house with light control need 4 square feet per bird, while those raised outside need 25 to 30 square feet per bird.

On most general farms, guinea keets are raised in small flocks, usually 30 to 40 to a brooder.

From 1 to 10 days, quail require 0.25 to 0.30 square foot per bird; from 11 days to 6 weeks, 0.3 to 0.5 square foot is needed. After 6 weeks quail need 0.75 to 1 square foot per bird. Breeding quail on the floor need 1 square foot per bird, and caged breeding pairs of two per cage need 1 square foot per pair.

Management: Poultry

Ducks and Geese

Growing fowl: Ducklings and goslings from 1 day to 2 weeks (goslings), or 3 weeks (ducklings), need 0.5 to 1 square foot per bird. Thereafter, floor space should be increased continually. In ducks, this should reach 2.5 square feet per bird by 7 weeks of age.

Geese, being larger, require greater increases of space. They ordinarily are allowed to pasture around 5 to 6 weeks of age with access to an open shed, barn, or other shelter in bad weather.

Breeding Fowl: Confined breeding ducks need 5 to 6 square feet per bird and 40 square feet per bird if outside. Breeding geese prefer to be outdoors as much as the weather permits.

Feed and Water Space

The best "rule of thumb" for feed or water space is to provide enough running (linear) feet or inches of feed trough or water space to enable all birds currently kept to eat or drink at once. Add up both sides of a trough feeder to get total number of linear feet.

Different shapes and capacities of feeding or watering equipment, bird densities, and environmental conditions will alter the guidelines presented.

Space needs are less with feed or water presented from a circular dish or pan arrangement because birds are less crowded eating and drinking around a circle than along a straight line.

Generally it is much safer to oversupply than undersupply feeder or waterer space. Never underestimate the space need for the cheapest feed ingredient, water. An extra waterer and even a feeder in locations where your birds tend to congregate most heavily during different times of the day or night can pay big health and productivity dividends.

Chickens

Feeders: For 100 birds from 1 day to 1 week, 1 feeder lid; 1 week to 4 weeks, 12 linear feet feeder trough (two 3-foot feeders); 4 weeks to 8 weeks, 20 linear feet; 8 to 12 weeks, 30 linear feet; and 12 weeks and older, 40 linear feet.

Waterers: For 100 birds from 1 day to 1 week, six 1-quart waterers; 1 week to 4 weeks, two 2-gallon waterers; 4 to 12 weeks, three 5-gallon waterers.

Turkeys

Feeders: For 100 poults from 1 day to 10 days, 3 poult box lids; 10 days to 10 weeks, 30 linear feet; and 10 weeks and older, 70 linear feet.

Waterers: For 100 poults from 1 day to 2 weeks, 3 round water fountains; and 2 weeks and older, gradually increase to three or four 5-gallon waterers.

Game Birds

Feeders: Generally, begin with 1 inch of feeder space per bird and increase to 2- or 3-linear inches by the 6th week. Quail require 0.5 inches per bird from 11 days to 6 weeks, and 1 to 1.5 inches per bird after 6 weeks.

Waterers: Ordinarily provide two, 1-gallon waterers per 100 birds and increase to two 3-gallon waterers per 100 by the 6th week.

Ducks and Geese

Feeders: For the first few days of feeding, use shallow pans or small feed hoppers. For each 100 confined birds on full feed, provide 8 feet of trough space and increase as birds grow.

Waterers: Plan for 8 feet of water trough space for 500 birds for the first 2 weeks of age; then, as needed, increase the space up to 20 feet. Keep indoor waterers on wire platforms with underdrainage to help keep the litter dry.

Reproductive Data

Male: Female Ratios. Chickens—1:11 or 12 (egg-type) and 1:8 or 9 (meat-type); older or wild breeds of turkeys (long legs, narrow breast)—1:15; modern broad-breasted turkeys—artificial insemination.

Guineas—1:4 or 5; Pheasants—1:8 to 12; Quail—1:1 or 2:2 pairs, or 1:4 in a colony; Ducks—1:6; and Geese—1:4 or 5 (lighter geese) and 1:2 or 3 (heavier geese).

Note: Increase number of males slightly at beginning of breeding season to allow for some fighting and culling losses.

Hatching Egg Production

Chickens—240 eggs per year (egg-type) and 175 per year (meat-type); turkeys—80 to 95 per year; guineas—100 to 185 per year.

Pheasants—80 to 90 (variable); quail—90 eggs (no artificial light) and 150 or more (special management and lighting); ducks—100 (variable); and geese—20 to 50 per season, with some breeds almost twice as many.

Incubation Times of Hatching Eggs (Days). Chickens—21 (including bantams); turkeys—26 to 28; wild turkeys—28 to 30; guineas—26 to 28; grouse—25; partridges—23 to 24; peafowl—27 to 30.

Pheasants—23 to 26; quail—23 to 24; coturnix quail—17; Muscovy ducks—33 to 37 and other ducks—28; Canada and Egyptian geese— 35 (average) and other geese 29 to 31; and swans—42.

Brooder temperatures should be adjusted so hatchlings are evenly distributed under the hover and comfortable. With proper temperature and ventilation the chicks should neither be crowded to the edge (too warm), to the center (too cool), or to one side (drafty). Sometimes overheating produces more serious after-effects than chilling.

It is highly advisable to run brooders at least 1 to 2 days before delivery of day-old birds to be certain all are operating properly and the room temperature has reached 70° to 75° F.

Ordinarily, brooding temperatures start at 90° to 95° F for the first week followed by 5° decreases each succeeding week until 70° F (room temperature) is reached at 5 weeks of age.

Some recommend that quail brooding temperatures start at 100° F with weekly decreases as already described. Ducklings and goslings can be started at 85° to 90° F with the described weekly reductions. Goslings may tolerate 10° weekly reductions to 70° F.

Large, healthy, louse-free, quiet-dispositioned broody chicken hens make excellent mothers for guineas and geese. They reportedly have been used to hatch eggs and brood up to 25 guinea keets or up to 5 goslings per hen.

Special Safety Tips

Do not catch breeder males by one leg as permanent joint injury may result and interfere with breeding performance.

Catch geese by the neck and then by the base of the wings or by the body. Never catch ducks or geese by their easily broken legs.

Marbles or clean stones in game birds' waterers can prevent drowning of hatchlings.

Do not allow orphan waterfowl to swim for at least the first week after hatching. The parents use their own oil glands to waterproof the new hatchlings' feathers.

Ducks are nervous in the dark and may stampede. Low intensity night lights, inside or outside, help avoid this problem.

Sand or sawdust litter consumption by hatchlings, especially quail chicks, may lead to starve-out mortality.

Severe poisonings readily occur in waterfowl consuming outer leaves of insecticide-sprayed lettuce, or herbicide-sprayed pasture.

Management: Pet Birds

By Edward T. Mallinson and
Jim A. Stunkard

Pet birds share many similar basic needs with poultry. This applies especially to sanitation, disease security and fundamental disease prevention.

Nutrition and housing needs, however, are quite different for pet birds as well as are details of their breeding needs and characteristics. The following provides an introduction to many of these differences.

(The authors wish to acknowledge use of *Suggested Adult Cage Bird Maintenance Diet* and *Suggested Aviculture Practices for Psittacines* by Dr. Greg J. Harrison, Lake Worth, Fla., for much of the detail in this chapter.)

Edward T. Mallinson is Associate Professor, Virginia-Maryland Regional College of Veterinary Medicine, University of Maryland campus, College Park. Jim A. Stunkard is Director of the Bowie Animal Hospital, Bowie, Md.

Nutrition

Whenever possible, make a determined effort to obtain a balanced commercial feed for your birds and to adapt them gradually to it.

In some instances, pet birds or their owners find complete manufactured feeds unacceptable. For example, birds may become "hooked" on seeds, especially sunflower seeds.

In such instances, a program of feeding a large variety of foods free choice may be a necessary second alternative. When so doing, it is wise to provide the assorted foods two times a day.

This allows the bird to become hungry as it would in the wild (nature). Birds fed this way will usually eat a bigger variety of foods. Additionally, feeding 2 to 3 times a day may improve your bond with your bird as it considers you a friend at feeding time.

Several tricks encourage

"picky eaters" to adapt to a more nutritionally balanced commercial mix or pellet. Feeding new feeds during the morning and seeds only in the late afternoon may, with patience and persistence, bring about the desired change. Your veterinarian can provide other feeding tips.

Diet Alternatives

Dietary alternatives to commercial feeds are provided below for the owner not yet able to obtain or use commercially formulated rations.

Canaries. Good canary mix: 3 parts canary seed, 1 part rape, ¼ part niger, ¼ part each flax and sesame. Available at all times: Mineral, mash, grit, and cuttlebone. Daily: Fresh dark greens, avoiding iceberg lettuce. Carrots can be used when good greens are not available.

Three times weekly: Egg food, song food, pound cake. Twice weekly: Oats, ground nuts or sunflower seed, drop of cod liver oil. Once weekly: Crushed hemp, sprouted rape and crushed lentil sprouts.

Adjustments for breeding season: Dried egg yolk twice daily for hens with young. Greens—twice daily. Hemp, song food, ground nuts, sprouted rape, crushed lentil

sprouts may be left available all day.

Cockatiels. Seeds: Canary mix, parakeet mix, sunflower, spray millet. Greens: Spinach, alfalfa cubes. Fresh vegetables: Primarily corn, carrots. Fruits: Apples and grapes (often not fond of fruit). Supplements: Salt, cuttlebone, mineral block, oyster shell, cheese, monkey biscuit, and vitamins.

Cockatoos. Psittacine or hook-bill bird diet: Sunflower seeds, monkey biscuits, corn on the cob, apples, oranges, cheese, spinach, carrots, legumes (soybeans and lentils), cooked eggs (especially hard-boiled shell and all), calcium supplements (such as calcium lactate, gluconate carbonate), oyster shells, cuttlebone, supplemental vitamins.

Conures. Psittacine diet described for cockatoos. Other feed: Seeds plus "bread mixture" made of whole wheat bread crumbled, endive, carrots, plus vitamin supplements.

Finches, Lovebirds

Finches. Seed eaters: Small finch mix, millet, thistle, canary, rape, pound cake. Insectivorous (Melbas, Auroras, Violet-ears, Cordon Bleus, etc.): Add a couple of mealworms daily (too many mealworms may lead to liver problems) or use Insectivorous Mixture with high protein content. Both types need additional calcium in the form of powdered calcium, cuttlebone, crushed eggshells and grit.

Some breeders advocate feeding fresh food twice a day at the exact same time each day. Offer ground up vegetables, fresh corn, fruits, monkey biscuit. (Use a variety— whatever is available: Carrots, endive, celery, onions, spinach, whole wheat, rye, pumpernickel, parmesan cheese, etc.). Also egg yolk and peanut butter in the a.m. Same diet, whether breeding or not.

Fruit and Nectar Eaters (Hummingbirds, Lorikeets, and Toucans). As a guide only, these birds need a diet consisting of properly stored commercial or homemade nectars. Homemade formula: 15 to 18 monkey biscuits, 1 medium apple, and ½ cup molasses blended with enough water (3 cups approximately) to produce a cake batter consistency. These soft, moist foods spoil rapidly and should be fed twice daily.

Lovebirds. Seeds: Sunflower, parakeet mix, canary mix, as described. Fresh foods: Apples, endive, corn on the cob, whole wheat bread, car-

rots, spinach. Protein supplement: Monkey biscuit, egg, cheese.

Calcium supplement: Cuttlebone, oyster shell. Vitamin supplement: May want to use during times of stress or molt. Increase amount of soft food available during laying and feeding of young.

Macaws. Psittacine diet as previously described for cockatoos, using monkey biscuits.

Parakeets to Eagles
Parakeets (Budgerigars). Fifty percent canary seed mix, 5 percent oats, 45 percent mixed millets, greens, monkey biscuit, cuttlebone, small seed sprouts, corn, carrot, and cheese, or as described for canaries.

Australian Parakeets. Psittacine diet as described for cockatoos; canary and parakeet mix, and wild seedling grasses.

Parrots (African Greys and Amazons). Psittacine diet as described for cockatoos along with canary and parakeet mix, occasionally oranges, meat, and egg.

Pigeons and Doves. Fresh commercial pigeon pellets available at many feed stores. Pelleted turkey or chicken feed, beans, peas, and

Marie T. Sebrechts

Birds make fun pets. However, species such as the macaw are very demanding while others like parakeets require relatively little care. It's a good idea to consider your own lifestyle and your family's before choosing a bird.

mixed grains plus vitamin/ mineral supplements.

Raptors (Falcons, Hawks, Other Birds of Prey). These are flesh eaters in the wild but the digestive tracts of the rodents and birds they eat also contain vegetable matter.

Some of the foods commonly fed to these birds include chicken necks, baby chicks, small rodents, their complete internal organs, and a vitamin mineral supplement that includes calcium, vitamin A, D_3, and B complex. They start accepting food with talons instead of their beak at about 4 weeks of age.

Note that the captive maintenance of raptors is strictly legislated. Their safe care requires great skill and caution.

Cage Needs

Hook nest boxes on outside of cages. Build wire enclosure over cage to prevent escape and predator damage. Lead-soldered wire can be toxic to birds.

Breeder cage dimensions are Length × Width × Height.

Canaries. Standard double breeder: $18'' \times 10'' \times 10\frac{1}{2}''$. If room permits, $24'' \times 16'' \times 16''$ is preferable. Flights: $6' \times 3' \times 3'$ stacked three high (floor of upper makes roof of lower). Each flight houses 30 birds. Stacking, however, can increase disease transmission.

Cockatiels. Single pet bird with clipped wing: $24'' \times 12'' \times 18''$ nontarnishing, aluminum variety cage. Untamed cage bird: $4' \times 2' \times 2'$; perches $6''$ from sides. Single breeding pair: $4' \times 2' \times 3'$. Young birds flight: $6' \times 3' \times 3'$.

Cockatoos. $4' \times 4' \times 8'$ minimum (preferably longer). Need enough space or hiding place so female can get away from male. Common for male to kill female during breeding season, either outright physical assault or harassment to the point of death due to stress, especially in Sulphur

108

and Citron-crested. Not as common in Bare eye, Rose-breast, Goffin, or Moluccan.

Conures. $4' \times 2' \times 4'$ or $4' \times 4' \times 4'$. Large conures need minimum of $8' \times 4' \times 4'$.

Finches. $2' \times 2' \times 2'$ up to $8' \times 3' \times 4'$ or larger outdoor aviaries. Use ¼" wire if outside to protect from snakes.

Fruit and Nectar Eaters. Variable. $8' \times 4' \times 4'$ larger birds, $3' \times 2' \times 3'$ smaller birds. Consult with knowledgeable breeders, aviculturists, and avian veterinary practitioners.

Lovebirds. $2'$ or $4' \times 4' \times 4'$. Can colony breed three pair in larger cage.

Macaws. $6' \times 6'$ and larger. Wire size: ½" $\times 3"$ in 12 to 14 gauge for all but Buffons, Greenwing, Hyacinth. For these use $1" \times 3"$, 8 to 10 gauge.

Parakeets (Budgerigars). Best results with one pair per cage: $24" \times 14" \times 8"$. Use ½" $\times 1"$ wire.

Fliers, Fighters

Australian Parakeets. All love to fly. Smallest grass parakeets (Elegants, Bourke's, Red-rumps, Scarlet Chested, Turquoisines) need $4' \times 2' \times 4'$ flight minimum. Larger Australian birds (Princess, Rosellas, etc.) need $4' \times 4' \times 4'$. May want smaller cage during breeding season, $3' \times 2' \times 3'$.

Most are fighters, so must keep pairs separate.

Can use small, light mesh wire, like chicken wire, as they are not chewers. Can house several pairs together if a mixed exhibit with a large cage and plenty of nests to choose and defend. Visual barriers help prevent fright and injury of fledglings.

Parrots (African Greys and Amazons). $4' \times 3' \times 4'$ minimum, $8' \times 4' \times 4'$ large flight. (Use smaller cage for breeding season.) Use ½" $\times 1"$ welded wire, 14 gauge. Galvanized after welding is best.

Pigeons and Doves. $1' \times 2' \times 2'$ with 1" perches. A pair of pigeons can be housed in a box 3 feet square and equipped with a wire front.

Raptors. $6' \times 6' \times 6'$, but $10' \times 20' \times 20'$ is better. Excessive room may cause bird to injure itself if frightened.

Remember, raptors are subject to special laws and safety precautions.

Reproductive Data

Cooperative programs, such as the proposed National Cage and Aviary Bird Improvement Plan, are expected to encourage official recognition of U.S.-hatched pet birds sold in retail shops and other trade channels.

Sexing. Proper sex determination is a must to prevent disappointment when what you may have supposed was a male/female breeding pair turns out to be two of the same. The following is a general guide at best. Consult experienced breeders and other authorities for more precise information.

Here are visible characteristics that usually suffice for sex determination: Canaries—singing, body positioning; cockatiels—feathering; cockatoos—eye color (female reddish brown, male black); finches—feathering, song, dancing behavior; lorikeets—generally males are larger and have wider, more flat, coarser skulls; parakeet—cere color 85 percent accurate (female brown, male blue) but unreliable in partial albinos, etc.; Australian parakeets—feathering sometimes, natural pairing when in groups of 6 to 8 young; and pigeons and doves—courting behavior, facial skin.

Surgical sexing usually is required for accurate identification of conures, lovebirds, macaws, and most parrots. Note: Sexing by steroid analyses of blood or droppings has been used.

Hatching Egg Production Per Clutch: Canaries—2 to 7 (last egg bluish hue); cockatiels—3 to 7; cockatoos—2 to 4; conures—4 to 6 (lay 4 to 5 clutches annually); finches—4 to 6; lorikeets—2 to 4 (2 average); lovebirds—3 to 8; macaws—2 to 4, but will continue to lay if eggs are harvested to incubator or foster parents (up to 25 per year); parakeets—4 to 10; Australian parakeets—4 to 6; parrots—1 to 5; pigeons—1 to 2; and raptors—2 to 3 clutches per year.

Many types—such as cockatiels, parakeets, and parrots—will continue to lay if their eggs are harvested.

Incubation Times of Hatching Eggs (Days): Canaries—14 to 15; cockatiels—21 to 23; cockatoos—28; conures—approximately 24; finches—14 to 19 (mostly 14); lorikeets—22 to 25 (average 24); lovebirds—23 to 24; macaws—28; parakeets—18 to 20; Australian parakeets—18 (smaller species) and 21 (larger species); parrots—28; pigeons—17 to 18, and raptors—28 to 42.

Persons keeping or dealing with pet birds often benefit from membership in local bird clubs and national aviculture associations such as the American Federation of Aviculture, P.O. Box 1568, Redondo Beach, Calif. 90278.

III. DAIRY AND BEEF CATTLE

USDA

Dairy Herd Management

By David M. Galton

Dairy cattle produce milk and related products by consuming vast quantities of roughages (hay, fermented feeds and byproduct feeds) that are inedible for human consumption. Dairy farming is a complex business that demands astute managers for the future if they want to return a reasonable profit. Average capital investment for a New York State dairy farm is about $425,000.

High quality milk starts with healthy cows in clean and sanitary environments which demand good overall management programs. Some dairy cattle are housed in confinement individual stall barns (stanchion, tie stalls). This housing system usually includes milking systems consisting of milking machine buckets or milking machines with mechanical milk transport.

Dairy cattle housed in confinement are usually turned outside for short periods of time in the colder months and inclement weather. In the warmer months, they are turned out to pastures or drylots for much of the time in between milkings. Good bedding is essential in confinement housing so that cows do not bruise their legs, udders, and bony prominences on concrete.

Another housing system is referred to as freestalls. Stalls are provided for cows, but the cows are free to move about to feed and water. Cattle are handled in groups based on milk production and stage of lactation, offering flexibility for mechanization and automation for greater efficiency.

David M. Galton is Assistant Professor of Dairy Cattle Management, College of Agriculture and Life Sciences, Cornell University, Ithaca, N.Y.

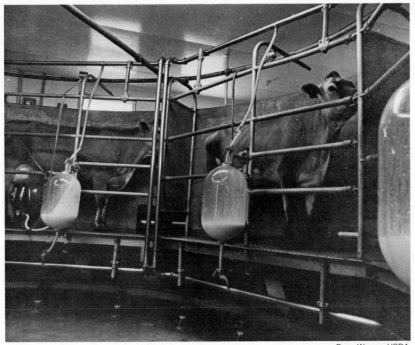

Dave Warren, USDA

High quality milk starts with healthy cows in a clean environment, as in this automated revolving milking parlor.

Cattle housed in freestalls can be milked in systems similar to stall barn systems or milked in milking parlors whereby more flexibility in efficiency can be realized. In warm climates, cows sometimes are housed in loafing type housing which is similar to management in freestall systems.

Avoiding Mastitis

Milking usually is done twice daily and most dairy farms attempt to milk as close to 12-hour intervals as possible. In some areas, three-times per day milking has gained acceptance.

Three-times-a-day milking does increase the milk production of cattle above that for twice a day milking, but obviously requires more labor. The additional milk production must therefore more than equal the additional labor costs in a herd for three times per day milking to be economically feasible.

Regardless of the fre-

courtesy of David Galton

Conventional confinement housing places each cow in a tie stall with neck straps (as shown) or in a stanchion.

quency of milking, the intervals between milking *must be constant* in order to avoid problems with mastitis. Dairy cattle are creatures of habit and the best dairy farmers adjust their day to accommodate this trait with strict regimentation of the daily feeding and milking schedule.

Dairy cattle are divided by stage of lactation since this factor has an impact on milk production, breeding status and nutritional requirements. Free stall barns are more labor efficient in this regard since cows can be grouped based on their stage of lacta-

tion. In confinement housing good dairy managers adjust the nutrition individually, based on production levels and stage of pregnancy.

A resting period or *dry period* usually is provided to dairy cows for 6 to 8 weeks prior to their next calving. This period allows the cow to replenish body stores before the onset of lactation and the stresses accompanying lactation.

Handling Waste
As herd size increases, fewer cattle will be housed in individual confinement stall

114

Erwin W. Cole, USDA-SCS

In warmer months, cattle are turned out to pastures or dry lots during much of the time between milkings.

barns. Housing must be integrated with several other systems to provide cow comfort, good herd health, quality milk production and efficient handling of milk, feed and animal waste.

For the most part manure removal is a daily chore and in today's management systems, it is a highly mechanized area. In conventional confinement barns, mechanized gutter cleaners work like large conveyor belts to remove manure from the gutter drop behind the cows. In loose housing or freestall barns, manure is scraped or plowed out of the alleyways adjacent to feed bunks by unloaders, bobcat tractors or other tractors.

Manure once removed from the barn is often used for fertilizer. In addition, farmers are working in conjunction with environmental experts in the development of large slurry systems to handle manure in the manner of sewage systems when large numbers of cattle are housed together.

Calf management is essential in order to have a successful management system. There generally are two accepted housing alternatives

Dairy Herd Management

Environmental experts working with farmers have developed slurry systems that efficiently move manure to a holding lagoon, when large numbers of cattle are housed together. Solid animal waste can then be converted into methane gas for fuel to run generators that provide electricity for the farm.

Tim McCabe, USDA-SCS

Dairy and Beef Cattle

for calves: cold housing (calves are kept in hutches or other structures where the temperature in the housing unit is similar to outside temperatures), or warm housing (insulated and mechanically ventilated).

Regardless of the housing system used, prevention of disease exposure, dry and clean environment and good management practices are essential for low calf mortality.

Dairy cows should be observed closely at the time of calving to insure a normal birth. Immediately after the calf is born, its naval should be dipped with a disinfectant and it should be provided colostrum (first milk) from its mother.

Most calves will nurse the mother by themselves, but if the calf's nursing ability is questionable, colostrum should be milked from the mother cow and given to the calf as soon after birth as possible and always before 12 hours of age. This colostrum provides passive antibody protection to the calf that will enable the calf to fend off infections during its first few weeks of age.

Leaving Mother

Thereafter, dairy calves usually are managed much differently than beef calves since they cannot stay with their mother during lactation. Dairy calves are removed from the mother within 1 to 3 days of birth and fed whole milk, colostrum, or commercial milk replacers for 6 to 8 weeks.

They are offered small quantities of high quality solid food such as coarse grain, good quality hay, and clean water even while on milk products so they can adjust to solid food as time goes on. Eventually at weaning (6 to 8 weeks) the calf is ready to exist on solid food.

Dairy farming is based on the cow and, therefore, most farmers raise only heifer calves. Bull calves usually are shipped to market for veal or sold to be raised as larger veal calves. Only extremely valuable genetic base male calves are kept to be used as breeding bulls.

Herd size and efficiency will be increased in the future which will command more interaction of dairymen and industry people such as veterinarians, extension agents and other resource people to provide needed educational resource input. Such input will be more important as the complexity of dairy farming increases.

Managing Beef Cattle

By Kenneth Tillapaugh

A healthy environment and good management are paramount in operating a successful and profitable beef cattle operation. One of the chief ingredients in any beef operation should be a good preventive medicine program. The profit and loss margin is greatly influenced by the frequency and degree of illness and injury in the herd or feedlot and how well or how quickly the animals recover from setbacks that occur for a variety of reasons.

Proper housing should be one of the first items addressed, whether for a cow/calf program or a feedlot operation. An open barn or shed, facing away from the direction of the prevailing winds, is much preferred to a closed building. Many diseases thrive in a warm, humid environment as found in some closed buildings. Drafts should be prevented as much as possible in open buildings.

Use of dry bedding of some type is important; pens should be cleaned frequently. Cattle should not be forced to lie in sloppy, filthy pens. Many cattlemen prefer to provide an adjoining outside exercise lot. Calves should not be forced to nurse on dams which have been lying in manure. Overcrowding in pens should be avoided. Pens with concrete floors are preferable to muddy lots.

In many feedlot operations, especially in areas of moderate temperatures, cattle are housed in open pens with no roof over them. In colder climates, a roof shelter with open sides is adequate. In warmer areas, some type of shade helps keep cattle comfortable and healthy.

Kenneth Tillapaugh, now retired, was Cornell University Beef Herd Superintendent, Ithaca, N.Y.

Dairy and Beef Cattle

Marie T. Sebrechts

In dirt feedlots, a few elevated areas or knolls allow cattle to relax in a dry situation out of mud. Dirt pushed up in a pile and packed down will also suffice. Maintaining cattle on dry surfaces helps prevent many foot problems such as foot rot.

Outdoor housing of the cow/calf herd in winter is preferred by many beef cattlemen throughout the United States and should receive serious consideration when planning a beef operation. This is an accepted practice even in the cold Northeast.

Advantages to keeping beef cattle outside year-round are many, not only for disease control but for economic reasons as well. Not only is the cost and maintenance of expensive barns avoided but also the cost and labor involved in

An open barn or shed that faces away from prevailing winds provides the best air circulation for cattle.

removing manure and supplying bedding.

Select an area with a fair-sized woodlot containing an abundance of evergreen trees for protection from cold winds and snow. A few rows of evergreen trees may provide sufficient shelter and an adequate windbreak. Beef cattle prefer being outside; their heavy coat of winter hair gives ample protection from cold temperatures.

Sufficient ground area should be provided to avoid heavy concentrations of manure. If a portion of regular pasture is used, scatter the manure with a pasture harrow in spring.

Managing Beef Cattle

Karen Rusinski, USDA-SCS

Cutting Calf Diseases

A small, adjacent, well-drained grazing area used only during the calving season will aid in minimizing baby calf diseases. Again, a wooded area should be available for protection from inclement weather.

The calving pasture is best located in a place that permits the cattleman to easily and frequently observe the cattle. To repeat, keep this area idle except during the calving period.

Devise a plan for caring for outdoor cattle during periods of severe weather condi-

Beef cattle prefer being outside. Their heavy coats of hair keep them warm in winter.

tions before a crisis develops. Always assure access to water.

If a wooded lot or a sufficient number of trees are not available, a satisfactory and inexpensive board windbreak can be constructed and will protect cattle effectively from cold winds. Several building plans for windbreaks are available from agricultural research centers.

The greatest enemies of disease are fresh air and a dry environment. These two elements are present in outdoor housing situations.

Pastures and Health

Good pasture management is vital in the successful beef cattle operation. Pastures should be rotated to prevent disease and parasite buildup. Proper nutrition is critical.

Cattle should not be forced to eat stubble and dirt when grass is short. Provide some type of supplemental feed when such conditions exist. Nutritionally healthy cattle fight off many diseases.

A pasture clipping program should be practiced; tall grasses and weeds can cause severe eye irritation. Some cattlemen believe this type of eye irritation can help cause pink eye. The stubble of mature weeds and grasses can in-

jure feet and lead to foot infections.

Carry out effective fly control; various methods work better in different geographical locations. Flies seem fewer in number in shady areas near flowing fresh water, and a shaded area near a creek is a cool and comfortable resting spot.

A shady area in the pasture will relieve discomfort caused by the hot summer sun. A few trees on a hillside where a breeze often is present provide comfort in a relaxed atmosphere on warm days.

Pastures should be gone over with a pasture harrow at least in the fall or spring to scatter clumps of manure. This disturbs the habitat enjoyed by flies and other parasites as well as breaking up clumps of manure which smother grasses. Of course, considerable fertilizer value can be gained when these clumps are broken up.

Hilly fields can be well utilized as pasture, and provide an area of higher elevation during wet periods.

Fencing

Adequate fencing should be maintained, and several types are available. The old standbys still exist—woven and barbed wire fences. Woven wire rusts and weakens after a few years, and barbed wire presents the danger of injury to cattle from the sharp barbs. Both require a fair amount of maintenance.

During recent years the Australian or New Zealand type of fencing has been introduced and used successfully in the United States. This is a strong and probably longer lasting smooth wire fence which is stretched tightly and fastened to pressure-treated posts that are driven into the ground to a depth of 3 to 4 feet. Thus, fewer posts are needed.

Varying numbers of strands of wire are used, depending on the type fence needed. An electrified fence with 3 to 5 strands of wire will do the job adequately. If electricity is not used, a 6 to 8 strand fence should be constructed.

Ratchet-type tighteners are placed on each strand in various places to tighten the wire when necessary. This type of fencing is adequate also for construction of feedlots, holding lots, and corrals.

Isolating New Cattle

A relatively small pasture or open shed located away from the main barns and the regularly used pasture will pay dividends when used to isolate newly purchased cattle from the native cattle.

Isolation will minimize the risk of bringing new illnesses to animals already on the farm as well as protecting the newly arrived cattle from diseases against which they have little or no immunity. A small area is recommended to allow for close observation of the new animals.

Serious consideration should be given to both location and method of construction of equipment needed to handle cattle. Corrals, chutes, and holding pens must allow for proper catching, handling, and restraint. Equipment should be strong enough and of adequate size to handle any size of beef animal.

These facilities need to be strategically located and arranged to minimize the stress put on cattle when catching and handling them is necessary. Overly stressed animals are more susceptible to disease, and recovery is slower than with those who have had less stress placed upon them. Gates to corrals and holding pens should be sufficiently wide to allow the animals easy entrance.

John Kucharski, USDA-APHIS

An appropriately designed squeeze chute and head gate allow efficient access to animals and ensure safety for the cattleman and/or veterinarian as well as the cattle.

Bait as Enticement

A little grain or high quality hay fed occasionally and then used as bait to entice cattle into a corral will save time and effort and is preferred over getting cattle excited before the work even begins. Move cattle from the catching pen through a funnel-shaped entranceway to the chutes. Pressure to force the cattle to advance forward can be applied with a gate behind the animals.

An appropriately designed squeeze chute and head gate should be used to allow efficient access to the animals and yet ensure safety for the cattlemen and/or veterinarian as well as the cattle.

It is vitally important to place the *least possible* amount of stress on cattle when handling them, regardless of whether they are healthy or ill. During periods of extremely hot weather, it is best to avoid working on cattle or getting them excited in any manner.

Most agricultural research centers will supply building plans for corrals, holding pens, and chutes. Excellent permanently installed equipment is available from commercial suppliers throughout the United States. These facilities are needed for many tasks, and investment in this equipment will pay large dividends.

Managing Beef Cattle

Nutrition

By Francis H. Kallfelz

Some of our most nutritious foods come from cattle. Beef and dairy cattle are the source of hamburger, steak, milk and cheese, to name a few. Such foods are very important for human growth and health.

To insure a plentiful supply of these foods, it is of course necessary to provide optimal feed for both beef and dairy cattle so they will grow, reproduce, produce milk, etc., for the benefit of mankind. Much research has been and continues to be done to determine the best way to feed both beef and dairy cattle in order to produce food for humans.

Cattle as well as sheep, goats and deer belong to a group of animals known as

ruminants. These animals have a digestive tract quite different from that of people, dogs, pigs and most other animals. A major difference is that the ruminant has four stomachs instead of one.

When a cow eats, the food swallowed enters the first stomach or *rumen* which is the largest of the four, containing in the adult cow a volume of some 30 gallons of mixed water and food.

The rumen is connected to the second stomach, the *reticulum*, and contents of the rumen can move freely into the reticulum and back again, through a large opening.

Forages (such as hay or silage) which are eaten by the cow remain in the *rumenoreticulum* for a considerable time period. During this time, the huge population of microorganisms present in the rumenoreticulum break down the fibrous portions of forages into smaller substances that

Francis H. Kallfelz is Professor of Clinical Nutrition, New York State College of Veterinary Medicine, Cornell University, Ithaca.

Dairy and Beef Cattle

courtesy of F.H. Kallfelz

Cattle belong to a group of animals known as ruminants; the major characteristic is that they have four stomachs rather than one.
a: rumen; b: reticulum; c: omasum; d: abomasum.

can be absorbed and used by the cow for growth, milk production, etc.

Besides breaking down the fiber, the micro-organisms in the rumen also synthesize (make) other substances such as protein and vitamins which subsequently can be absorbed and used by the cow.

Mixing It Up

The first two stomachs undergo periodic contractions (every minute or so) which help to mix the food particles with the micro-organisms present. Cows also chew their cuds or *ruminate*. By this is

meant that small portions of the food present in the rumen are periodically brought back to the mouth for further chewing and then reswallowed. This tends to further reduce the size of food particles so that they can be more easily broken down chemically by the rumen micro-organisms.

After leaving the rumen and reticulum, the food passes through a very small tunnel into the third stomach, or omasum. This stomach is round and about the size of a volleyball. Here it is thought that water is removed from the food. The food then moves

Nutrition

through another small tunnel into the fourth stomach, the abomasum, which is similar to the stomach of humans and non-ruminant animals.

In the abomasum, food which was eaten but not acted upon by the micro-organisms in the rumen, substances made by the micro-organisms as well as some of the micro-organisms themselves begin to be digested and made ready for absorption in the small intestine.

While some very small chemical substances can be absorbed through the rumen wall, most absorption of broken down food occurs in the small intestine of the cow as is the case in other animals. The absorbed food is then used for such things as energy, growth, and milk production.

Because cows have rumens containing micro-organisms capable of breaking down fiber (the woody parts of plants), they can digest inexpensive feedstuffs like grass, hay and cornstalks—which cannot be digested by other animals—and convert them into foods (meat, milk) which can be used by humans. The goal of cattle farmers is to obtain inexpensive feedstuffs which provide a complete and balanced diet for their cattle

in order to produce meat and milk which can be sold for a profit.

Feedstuffs for cattle include forages, concentrates, and supplements.

Forages consist of grasses, legumes, hay, corn silage, and other substances which have relatively high levels of fiber. While historically these were sufficient to supply all the needs of cattle in the wild, modern day cattle have been genetically selected for high production. Forages alone are often incapable of providing the nutrient needs of these super-efficient "food factories" since the digestibility of forages frequently is quite low.

Thus more concentrated types of feeds must also be fed in most contemporary cattle operations. The term *concentrate* really means a feed which contains more available energy per pound than is found in forages. Grains such as corn, wheat, and oats are used as concentrates.

Rations of high-producing cattle often must be supplemented as well with protein, minerals, and vitamins. Feeds such as soybeans, cottonseed, and corn gluten can be used to provide extra protein and often are included in the concentrate portion of cattle rations. Supplements containing minerals and vitamins also are frequently added to concentrates when additional amounts of these substances are needed.

The specific nutrients of ruminants, including cattle, are similar to those of other animals. Since the rumen micro-organisms can manufacture many of these nutrients, however, the rations fed depend upon the nutrient requirements of the rumen micro-organisms as well as those of the cow. Also, nutrient requirements differ with age (young as compared to adult animals), product (milk as compared to meat), level of production (high producing as compared to average dairy cows), pregnancy, and so forth.

The nutrient requirements of adult beef cattle are not too high. Good quality grass pasture or grass hay in sufficient quantity is sufficient to supply adequate levels of protein, energy, fiber, and most minerals for both pregnant and lactating beef cows.

Water, Salt

It is essential that clean water be available at all times. This sometimes can be a problem with cows on pasture during the winter when water sources may freeze. Also, trace mineralized salt should be available. If pasture or hay quality is poor, then supplementation with protein, energy, minerals, and vitamins may be needed.

Nutrient requirements of non-producing and pregnant dairy cows are similar to those of beef cattle. These animals can obtain all nutrient needs from a good quality hay, trace mineralized salt, and water.

The high producing milking dairy cow, however, has greatly increased nutrient needs. A cow producing 90 to 100 pounds of milk per day may require over five times as much protein and several times as much energy and minerals as a non-producing cow. While the lactating cow will eat more, it also is necessary to increase the concentration of protein, energy and minerals in the ration of these animals in order to provide adequate nutrient intake.

Concentrates play an important role in supplying the significant additional nutrient needs of the lactating dairy cow. A constant availability of salt and clean water also is essential. Lactating cows can require over 40 gallons of water a day.

Harry W. Oneth, USDA-SCS

USDA-APHIS

Erwin W. Cole, USDA-SCS

Good grass, well-balanced feed and plenty of clean water— key ingredients for maximum growth.

128

Dairy and Beef Cattle

Growth Factors

The age of cattle also affects nutrient requirements. Higher amounts of all nutrients are needed during growth as compared to adult maintenance needs. Another fact is that the rumen does not begin to function until a calf is about 6 to 8 weeks old. Before this time, therefore, the calf requires a diet similar to that of non-ruminant animals, one which contains all the energy, protein, vitamins, etc., in a readily digestible form.

Whole milk, of course, is the best food for the young calf, but many milk replacer products are also available for this purpose.

After the rumen begins to function, dairy calves must be fed rations that contain all nutrients at levels high enough to support growth. With beef cattle, however, the growth period is most important since this is the time during which the meat (muscle) is formed. Therefore, the diet must be designed to promote rapid growth and formation of the right combination of muscle and fat to produce quality meat.

Growing and finishing (being readied for market) beef cattle require slightly higher protein and considerably higher energy levels than

do growing dairy cattle. High levels of concentrate feeding are most often used with just enough forage included to keep the rumen functioning normally.

Growth Stimulants

Another technique that promotes weight gain in beef cattle is the use of growth stimulants. These are substances that increase the efficiency of conversion of food to muscle (meat).

For example, some antibiotics when mixed in small amounts with the feed will alter the microbial population of the rumen and intestine, resulting in improved growth and feed efficiency. Also, certain chemicals and hormones stimulate growth by altering chemical reactions in the body. These substances can be formed into pellets and placed under the skin (implanted) in growing beef cattle. The active chemicals then are slowly dissolved into the blood over several months, resulting in long term stimulation of growth.

When formulating rations (deciding upon the mixture of various feeds) of dairy or beef cattle for various functions such as growth and production, be sure the ration is balanced—that is, contains all the necessary nutrients at appropriate concentrations. This requires a knowledge of those requirements. Such information is available in several textbooks and government publications.

One must also know what basic feeds and supplements are available for use and at what cost. Availability and cost of ingredients differ in various parts of the United States.

On dairy farms, the roughages such as corn silage or hay often are grown on the farm and hence are used as the basis of the ration. Many farmers have these forages analyzed in order to be sure of the nutrient content. The amounts to be fed daily to each animal will depend upon the number of animals, the total amount of feed available, and the number of days during which the feed will be used.

Ration Balancing

Information on nutrient content of the forages as well as how much will be fed per animal each day can then be combined to determine how much of each essential nutrient (protein, energy, minerals) is supplied by the forages to be used.

Comparing this informa-

tion with the nutrient requirements allows a calculation of how much of each essential nutrient must be provided by the concentrate, protein and mineral supplements, etc. This procedure is known as ration balancing. This can be done by hand; however, today many computer programs can also be used for this purpose.

Frequently, in feedlot situations where finishing cattle are fed, purchase of all feeds is necessary. In this case a "least cost" approach often is used in balancing rations. That requires considering costs of the available feeds as well as their nutrient content.

While least cost ration balancing is complex, computer programs are available which can be used to formulate a balanced ration by using the most economical combination of the feeds and supplements available. The least cost technique also can be used to balance rations for dairy cattle and other animals.

When, for any number of reasons, balanced rations in adequate amounts are not fed, nutritional disease results. Both underfeeding and overfeeding of any or all essential nutrients can result in disease problems.

Starvation Syndrome

Failure to provide adequate amounts of nutrients in general results in various degrees of starvation syndrome. In animals that are mildly underfed, a slightly decreased growth rate may be the only sign in growing cattle, with decreased production seen in adults.

Moderate underfeeding will result in a significant decrease in size compared to age in young animals, and decreased production and weight loss in adults. Severe underfeeding results in weight loss and eventual death in both young and adult animals.

Overfeeding of a balanced ration results in overconditioned cattle which can also result in disease problems, particularly at and shortly after calving.

Individual nutrient deficiencies can result in specific diseases in both beef and dairy cattle. For example, a frequent problem in beef cattle on pasture in the winter is *hypomagnesemic tetany* or *winter tetany*.

This disease is the result of low blood magnesium levels caused by too little magnesium in the diet, and is most common in beef cows with nursing calves. Signs of the disease include nervousness and a stiff gait progressing to falling down, paddling, and convulsions. Death occurs within a few hours of the onset of convulsions. Sometimes cows are just found dead in the pasture.

Treatment of affected animals must be accomplished quickly by intravenous administration of magnesium and calcium.

A similar disease known as *grass tetany* can occur in beef or dairy cattle on lush grass pastures in the spring. The disease can be prevented by insuring adequate intake of magnesium.

Grain Overload

Overfeeding of specific dietary ingredients can cause serious disease problems. Grain overload is a common disease of this type in feedlot beef cattle. Micro-organisms of the rumen in cattle fed forage are adapted to breaking down fiber. Feedlot cattle must be slowly changed to a high concentrate ration which contains high levels of starch and sugar. When too much grain is fed to unadapted cattle, the starch and sugar is broken down to acids.

The consequences of this are many, including overdistention of the rumen with fluid, dehydration of the animal, death of the rumen wall, founder, severe metabolic changes, and death of the animal. A similar problem can occur in dairy cattle if they suddenly consume large amounts of grain. This disease can be prevented by slowly increasing the concentrate intake so that micro-organisms in the rumen can adapt to breaking down starch and sugar rather than fiber.

Salt Deficiency

Disease problems as a result of improper nutrition also occur frequently in dairy cattle. One problem related to undernutrition is salt deficiency.

Dairy cows producing large amounts of milk can require a quarter of a pound or more of salt per day. Forages and grain contain very low levels of salt, so it is essential to add it as a supplement.

When balancing rations, farmers and feed dealers sometimes fail to consider the salt requirement and this results in salt deficiency. Symptoms include a severe drop in milk production, loss of body weight, and a significant increase in water consumption and urine production.

This condition can be treated and prevented by being sure sufficient salt is added to the ration. Also,

since cattle needing salt will develop a hunger for it, having salt available free choice is a good management practice. However, this does not hold for other minerals; cattle deficient in calcium, for example, will not necessarily consume a calcium supplement made available free choice.

Overfeeding of calcium can be a problem in dairy cattle. While calcium is required at high levels during lactation, much lower levels are needed during late pregnancy after milk production has ceased (the dry period). During this time, dairy cows are fed mainly forages but some of these can contain high levels of calcium—resulting in overfeeding of this nutrient.

Milk Fever

When the cow gives birth, milk production begins again and large amounts of calcium are needed for this. During early lactation, much of the calcium is obtained by removal from bone. Overfeeding of calcium in late pregnancy causes the bone to become resistant to calcium removal. Thus when milk production begins, blood calcium levels quickly fall, resulting in a disease called parturient hypocalcemia or milk fever.

The cow becomes very

Salt that is readily available will eliminate the risk of under-nutrition due to salt deficiency.

weak and usually is found lying down with the head turned into the flank. Her body temperature is low and skin cold. The pulse is rapid but weak.

Cows with milk fever are treated by intravenous and subcutaneous administration of calcium which often results in rapid and complete recovery. To prevent the disease, carefully control calcium level of the diet of cows in late pregnancy to avoid over-feeding.

Most nutritional disorders are classified as metabolic diseases. Such problems are the result of abnormal metabolism (the term *metabolism* meaning the chemical reactions occurring in the body) rather than being caused by bacterial or viral infections.

Ketosis
Metabolic diseases can cause serious losses in both beef and dairy cattle. In addition to winter tetany, grain overload and milk fever, which have

Nutrition

just been described, another very common metabolic disease is ketosis.

After calving, milk production in the dairy cow increases rapidly. Feed intake also increases but, frequently during the first few weeks of lactation, not rapidly enough to provide all the nutrients needed for milk production. In such cases, the cow can become energy deficient.

The blood sugar level falls and the cow begins to break down body fat to meet the energy demands of milk production. If the fat is not efficiently utilized, small breakdown products of fat called *ketones* are formed and the blood level of these ketones can become quite high. The ketones affect the cow in such a way that she reduces her feed intake, and milk production falls.

Treatment of this disease (ketosis) involves intravenous administration of sugar and other techniques to improve feed intake and thus provide the extra energy needed for milk production.

Of course if the cow becomes sick for some reason and stops eating as much as she should, ketosis may be a result. Another metabolic disease in which ketosis frequently is a problem is *dis-placed abomasum.*

The abomasum is located on the right side of the cow and sits on the floor of the abdomen (the space containing the stomachs, intestines, etc.). It is attached at the front end to the omasum and at the back end to the small intestine. The mid-portion of the abomasum is not held rigidly in place by other structures; however, the weight of material within it usually keeps it in place on the floor of the abdomen.

Sometimes, however, when metabolism of the stomach is abnormal, the abomasum slides under the rumen, becomes partially filled with gas, and rises on the left side between the rumen and the body wall. This causes the cow to feel sick and stop eating, and she develops ketosis. In this condition, if one thumps the left side of the cow (behind the ribs) while listening with a stethoscope, a high-pitched ping (from the gas-filled abomasum) can be heard.

Treatment for this condition involves rolling the cow onto her back to get the abomasum back into its normal position or performing surgery to fasten the abomasum in such a way that it is no longer free to move.

Reproduction

By Stephen Roberts

Bovine infertility and re productive diseases exact an enormous yearly toll of over a quarter of a billion dollars annually on the cattle industry in the United States. Thus it is very important that cattle owners and breeders understand the normal bovine reproduction process in both a managerial and nutritional sense, as well as the adverse conditions and diseases which have a major impact on this process which is so vital to the success and profitable rearing of cattle.

Reproduction is a "luxury" function which is not necessary to the life of the bovine animal. So any severe condition affecting the cow or bull will have a marked effect on its reproductive functions.

Stephen Roberts, Professor Emeritus of Obstetrics, New York State College of Veterinary Medicine, Ithaca, is currently a private practitioner in Woodstock, Vt.

The Estrous cycle commences in heifers at a variable period of from 6 or 7 to 18-25 months, depending upon the level of nutrition, rate of growth, and breed of cattle. Most dairy breeds are fed adequately, resulting in heifers weighing 500 to 750 pounds at 13 to 18 months of age, which is the usual time of breeding.

In older cows, the "heat" cycles usually commence and are observable about 30 to 60 days after calving; a wide range would be 20 to 90 days after calving. In cows suckling calves, the onset of these estrous cycles is usually delayed one or two months.

The "heat" or estrous period is characterized by the female standing to be mounted by other females or a male. It occurs about every 21 days with a range of 18 to 24 days. This "heat" period lasts about 10 to 21 hours but may range from 6 to 27 hours in certain breeds and individuals.

Reproduction

The estrous cycle and "heat" period is brought about by a complex chain of events caused by a variety of hormones and results in ovulation. This is the release of the egg from a follicle or egg sac on the cow's ovary about 10 to 15 hours (range 2 to 24 hours) after the end of the standing "heat" or estrus.

Insemination

Unless a fertile bull is placed with the cows to breed them during this "heat" period, the cows must be artificially inseminated. It is essential that semen used in breeding be of good quality, regardless of whether natural or artificial insemination is chosen.

If artificial insemination is used, semen should be obtained from a reputable bull stud employing skilled technicians. To be most effective, this insemination must be performed during the estrous or "heat" period, or within a few hours after the end of estrus, so that the living fertile male sperm cells are in the female's uterus and oviducts before the "egg" is ovulated from the ovary.

The "egg" or ovum can survive only a few hours without being fertilized, while the sperm cells usually survive for about 24 to 36 hours in the fe-male reproductive tract. Therefore, two or three times a day the owner or herdsman must watch the cycling cows while they are in the barnyard or pasture to detect the occurrence of estrus so that they may be artificially inseminated at the proper time.

Careful, frequent heat detection and recording is extremely important for a successful reproductive program in herds using artificial insemination.

Causes of Failure

Failure to detect "heat" periods or estrum in nonpregnant cycling heifers or cows is most commonly due to a failure of the herdsmen or owners to observe these females frequently enough or for a long enough period of time (20 to 30 minutes) when the animals are able to interact and mount each other.

The second most common cause for failure of cows or heifers to show estrus is a lack of feed, energy, or total digestible nutrients, and occasionally protein and minerals to provide the nutritional needs of the female for growth, milk production, and a "luxury" level for reproduction. Usually these undernourished females are thin and in poor condition.

A third group of lesser causes for failure of estrus or heat includes a variety of abnormalities such as cystic ovaries (especially in dairy cows), severe chronic infections of the uterus, metritis or pyometra, pregnancy with or without death of the embryo or fetus, and severe chronic systemic or general diseases causing a marked loss of body condition.

Consultation with a knowledgeable veterinarian, or a university dairy specialist or nutritionist can be very helpful. They can give recommendations and advice on the diagnosis and prevention of problems associated with failure of estrus in dairy or beef herds which results in infertility and a loss of income.

A number of aids have been developed to assist farmers in detecting or regulating "heats," including hormones, Kamar pads or chalk on tailheads, operations to produce "detector" bulls, and rectal examination of the genital tract to predict estrus and detect abnormalities. However, none of these can replace careful, frequent observation.

The *gestation period* in cattle, the period from conception to birth, varies from 273 to 296 days; the larger breeds have longer gestation periods. Twinning and other diseases causing abortion may shorten the length of this period. Twinning occurs in 0.5 to 8 percent of bovine births. Beef breeds and dairy heifers produce fewer twins than the larger dairy breeds, and less than the mature or older cows of these breeds.

Occasionally, pregnant cows show signs of heat or estrus, especially during the first 3 to 4 months of gestation.

Early death of the embryo is quite common in cattle, especially during the first two months of gestation when the tissues and organs of the embryo are undergoing very rapid but defective development or when disease or infection in the uterus kills the embryo.

Venereal Disease

These early embryonic deaths and apparent infertility may signal the venereal diseases of vibriosis and trichomoniasis. This is especially true in cattle, usually of the beef breeds, that are bred naturally to older infected bulls.

The organisms introduced into the female genital tract by the bull at service may invade the uterus and cause infection of the uterus, death of the early embryo, and occa-

Reproduction

USDA

Reproductive diseases such as brucellosis cost the U.S. cattle industry over one-quarter of a billion dollars annually. Here is a cow and her aborted fetus.

Dairy and Beef Cattle

sionally abortion around mid-gestation.

After a period of costly infertility lasting 2 to 6 months, most cows develop sufficient immunity to these two diseases to carry their calves normally. Effective vaccine given several months prior to breeding can control loss due to vibriosis, but no effective vaccine exists for trichomoniasis.

A number of other "wound-infection" organisms commonly found in the vulva of cows and the sheath of bulls may occasionally become virulent in certain herds and cause periods of infertility.

There are about 40 or more bacteria, viruses, molds, protozoa, toxic chemicals, hormones, and other agents known to cause abortion in cattle. Of these, the diseases of brucellosis, leptospirosis, infectious bovine rhinotracheitis (IBR), and bovine virus diarrhea (BVD), are most common and usually result in abortion of the fetus in the latter half of gestation. Vaccines are available commercially for these diseases and should be administered on the advice of and by the local veterinarian.

Bovine brucellosis due to *Br. abortus* can cause severe herd losses in nonvaccinated cattle and undulant fever in humans. An active campaign with blood and milk testing to detect infected cattle and herds is presently being carried out in the United States. Quarantine and depopulation are necessary to eliminate brucellosis in cattle.

If the incidence of abortion in a herd exceeds 5 to 7 percent, a highly competent diagnostic laboratory should be employed to determine the causative factors.

Birth or calving

Dairy cows should be given a six-week dry or non-lactating period before calving. Cows due to calve have enlarged udders and relaxed pelvic ligaments and vulvas. They should be placed in a clean, well-bedded boxstall or in a clean pasture where they can be closely observed every few hours.

Once labor or birth begins, as noted by abdominal contractions, the heifer or cow should deliver the calf within half an hour to 3 hours. Heifers require a longer time for delivery than do cows. After a normal delivery (one in which the calf's head and forefeet come first as in 95 percent of births), the fetal membranes, placenta, or afterbirth is dropped in about 1 to 8 hours.

Once labor occurs, the calf

Reproduction

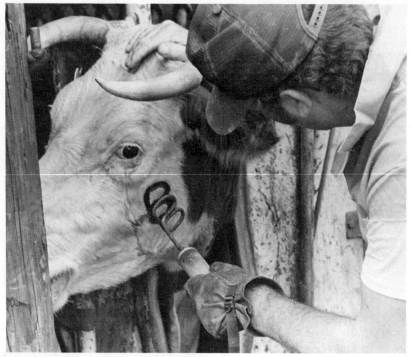

George Robinson, USDA

Chuck Herron, USDA-APHIS

To help fight brucellosis, which can cause severe herd losses in non-vaccinated cattle and undulant fever in humans, cattle producers actively participate in a program of calfhood vaccination, blood and milk testing, and marking and eliminating infected cattle.

Chuck Herron, USDA-APHIS

colostrum or first milk within a few hours to give it the necessary immune antibodies to survive.

At or after calving, other serious problems requiring veterinary or skilled attention may occur. These include milk fever (hypocalcemia), retained placenta, and uterine infection, prolapse of the uterus, ketosis, mastitis, and displaced abomasum. These conditions are much more common and serious in dairy cattle than in beef cattle.

In a successful reproduction health program, cattle owners and breeders should strive for a 12 to 13 month calving interval, a 60 percent or higher first service conception rate, 1.6 to 1.8 services per conception, a range of 85 to 115 days open period postcalving, a less than 5 percent abortion rate, and less than 10 percent reproductive problem cattle.

should be progressively expelled. If this does not occur and the process is stalled, prompt assistance usually is indicated and a knowledgeable veterinarian or possibly a skilled, experienced layman is generally required. In small, poorly grown beef heifers, a cesarean operation or other operations may be required.

Hasty, ill-considered and improper traction on a calf not in the proper position should be avoided.

Following calving, it is essential the calf receives some

To attain these goals requires careful, competent herd management by the owner or herdsman, the veterinarian and the inseminator (if the herd is bred by artificial insemination). The herd must also be free of contagious or infectious diseases, most commonly acquired by purchase of cattle from unknown or questionable sources.

Reproduction

Bovine Mastitis

By Frances D. Barnes

Bovine mastitis is inflammation of the milk-secreting gland or udder of the dairy cow. Micro-organisms (micro meaning "small" or "tiny", and organisms meaning "living things") are the usual cause of inflammation in the udder.

The most common mastitis-causing micro-organisms are bacteria: Streptococci, staphylococci, and coliforms. Other organisms include various gram negative and gram positive bacteria, fungi (yeasts and molds), algae (prototheca) and mycoplasmas.

Signs of mastitis may be put into two groups: Clinical—that which is obvious to the naked eye, or subclinical—that which cannot be detected by visual examination.

Frances D. Barnes is Senior Research Specialist, Mastitis Control Laboratory, New York State College of Veterinary Medicine, Cornell University, Ithaca.

The clinical type of mastitis accounts for only a small portion of total infections, and is manifested by clots, pus, swelling, or heat. Dairymen often are unaware of the extent of infections in their herds without using some other means of detection such as somatic cell counts or laboratory culture.

Somatic cells (soma means body) come from the body's defense mechanisms against infection. These cells are mainly white blood cells or leucocytes sent to the site of the infection or injury by the body's defense mechanism.

The purpose of these cells is to eliminate foreign particles such as bacteria by engulfing them, breaking them down by enzymes, and ridding the host's body of them. Often this mechanism is adequate to rid the host of disease-causing organisms before they can multiply enough to cause an infection.

Dairy and Beef Cattle

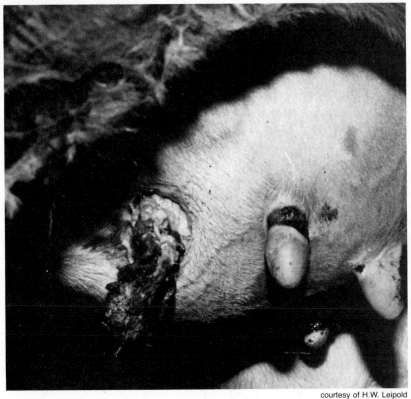

courtesy of H.W. Leipold

When quantities of somatic cells accumulate in one area, it may become obvious by the formation of pus. When there are fewer numbers in the udder, they must be detected by testing procedures.

Udder edema and mastitis in Jersey cow.

Somatic cells are our best indicator of udder health or, more specifically, the level of infection or irritation in the udder. Somatic cells may be detected either at cow-side by the California Mastitis Test or by laboratory techniques. The Wisconsin Mastitis Test, Di-

Bovine Mastitis

143

rect Microscopic Somatic Cell Count, or electronic equipment manufactured for this purpose are a few of the common techniques used.

Diagnostic laboratory culture of milk for micro-organisms is important because it identifies the types of bacteria or organisms causing the infections. Prognosis, control measures, and antibiotic therapy depend upon the causative agent.

Two Types of Organisms

The source of mastitis-causing organisms may be divided into two groups: Those that are contagious, such as *Streptococcus agalactiae, Staphylococcus aureus,* and mycoplasma, and those that are environmental such as coliforms and streptococcal species.

The contagious organisms do not survive well in the environment and require the host (cow) as a reservoir. These organisms are spread from cow to cow, often during the milking process.

On the other hand, environmental organisms readily survive in the environment. Dirty, wet environments are conducive to bacterial growth and, when the numbers of organisms are high, chances for them to cause mastitis increase. Good management

practices are extremely important in the control of all types of mastitis.

Treatment responses of mastitis infection by antibiotics are variable. Mastitis may be caused by a variety of micro-organisms. Therefore, it is important to know which organism is causing the infection for proper antibiotic treatment.

Some organisms, such as *Streptococcus agalactiae,* respond readily to a broad spectrum of antibiotics. Other organisms such as yeast, prototheca, nocardia, and mycoplasma are refractory (or resistant) to most if not all antibiotics and, therefore, do not respond to or may be worsened by antibiotic therapy.

Infections due to types of bacteria, such as *Staphylococcus aureus,* streptococcus species, and coliforms, fall somewhere in between; they may respond to certain antibiotics but not to others. Laboratory tests for resistance patterns are helpful in these situations.

Antibiotics should never be used indiscriminately. Excessive use of antibiotics may cause development of resistant strains of some bacteria.

Loss Estimates

Researchers have attempted to assign a lost dollar value

due to mastitis to the average dairyman. Figures of between $150 to $200 per cow per year in a herd are estimated losses. Using these figures, mastitis costs the owner of a 100-cow herd between $15,000 and $20,000 each year.

Most of these losses are due to decreased milk production, as an infected udder does not produce to its potential. Mastitis may cause up to 20 percent lower milk production, or more in severe cases. Other dollar losses are due to antibiotic and treatment costs, discarded milk, and death or premature culling.

Public health significance of mastitis has been greatly reduced by pasteurization. However, consumers of raw, unprocessed milk are candidates for infections associated with bacteria from mastitis milk.

Human Group B strep, not unlike *Streptococcus agalactiae,* has been isolated from human infections. A direct link to the dairy industry has not been found in these cases, but caution should be advised when working with or drinking raw milk from infected animals. Subclinical mastitis—the kind you cannot see— is probably the most dangerous since the milk looks normal but bacteria are present, often in high enough numbers to be significant.

Quality Affected

Milk quality is affected by mastitis. As the somatic cell level increases, the nutritive substances of milk—such as lactose, total protein, casein, solids not fat, total solids, fat, calcium, phosphorus, and potassium—all decrease. Undesirable components such as immunoglobulins, lipase, sodium chloride, trace minerals and whey protein all increase.

Cheese manufacturers have also discovered that milk containing high somatic cell levels and undesirable components will yield less cheese per pound than higher quality milk.

This review is intended only to scratch the surface of a complex, multi-faceted disease. Many factors influence the incidence of mastitis: Environmental sanitation, housing, nutrition, milking systems, and milking procedures are a few. It is not the interest here to guide one in management of mastitis, but only to make the reader aware of the complexity of the disease, its cause, control, and cure. Said best in the words used by many in the mastitis field: "Prevention is the key to mastitis control."

Respiratory Diseases

By William C. Rebhun

Bacterial bronchopneumonia is the most common cause of contagious respiratory infections in calves and adult cows. There are several bacteria capable of inducing pneumonia, but the most common organisms are *Pasteurella multocida, Pasteurella hemolytica,* and *Hemophilus somnus.*

These organisms may create disease individually, in cooperation with one another, or work in combination with viruses and mycoplasma organisms which will be discussed separately.

When bacterial pneumonia occurs in calves, it usually involves 10 to 80 percent of the calves on a farm and is

William C. Rebhun is Associate Professor of Veterinary Medicine and Ophthalmology, New York State College of Veterinary Medicine, Cornell University, Ithaca. He is chief editor/writer for this section.

termed Enzootic Calf Pneumonia. In adult cows, bacterial pneumonia is termed Shipping Fever and occurs in outbreaks that involve a high percentage of cattle on the premises.

Laymen and veterinarians called bacterial pneumonia Shipping Fever because it frequently developed in cattle shipped long distances, transported to shows and fairs, or assembled in sales or feedlots.

The signs of bacterial pneumonia include fever, coughing, nasal discharge, increased respiratory rate, depression, and decreased appetite. Inflammatory cells and exudates in the airways of the lungs cause abnormal sounds called "rales" as air moves into and out of the airways (bronchioles) of the lungs. These sounds can be heard only with a stethoscope and are important diagnostic signs for the veterinarian examin-

USDA-APHIS

Bacterial pneumonia is often called Shipping Fever because it frequently develops in cattle shipped long distances.

ing calves or cows affected with bacterial bronchopneumonia.

The majority of the damage occurs in the lower lung area and, in severe cases, the infection results in consolidation or total destruction of the lower lungs. This results in chronic pneumonia, poor growth, or death in these severely affected animals.

Spread by Air

The organisms are spread from one animal to another through the air or through nasal discharges and coughing of infected secretions. This airborne transmission makes it

easy for the causative organism to infect many cattle when they are confined to a barn or feedlot area. The infection rate is high if cattle are confined in a poorly ventilated area or a totally enclosed structure, since air movement and subsequent diffusion of organisms is reduced in these settings.

Fortunately, humans and other species of animals are not at risk from bacterial bronchopneumonias in cattle since each species (including man) tends to suffer from species-specific pneumonias.

This disease occurs all across the United States but

Respiratory Diseases

George Robinson, USDA

Good ventilation will help eliminate ammonia fumes from urine and manure that can damage the cattle's normal defense mechanisms against respiratory diseases.

has a higher incidence in the mid-fall and early spring, when the weather is changeable, and especially in the cold months in the Northern United States since cattle are confined in smaller units or barns during these months.

The disease has a tremendous economic impact on cattle owners and consumers due to decreased production, drug costs for treatment, and mortality of affected cattle.

In beef animals, cattle affected with bacterial bronchopneumonia may grow poorly, need more time and feed to reach market weight, or may die. All these problems result in higher costs of beef for the consumer.

Treatment requires antibiotics to kill the causative bacteria, nursing care, well-ventilated shelter, and supportive drugs that may hasten recovery. Supportive drugs and antibiotics are selected by veterinarians based on their experience as well as specific cultures of bacteria obtained from affected calves or cows.

Cultures are obtained from the airways of affected live cattle or the lungs of cattle that have died from the disease. Antibiotics such as penicillin, tetracycline, sulfas and erythromycin may be used, but antibiotic selection should be at the discretion of the attending veterinarian.

When ventilation is poor, ammonia fumes from urine and manure build up and cause chemical damage to defense mechanisms of the lungs. Humidity also builds up and predisposes to cross infection through aerosol transmission. Unless ventilation is improved immediately, further spread of the disease may occur and affected animals may fail to improve following therapy.

Prevention is difficult since many predisposing factors such as transport of cattle, confinement of cattle, and grouping of calves and cattle are inevitable and necessary management components of the livestock industry.

Vaccines are available for some bacterial causes of pneumonia such as *Hemophilus somnus* and can prevent this disease if ventilation and management are good. Vaccines against *Pasteurella* pneumonias are controversial and most veterinarians agree that these vaccines cannot adequately protect cattle against *Pasteurella*—especially if management techniques or ventilation predispose to disease.

Viral Diseases

Viral infections of the respiratory tract in cattle occur frequently and damage tissue in the upper airway, trachea (windpipe), or bronchi and lungs. There are many known viruses capable of causing respiratory disease in cattle, and probably some viruses which are yet to be isolated or discovered.

Viral infection sometimes occurs before or in conjunction with bacterial pneumonia in cattle and is thought to predispose to bacterial pneumonia because it weakens the defense mechanism and lining tissues of the respiratory tract.

Because of this interaction of viruses and bacteria, the term Shipping Fever Com-

Respiratory Diseases

plex often is used to describe the myriad of organisms involved in an outbreak of respiratory disease in cattle or calves. This term is especially appropriate if management factors such as grouping, transporting, or poor ventilation for cattle are present in addition to bacteria and viruses.

Stresses created by management allow infections to develop more easily because cattle are weakened by these stresses. This is exactly like the situation in a human being when lack of sleep, driving long distances, or attending meetings where one encounters hundreds of other people predispose all of us to the common cold. This common cold is a viral disease but may develop into a bacterial pneumonia if we are further stressed or chilled.

Specific viruses that cause respiratory diseases in cattle include Infectious Bovine Rhinotracheitis (IBR, "Rednose"), Bovine Respiratory Syncytial Virus, Bovine Adenovirus, and Bovine Parainfluenza virus (PI3). All of these viruses cause high fever (105° to 108° F), depression, increased respiratory rate, nasal discharge, ocular discharge, coughing, and predispose to secondary bacterial

pneumonias as discussed previously.

Without cultures of affected tissues it often is difficult to determine exactly which virus is involved. IBR does cause specific lesions in the nasal cavity, trachea, and occasionally the eyes, which allows a definitive diagnosis through inspection by an experienced veterinarian. Unfortunately, the other viruses cause symptoms that are hard to differentiate.

In all instances, however, the fever and signs of respiratory disease fail to respond to antibiotic therapy, and this fact alerts the veterinarian to a viral cause. Usually 10 to 50 percent of the animals on a premise will be affected, and transmission occurs by airborne or aerosol transmission from affected to non-affected cattle. Other species are not affected.

Treatment is supportive and may include drugs to reduce fever (aspirin), antihistamines, and antibiotics if a secondary baterial pneumonia is suspected.

These viruses are of great economic importance since they result in treatment costs, poor growth or production, and deaths. Control and prevention are possible through vaccination for IBR and PI3 and may soon be available for some of the other respiratory viruses of cattle.

Mycoplasma

Mycoplasma are microbes that are neither bacteria nor viruses but are intermediate in size and characteristics between bacteria and viruses. They can cause subclinical (undetected) or actual respiratory disease in calves and adult cattle.

Mycoplasma can be cultured from the lungs of many apparently healthy cattle and, therefore, the pathogenicity is difficult to determine. However, as part of the Shipping Fever Complex, mycoplasma have at least a role in respiratory disease.

When coupled with bacteria, viruses, or both, mycoplasma probably contribute to respiratory disease and complicate the problem. Occasionally, mycoplasma are the only organism isolated from outbreaks of pneumonia in calves, but usually mycoplasma *and* a bacteria are isolated and the combination of organisms is thought to add to the severity of disease.

Signs of disease may be mild in pure mycoplasma infections and include fever, nasal and ocular discharge, and a moist cough. In calves and growing beef animals, an infectious arthritis occasionally may be detected in one or more joints. Fever may not respond to routine therapy with antibiotics, but seldom is as high as that occurring in viral respiratory infections. When symptoms indicate a severe pneumonia, usually other organisms coexist with the mycoplasma.

Transmission is through airborne and aerosol mechanisms. Treatment should be directed at any associated bacterial organisms and include supportive therapy as well as improved ventilation. If mycoplasma is the only organism isolated, antibacterial therapy with tetracyclines or tylosine may be employed by your veterinarian.

No specific control or prevention exists for this problem, and the ubiquitous nature of the organism in cattle makes it likely that this organism will continue to be a component of the respiratory disease complex in cattle.

Verminous Pneumonia

A common parasitic pneumonia of cattle is caused by the lungworm, *Dictyocaulus viviparous*. The worm lives within the airway or bronchi in cattle and causes irritation to the airways. This irritation leads to exudates, fluids, and may predispose to secondary bacterial pneumonias.

Signs of verminous pneumonia include mild fever, a deep, moist, frequent cough, and a rapid respiratory rate. Chronic cases have labored breathing that may result in open mouth breathing. Rales can be heard over the entire lung area when the chest is listened to with a stethoscope.

Diagnosis requires a special technique called the Baermann technique which identifies larval forms of *Dictyocaulus viviparous* in the feces of affected cattle. This diagnostic test depends upon the fact that the adult worms in the lungs produce offspring, or larvae, which are coughed up from the lung, swallowed by the cow or calf, and then shed in the feces.

It follows that the disease spreads by fecal contamination of boxstalls, foodstuffs, or pastures, and oral ingestion by susceptible cattle. The parasite then penetrates the gut wall and migrates to the lung where it completes its development into the adult phase.

Moisture aids in propagation of the parasite. Thus swampy pastures, dirty boxstalls, or loose housing that allows manure buildup predispose to infection.

The parasite is not spread to other livestock or man. Levamisol, a modern anthelmintic, can be given orally or via injection to kill this parasite and control infection. Management controls such as fencing off lowlands or swampy areas, preventing fecal contamination of water and feed, or cleaning manure from boxstalls or loose housing areas are important adjuncts to vermicidal therapy.

Vaccines with irradiated *Dictyocaulus viviparous* larvae have been used successfully in endemic areas such as Great Britain but are not used currently in the United States.

Although *Dictyocaulus viviparous* infestation is an important cause of pneumonia in endemic areas, it is not as important as the infectious causes of pneumonia in cattle previously described.

Prevention of respiratory disease and pneumonia includes management principles, vaccines, and a program tailored individually for each farm or feedlot. This is best designed by active cooperation between the livestock owner and veterinarian in each case and a consideration of the type of cattle, type of management, geographic area, and climatic conditions.

Digestive Diseases

By William C. Rebhun

Calf diarrhea is the number one cause of death losses in newborn calves. Calf diarrhea, or "calf scours" in layman's terminology, can be caused by several infectious agents.

The most common causative agent is *Escherichia coli* (*E. coli*), a bacteria which colonizes within the epithelium of the small intestine in calves and produces a secretory diarrhea. Although digestive tracts of all animals and man contain *E. coli* of various types, pathogenic *E. coli* in calves tend to be a specific subgroup called K-99 *E. coli*.

Signs of disease are specific in calves less than 2 weeks old and include diarrhea, usually a fever of 103°

William C. Rebhun is Associate Professor of Veterinary Medicine and Ophthalmology, New York State College of Veterinary Medicine, Cornell University, Ithaca.

to 105° F, dehydration due to fluid loss in the form of diarrhea, depression, and decreased appetite. Because of the young age of these calves, dehydration, electrolyte (salt) losses, and acidosis may result in death in the most severe cases.

In addition, septicemia (blood poisoning) sometimes occurs due to spread of the organism from the intestine into the systemic circulation and subsequent infection of other major organs. Up to 100 percent of the newborn calves on a farm may develop calf diarrhea in severe outbreaks.

The disease can spread from calf to calf through fecal/oral transmission. Once the organism is established on a farm, any manure that the calf is exposed to may contain the organism. Therefore, the calf can ingest the organism from the udder of its dam, feedstuffs, buckets with slight manure contamination, or

Digestive Diseases

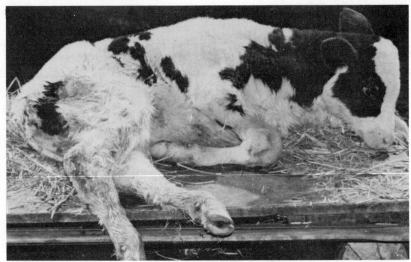

Cornell University

USDA

Several infectious agents can cause calf diarrhea, leaving the animal in a weakened, dehydrated condition. Prevention is important. A clean barn and adequate intake of colostrum, mother's first milk, will eliminate most cases.

from the floor, ground, or bedding.

Calves that have not been given colostrum with its protective antibodies within 12 hours of birth are definitely more at risk to the development of *E. coli* diarrhea. Calves older than 2 weeks may develop diarrhea, but it is seldom life-threatening since they are not as likely to suffer severe dehydration as newborn calves.

Calves do not transmit this disease to other species or humans since each species has specific *E. coli* subtypes which cause disease.

Treating, Prevention

Treatment consists of oral protectants, oral antibiotics such as neomycin, sulfa or tetracycline in some cases, oral supplementation with electrolytes (salt) and fluids, and decreasing the amount of milk fed for 1 to 4 feedings. Intravenous fluids and antibiotics may be necessary in severe cases where dehydration, acidosis, endotoxemia, or septicemia occur.

Prevention includes management changes to insure adequate colostral intake by the newborn calf, physical cleansing of the barn and maternity areas, and avoiding overcrowding.

Passive antibodies can be given for the newborn calf at birth by means of a new vaccine containing *E. coli* antibodies, or by adequate colostrum containing antibodies to *E. coli* created by vaccinating the dam with *E. coli* killed vaccines before calving. The vaccine should be discussed with a veterinarian familiar with these problems.

Other organisms such as Rota virus and Corona virus can cause similar diarrhea in calves less than 2 to 3 weeks old. These agents result in diarrhea and signs indistinguishable from mild to moderate *E. coli* diarrhea. Although the viruses can result in dehydration and occasional death, their major impact is to combine with pathogenic *E. coli* and result in severe diarrhea or death.

Vaccines are available against Rota and Corona viruses in calves. These vaccines are modified-live products that are given orally to the newborn calf at birth, or given to the dam before calving to cause antibodies to be present in her colostrum which the calf ingests.

When faced with neonatal diarrhea that results in calf mortality or severe illness in a number of calves, farmers should work in conjunction with their veterinarian to discover the cause. This is best done through bacterial and viral cultures of fecal material from affected calves.

Only through identifying an exact cause can management changes, medical therapy, and preventive vaccines be employed to solve the problem.

BVD Disease

Bovine Virus Diarrhea (BVD or BVD-Mucosal disease) is a contagious viral disease responsible for major losses in both beef and dairy cattle. The virus is spread through fecal contamination and secretions from infected to non-infected cattle.

Although most cows have subclinical disease or are immune from prior exposure, a percentage of unprotected calves or cows show clinical signs when exposed to this virus.

Signs may be mild, consisting of fever (103° to 108° F), salivation, falloff of appetite, mild oral lesions, and mild diarrhea. Or signs may be radical with severe diarrhea, fever, total loss of appetite, and erosions of mucous membranes in the oral cavity, nasal cavity, esophagus, rumen, intestine, and feet at the skin/claw junctures.

A wide variation in signs is possible with this disease. Laboratory work or autopsy of fatal cases often is necessary to confirm the disease. In general, affected animals have decreased numbers of white blood cells and reduced ability to fight off other infections (immunodeficiency) when affected with BVD.

Autopsy lesions include those mentioned earlier and destruction of lymphoid areas in the intestine. State diagnostic laboratories may culture the organisms from blood or tissues of affected animals.

Abortions may occur in cows that are affected in late pregnancy, and fetal anomalies can be present in calves from cows that were infected during the middle months of their pregnancy.

The causative virus is widespread in the United States and can cause disease in beef and dairy cattle of all ages. Its importance lies not only in death losses and abortions, but decreased production or growth in affected animals, and predisposition of affected animals to various secondary diseases.

Treatment is supportive primarily, with oral or intravenous fluids and electrolytes (salts), and antibiotics if secondary bacterial diseases occur. Blood transfusions to supply passive antibodies and white blood cells have appeared to help some severe clinical cases.

Control and prevention are now possible through vaccines. Although modified-live virus vaccines have long been available, they occasionally have been unprotective and in some instances have introduced the disease to a premise. New killed vaccines generally are indicated in herds or geographic areas that have a high incidence of BVD.

Salmonellosis

Diarrhea due to bacterial infection of the intestine with *Salmonella sp* is an increasingly common disease in cattle and calves. There are many different strains and serotypes of Salmonella, and these many strains vary in the severity of disease they produce.

Type B salmonella such as *S. typhimurium* are the most common types in the northeastern United States but Type E such as *S. anatum* and Type C salmonella such as *S. litchfield* also have been associated with herd outbreaks of diarrhea in calves and cows. *Salmonella dublin*, which can cause severe outbreaks of diarrhea and mor-

tality, has been a problem in the western United States and in Europe.

In past decades it was rare to see herd outbreaks of Salmonellosis, and most clinical cases were in individual cows or calves that were stressed by concurrent disease and thus predisposed to infection by Salmonella organisms. This situation has not changed drastically, but outbreaks involving several animals or entire herds now are the rule in many cases.

Signs of the disease include diarrhea, depression, dehydration, and fever (103° to 106° F), which can precede the onset of diarrhea by 12 to 24 hours. In addition, fresh blood may be present in the feces.

Character of the diarrhea varies from loose manure to profuse watery diarrhea containing virtually no solids. It follows that the most severely ill animals are those with profuse watery diarrhea since they will have greater degrees of dehydration and electrolyte (salt) losses.

The disease is not age dependent, and it is common to see calves of all ages as well as adult cattle affected in a herd. Usually 10 to 80 percent of the cattle in a group are affected. With more vicious strains, mortality may approach 50 percent of affected animals. Animals in close proximity to one another, such as veal calves or confined cattle, are at greater risk, since fecal shedding of the organisms is more likely to cause cross infection.

Affects Humans

Salmonellosis is one disease of cattle that can affect other species and, therefore, has tremendous public health significance. Not only can humans and other species be affected, but the reverse applies as well—dogs, horses, or people affected with salmonella can shed this organism in their feces and cross-infect cattle.

Regardless of the species, signs are similar and young animals always are at greater risk since they tend to dehydrate more rapidly than adults. Milk from affected cattle must be pasteurized to destroy the organisms which can be shed into the mammary gland and milk.

Treatment consists of oral or intravenous fluids and electrolytes (salts) to replenish fluids lost in the feces. In the more severe forms of disease, specific antibiotics such as tetracycline, ampicillin, or sulfa drugs are indicated since septicemia (blood poisoning) or spread of the organisms from the intestine to the rest of the body can occur, resulting in infections in many other organs.

Management must attempt to isolate affected cases, dilute highly concentrated populations of animals, and prevent further stresses or concurrent disease. Handlers of affected cattle must be extremely careful and sanitary in handling manure from affected cattle to prevent ingestion of organisms and subsequent disease.

Prevention is best accomplished through management procedures previously discussed. Although not always successful, bacterins made from killed organisms are sometimes used in endemic herds to control the problem.

Salmonella, like *E. coli*, can live happily in the intestinal tract of many healthy animals, but it tends to proliferate and be shed in the manure when these animals are stressed by other diseases or by shipment. This makes detection of carrier animals very difficult, and the problem exists in all species, including man.

Johne's Disease

Johne's Disease (Paratuberculosis) is an insidious, chronic disease of cattle caused by

Mycobacterium paratuberculosis, an acid-fast bacteria which can live in fecal material for long periods of time outside the cow's body.

Unlike the diseases previously discussed, Johne's disease does not make cattle appear ill until late in its course. The infection is generally acquired by calves that ingest the organisms in milk or feed contaminated by manure from an affected cow.

The organism establishes an infection in the terminal small intestine and large intestine and lives within cells and lymphatics in this region. From the time of infection, 12 to 24 months usually are required before diarrhea occurs or becomes obvious in these animals. Therefore, it is unusual to diagnose Johne's disease in cattle less than 2 years old.

Control Measures

Currently there is no treatment for Johne's disease so control depends upon accurate diagnosis and culling of affected animals. In addition, several other procedures should be employed. These include:

Removing calves from their dams immediately after birth and feeding them colostrum free of fecal contamination; raising all calves in a facility totally separate from the adult cows; fecal culturing of all cows in a herd and culling affected animals; repeating cultures at 6-month intervals to detect new cases early (it should be remembered that affected cows can shed organisms *before* they show signs of diarrhea).

Also, liming pastures and fields to increase the soil pH, which discourages growth of the organism on contaminated soil; and physical cleansing of manure from the barn or confinement areas to prevent buildup of the organisms which can survive in fecal material for months or years.

Currently, newer diagnostic tests are being developed, and vaccines are being used in endemic areas. These vaccines do not totally control the problem since cattle can still shed the organisms despite remaining free of disease.

Incidence in affected herds varies from 5 to 20 percent. During past decades, the disease was diagnosed in beef herds where calves reared at their mother's side were at great risk, and in purebred dairy herds where all heifer calves were kept in close proximity to the adult cows.

In the past decade, the disease has become much

more common due to more intensive methods of housing cattle and the introduction of infected cattle into clean herds through purchase—especially in purebred cattle. It is now considered one of the major diseases of dairy and beef cattle, and the insidious nature of the disease contributes to its distribution.

The signs of clinical disease consist of weight loss, decreased production, and diarrhea that varies in consistency from merely loose to a typical pea-soup consistency. In all cases, the manure is more fluid than that of unaffected herd mates on a similar diet.

The diarrhea also may increase or decrease with changes in diet and can become more obvious when the cow is stressed by concurrent disease or calving. Cows may have subtle diarrhea for weeks or months before signs of general unthriftiness such as rough haircoat, weight loss, and decreased milk production occur.

Most ruminant species, including goats, bison, and cattle, are susceptible to this disease. Laboratory work generally reveals only low serum protein levels due to protein loss into the intestinal tract.

The disease occurs all across the United States and in many foreign countries. It is one of the most economically important diseases of cattle, especially since frequently it involves valuable purebred stock.

Diagnosis can be difficult because blood tests, skin tests (Johnin test), and other superficial diagnostic tests are highly unreliable. The most accurate test of practical value is the culture of feces for the organisms.

This culturing procedure is time-consuming since 4 to 6 months are required for diagnosis due to slow growth of the bacteria. In addition, only a few State diagnostic laboratories have the necessary facilities and expertise for this technique.

Histologic examination of tissue from the affected area of intestine also is highly diagnostic. This tissue can be obtained from surgical biopsies of live cattle and autopsy of cows that have died. The tissues are stained with special stains that highlight the causative acid-fast organisms.

Skin Diseases

By William C. Rebhun

Ringworm is a fungal infection of the skin (dermatomycosis) that occurs commonly in calves and occasionally in adult cattle. It is contagious; therefore, when one calf in a group develops the problem, many calves usually are affected. The causative agent generally is *Trichophyton verrucosum*, a fungus that lives on the skin of cattle and other livestock.

The signs of ringworm are hair loss and development of heavy gray-white crusts at the site of infection. The lesions do not cause itching. If the crusts are scraped or cleared away, a raw area of skin devoid of hair is found. The lesions are roughly circular and usually 1 to 10 centimeters in diameter.

William C. Rebhun is Associate Professor of Veterinary Medicine and Ophthalmology, New York State College of Veterinary Medicine, Cornell University, Ithaca.

Calves commonly are affected in several spots around the face, eyelids, ears, and neck, although lesions can occur anywhere on the body. Adult cattle, when affected, tend to have more generalized lesions on the face, neck, trunk, and tail region.

Spread of ringworm occurs through body contact and inanimate objects such as brushes or blankets used on an infected animal and then used on other animals. This problem can be transmitted to humans very easily and is an important public health problem for farm workers and veterinarians that handle affected animals.

If ringworm is suspected in a human who has been in contact with cattle, a physician should be contacted for appropriate treatment.

Treatment is difficult because of the multiple sites and large number of animals that tend to be affected. For an in-

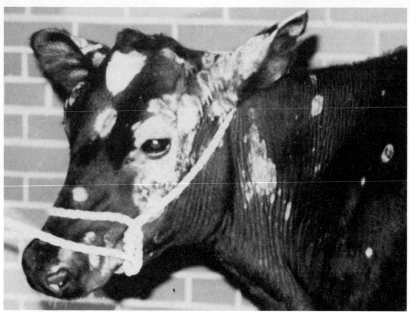

Cornell University

Ringworm is a fungal infection of skin that causes circular areas of hair loss and crusting of the infected skin.

dividual animal, the crusts can be carefully removed and topical applications of iodine, chlorox, captan, or thiabendazole applied.

For widespread lesions or multiple animal problems, captan sprays, oral griseofulvin, or other preparations may be used. It is best to consult with a veterinarian if the problem is widespread.

Fortunately, the disease tends to be self-limiting, and affected animals usually recover spontaneously within several months. Vitamins A and D sometimes are administered as empiric treatment,

and sunlight is felt to be helpful in resolving the problem.

Because of the risk of contagion, affected animals usually are not allowed to be shown in cattle shows.

Warts And Calves

Warts, or fibropapillomas, are benign skin tumors that tend to occur in calves between 4 to 24 months of age. The tumors are caused by infection of the skin with the bovine papilloma virus.

These are contagious through direct contact—especially at sites of skin abrasion or injury. The virus also can

162

Dairy and Beef Cattle

be inoculated into the skin by dehorners, castration devices, and eartags which have been contaminated by affected animals.

Usual signs include raised growths that have a gray appearance and are covered by a crust. Warts usually are 1 to 10 centimeters in diameter. A calf rarely will develop "atypical warts," which are large, very numerous, and tend to affect large areas of the body. Warts tend to occur on the face, head, eyelids, ear, neck, and topline.

These warts are not contagious to people and tend to resolve spontaneously over a course of several months in affected calves and heifers. There is no specific treatment, but large warts can be removed surgically.

Wart bacterins or vaccines are used sometimes in an attempt to prevent the disease or speed resolution of the problem, but the results are variable. These vaccines should be discussed with a veterinarian if a high incidence of warts exists on a farm.

Again, as in ringworm, the contagious nature of this problem may preclude moving affected animals to shows.

Mange Problems
Cattle mange is caused by mange mites of four major types. In general, mange causes loss of hair and tremendous itching due to movement of these tiny parasites within the skin layers.

Chorioptic mange or "tail mange" is probably the most commonly recognized clinical problem and causes loss of hair over the tailhead, escutcheon, and rear udder attachment, itchiness, skin crustiness, treading of the feet, and decreased production due to the irritating nature of the disorder. This parasite also may affect horses, sheep and goats, although the signs are somewhat different than those seen in cattle.

Sarcoptic mange, or *barn itch*, causes a severe, generalized loss of hair, reddening of the skin, and profound itching. Affected animals lose condition dramatically and decrease in production due to the irritation and itching caused by the parasites. The parasite can affect other species of livestock, such as horses, sheep, pigs, and goats, as well as people.

Psoroptic mange causes an itchy, crusty dermatitis on the neck, withers, and tailhead of affected cattle. The dermatitis can become generalized in some instances. This type mange tends to be spe-

Skin Diseases

Murray Lemmon, USDA

This barbed wire fence became a scratching post for cattle so severely bothered by scabies mites that they rubbed their hides raw to try and relieve the itching. Signs like these are signals that parasites such as scabies mites or sarcoptic mange may be affecting a herd.

cies specific and, therefore, the cattle psoroptic mange mite does not usually spread to other species.

Demodectic mange tends to be the most innocuous of the manges affecting cattle, and it consists of nodules or pustules on the neck, shoulders, and trunk of affected cattle. It does not tend to cause itching and is of concern mainly because of possible damage to the hide of affected animals. Demodectic mange tends to be species specific, and cattle do not spread this problem to other livestock species.

Diagnosis of mange requires a veterinarian to do skin scrapings or a skin biopsy and identify these specific parasites under a microscope. Whenever mange is suspected or diagnosed, a veterinarian should be notified for recommendations.

In cases of psoroptic or sarcoptic mange, State or Federal officials may need to be notified to enact treatment and control procedures. These include quarantine and chemical dips or sprays to kill the mange mites on all animals. The diseases are highly contagious to all animals within a

Murray Lemmon, USDA

Murray Lemmon, USDA

When severe loss of hair, reddening of the skin and profound itching is noticed in a herd, diagnosis requires a veterinarian to do skin scrapings or skin biopsy to identify the specific parasite so that correct treatment can be performed.

herd and early recognition is necessary to allow successful therapy.

Demodectic mange seldom requires treatment in cattle, and chorioptic mange usually is managed by specific sprays containing lime sulfur or ciodrin.

Louse Infestation

Both biting and sucking types of lice infest cattle. Louse infestation tends to be more of a problem during colder months when cattle have longer coats and are confined in close proximity to one another. Lice are species specific for the most part and cattle lice tend not to affect other species of animals or humans.

The major signs are itching and loss of hair in affected calves and cattle. Hair loss is

Skin Diseases

self-induced due to rubbing and licking by affected animals who are greatly irritated by the lice. In severe cases, blood-loss anemia may develop due to thousands of lice draining blood from a single animal. This most often occurs in younger animals that are exposed to large numbers of lice.

Many effective insecticides are available to control lice. These can be applied as powders, sprays, pour-ons, or dust bags. In any event, precautions should be taken to be sure the insecticide used is approved and safe for the breed, sex, age, and function of animal to be treated.

Streptothricosis

Streptothricosis, or Dermatophilosis, is a disease caused by *Dermatophilus congolensis*, a microbe that grows best in moist areas. In cattle, infection of the skin tends to occur when the hair coat is long.

Conditions that favor long hair coats, wet hair coats, matting of the hair, or skin abrasions favor growth of the organism. The skin lesions consist of crusts and clumps of hair that can be plucked off, leaving a raw area of dermatitis covered with a purulent discharge.

The majority of lesions occur on the topline of affected cattle, but in severe cases lesions can be generalized and affect the legs, udder, and trunk.

The organism is spread by contact, and other species such as sheep and horses can be affected—as well as people. Treatment necessitates grooming and clipping of hair if the hair coat is excessively long or moist. Grooming will remove the tufts and clumps of hair to reveal the raw skin lesions which then can be treated with iodine shampoos. In severe cases, systemic penicillin and streptomycin may be needed to help destroy the organisms.

Warbles or back grubs. This important parasite of cattle is responsible for tremendous economic loss in the form of damaged hides from affected cattle. The adult parasite is a large fly, *Hypoderma bovis* or *H. lineata*, that deposits its eggs on the hair of cattle during the fly season.

These eggs hatch, the larvae migrate through the skin of the host cow and through several other tissue layers until they reach the subcutaneous tissue on the back. At this point, they establish air holes in the skin and remain under the skin until mature, at which time they emerge

Many effective insecticides are available for treating parasites. Remember —it is extremely important to read the label. Safe and effective use depends upon many variables, including sex, breed, age and function of the animal as well as time of the year.

Murray Lemmon, USDA

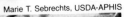

Marie T. Sebrechts, USDA-APHIS

and drop to the ground. They then mature into adult flies and complete the life cycle. Younger animals tend to be more severely affected than older cows.

Insecticides are available to kill these larvae before they complete their migration. However, it is *extremely* important to treat according to directions since treating at the wrong time of the year can lead to severe reactions. Each geographic area has its own specific time of treatment, and treatment to prevent grubs should be discussed with a veterinarian.

Skin Diseases

Other Infectious Diseases

By William C. Rebhun

Lymphosarcoma (Bovine Leukemia, Bovine Leukosis) is an infectious disease that results in leukemia and lymphoid tumor formation in some cattle infected with the bovine leukemia virus. The bovine leukemia virus is widespread, especially in dairy cattle, and current statistics estimate that 20 to 25 percent of dairy cattle in the United States may be infected with it.

Most cattle that are infected with the virus merely form antibodies against the virus and do not develop disease. However, of the total number of cows affected, a low percentage (probably less than 5 percent) develop clinical tumors that result in death. These clinical cases usually form antibodies to the virus but the antibodies do not protect them from tumor formation.

Signs observed in cattle with lymphosarcoma tumors are tremendously variable, based on location of the tumors and the number of major organs involved. Typical cases have multiple enlarged lymph nodes externally or internally and tumors in the heart, abomasum, spinal canal, uterus, and behind the eye.

However, each case is slightly different, and a major tumor in any location can lead to signs referrable to the involved organ. In some cases only a single tumor is found, but this is rare.

Because of the typical organ location of tumors, clinical cases may have heart failure, bleeding from the abomasum with a black color imparted to the feces, reproductive failures, bulging eyes, or paralysis. In addition, rare cases of multiple skin tumors

William C. Rebhun is Associate Professor of Veterinary Medicine and Ophthalmology, New York State College Of Veterinary Medicine, Cornell University, Ithaca.

(skin form), enlargement of the thymus gland (thymic form), and multiple lymph node enlargement (juvenile form) occur in calves and young cattle.

The virus lives in white blood cells of infected cattle. Therefore, secretions and blood contain the virus. The infection is spread by biting insects, needles and syringes contaminated with blood from infected cows, and in some secretions from infected cows. In affected herds, the virus can spread to involve up to 80 percent or more of the cattle.

Infection with the virus usually is innocuous, and only a low percentage of infected cattle develop tumors.

Calves generally are not infected before birth or via milk from infected cows. Although the virus may be able to infect sheep, it appears that other species—and people—are not at risk.

Economic Aspects

There is no treatment or vaccine for this disease. Bovine leukemia has tremendous economic implications because it results in mortality and carcass condemnation, as well as the fact that many foreign countries will not accept cattle or products of cattle such as semen which are infected.

Diagnosis of infection is best accomplished by blood tests via radioimmunoassay or agar-gel immunodiffusion that detect antibodies to the virus. In addition, some cattle infected with the virus have persistent elevations in the number of lymphocytes in their peripheral blood.

Control of the disease is very difficult and requires housing non-infected animals away from infected ones. Since many infected cattle are valuable production and breeding cattle, slaughter of all infected cattle is impractical and unwarranted since usually they do not develop clinical disease.

Genetics are very important in this disease because certain lines of cattle are less resistant to the virus and more prone to clinical tumor formation.

Because of the complex nature of this virus, the clinical disease, and the means of spread of the virus, the herd owner should discuss control with a veterinarian.

Pinkeye

Pinkeye, or Infectious Bovine Keratoconjunctivitis, is a highly infectious ocular disease of calves and cattle caused by the bacteria *Moraxella bovis*.

Other Infectious Diseases

Karen Rusinski, USDA-SCS

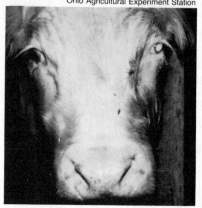

Ohio Agricultural Experiment Station

Face flies are not only annoying to cattle, but also can carry organisms, such as Moraxella bovis, a bacteria which causes pinkeye, a highly infectious eye disease. Although control of face flies is difficult, it is essential for combating pinkeye. Insecticide ear tags, dust bags and manure removal are important components of fly control.

Kevin Shields

This bacteria lives in the conjunctiva of recovered adult cattle and calves. It is present in a non-virulent form in these animals until activated by sunlight into a virulent form. Face flies then carry this organism from recovered or infected cattle to non-infected calves and adults.

Signs of the disease consist of ocular discharge which at first is watery and later contains pus. Within a few days following watery discharge and inflammation in the conjunctiva (red eye), a painful ulcer develops on the cornea of the eye and the bacteria invades the cornea to cause an obvious deep ulcer.

The affected eye appears gray, red, yellow, or a combination of all these colors. One or both eyes may be affected.

The infection spreads quickly during the fly season to involve most calves and some adult cattle that have not been exposed previously to this organism.

Other species are not affected. The disease occurs all across the United States and probably is more of a problem in beef cattle since they are usually pastured and thus exposed to sunlight and a greater population of face flies.

This disease causes serious economic loss due to poor growth and gain in affected calves, blindness, as well as drug and labor costs for treatment.

Treatment includes topical antibiotics such as penicillin, tetracycline, or furacin; antibiotics injected into the con-

Other Infectious Diseases

junctiva of the eye; and eye patches to protect the painful eye from sunlight.

Treatment procedures are easy in theory but difficult to carry out in practice. Any owner or veterinarian who has had to catch and restrain 100 beef calves for eye treatment every day for a week needs no further explanation.

Control of face flies is essential. Insecticide ear tags, dust bags, and manure removal are important components of fly control.

Although massive research has been devoted towards a vaccine against pinkeye, only recently has a new vaccine been developed which may help prevent the disease. This vaccine does not guarantee total protection but may help prevent disease in 70 percent or more of the animals at risk.

Anaplasmosis

This disease is caused by a protozoan organism *Anaplasma marginale* that parasitizes red blood cells of infected cattle. It occurs primarily in young adult or adult animals that are infected by the organism. Stress such as concurrent disease, transportation, or feed shortages often precipitates the disease.

Calves may be infected and develop immunity while continuing to harbor the organism. Adult animals that are infected often show an acute disease with fever, anemia, jaundice, and emaciation. Mortality may reach or exceed 50 percent in these acute infections.

Signs may be subacute with fever, anemia, jaundice, and weight loss, or peracute with all the aforementioned signs plus respiratory distress and death occurring quickly.

Insects are extremely important in transmission of this disease since blood must be transferred from infected to non-infected cattle. The most common insects involved are ticks such as *Boophilus* and *Dermacentor* species and tabanid flies. It also should be remembered that syringes and instruments contaminated with blood could transmit the disease.

In some instances, sheep, goats, and wild ruminants also may be infected and have subclinical or clinical disease. Humans are not affected.

Economic losses due to the disease are important and have been quoted by one source to approach $35 million annually. Therefore, treatment and prevention are important.

Diagnosis is confirmed by blood tests such as the complement fixation test. Treatment consists of high levels of tetracycline by injection and this is used for both clinical cases and carrier animals identified by blood testing. Imidocarb, another anti-protozoan drug, also has been used in treatment.

Prevention is difficult because of the number of subclinical and carrier cattle. Vaccines help minimize losses due to this disease, and their use should be discussed with a veterinarian.

Babesiasis

Babesiasis is a disease caused by protozoans of the *Babesia* species that parasitize red blood cells of infected animals. It usually occurs in animals between 6 to 12 months old that have not had prior exposure to the causative protozoan.

In endemic areas, cattle usually are protected by antibodies developed by exposure to *Babesia* at a young age. The disease also is rare in adult or older cattle unless they are introduced into an endemic area and have never been exposed in the past.

Signs include an acute onset of fever, anemia, depression, falloff of appetite, jaundice, hemoglobinemia, and hemoglobinuria. These last two signs are suggestive of rapid red blood cell destruction in the vascular space and provide important differentials when one is confused between Anaplasmosis and Babesiasis.

Each species has its own type of *Babesia* and, therefore, cattle only spread this to other cattle through the necessary insect vectors—ticks, mainly of the *Boophilus* genus. Again, as with Anaplasmosis, it should be emphasized that blood-contaminated instruments can carry the disease. Babesiasis does not affect humans.

Diagnosis depends upon identifying the tick vector, blood tests for antibodies, and blood smears to identify the causative parasite in infected red blood cells.

Treatment consists of chemicals such as Imidocarb (Imizol) that kill the protozoans, or quinuronium type drugs such as Acaprin which work against some of the organisms. Prevention can be attained by prophylactic treatment with Imidocarb or with vaccines. Eradication is possible only if the tick vectors can be eliminated from the geographic area.

Other Infectious Diseases

Common Causes of Lameness

By Francis H. Fox

Books have been written on this important subject (such as *Lameness in Cattle* by Greenough et al) which attests to its importance and widespread occurrence among cattle. As in any other species in which lameness is common, there are numerous causes, but specific problems involving the feet would probably account for about 95 percent of the cases encountered.

Foot rot is the term used to denote the most common form of lameness in cattle. This can appear initially as an inflammation and swelling of the soft tissue between the toes which may or may not extend to and include one or both bulbs of the heels.

Its cause is considered by most to be an infectious organism which thrives in moist and manure-littered soil. Others believe that although a single organism is almost never isolated from a lesion, something has to first break the protective integrity of the skin for the organism to gain entrance and do its damage.

Frequently incriminated items would include small sharp stones such as shale or cinders, sharp brush, or hedges which remain at the surface of the ground after they have been trimmed, and even overabundant use of anti-slip materials such as calcite.

Additionally, it is frequently observed by many that foot rot outbreaks are exceptionally high in periods of excessive weather, such as either extremely dry years or extremely wet ones.

In wet years, it seems logical to assume that the wetness favors excessive growth

Francis H. Fox is Professor of Veterinary Medicine and Obstetrics, New York State College of Veterinary Medicine, Cornell University, Ithaca.

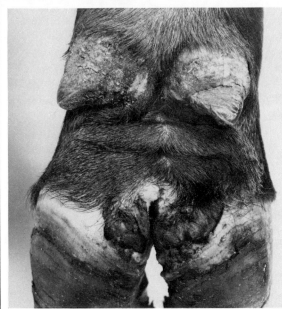

Foot rot—the most common form of lameness in cattle.

USDA

of the organism as well as aiding mechanically in allowing mud buildup between the toes. If the mud contains any abrasive materials such as sharp gravel, this logically accounts for the initial cut or injury.

In dry years, many feel that the interdigital skin and skin at the heels literally becomes dried out and cracks, thus allowing entrance of the infectious organism.

Signs Are Obvious

The signs are quite obvious to those with any experience. The animal is observed to be lame, usually in one limb, and the severity can range from a slight limp to so-called "three-legged lameness," in which the animal prefers not to touch the affected foot to the ground or floor.

Upon closer examination, one observes varying degrees of redness, swelling, and tenderness between the toes and/or involving one or both heels.

Neglected cases may demonstrate extension of the swelling/infection so that it involves the pastern area below the dewclaws and eventually may extend upward above the dewclaws to a point about midway between the ankle and the knee or hock. This indicates the infection has spread and involves soft tissues of the area including the

Common Causes of Lameness

muscles and tendon sheaths and, in the most severe cases, also extends into the fetlock joint causing a severe septic arthritis.

The possibility of foot rot spreading from cow to cow has been a controversial subject for many years, and no final conclusion has been reached as yet.

Up to half of the animals in a herd may be affected in a severe outbreak; some people are inclined to say that such a high incidence proves the disease's infectious nature. However, others do not agree it is truly an infectious disease in the context of spreading from cow to cow but rather that if the environmental agents (injury and organisms) are present, then "one animal gets the disease from where the others did." I tend to favor this latter concept.

Economic Losses

The economic significance is of considerable importance. The affected animal rapidly loses considerable weight and body conditioning and if lactating, milk production may drop as much as 50 percent. The reason for these effects includes the severe pain that obviously accompanies the swollen limb and, perhaps more importantly, the fact that the animal prefers to lie down most of the time. Whether an animal obtains its feed by grazing or by standing at a feed bunk, neither is possible while lying down. The same is true of water intake.

Treatment, especially if initiated early in the disease, is usually successful, though somewhat difficult and costly depending upon the facilities available to properly restrain the animal.

Ideally, the foot should be cleaned (and trimmed if needed) to ensure that a foreign object such as a small sharp stone does not remain between the toes or lodged under the hard sole or heel regions.

Following this, many apply a healing ointment, liquid, or powder, and bandage. The bandage is removed in 3 to 5 days, at which time the healing usually is complete. Others, as during an outbreak in a large feedlot operation, prefer to treat the animal systemically by administering an antibiotic such as penicillin and/or sulfonamide. Still others combine both methods, but in lactating dairy cattle it must be remembered that the milk must be withheld for the prescribed time period after antibiotics or sulfonamides have been administered.

Dairy and Beef Cattle

Prevention is important, particularly if large numbers in an outbreak are becoming affected. If the most likely cause is obvious, its removal is relatively easily accomplished and the results are rewarding. Fencing a mudhole, changing or resurfacing an offending laneway, or changing offending anti-slip material on cement surfaces can bring about dramatic results.

Also, in mature animals (both beef and dairy) whose feet have become overgrown with extra long toes, proper trimming can dramatically reduce the number of cases of foot rot. Overgrown hooves invite heel injury (long toes tip the weightbearing surface back to the soft heel tissue, inviting cuts and bruising); unworn and/or untrimmed walls frequently extend over the soles, creating pockets for stones or other foreign material to become imbedded.

Footbaths. Another worthwhile method of reducing incidence in a herd experiencing an outbreak consists in having the herd walk through a wet or dry footbath once or twice daily. This can be accomplished easily by constructing the bath at the entrance or exit of the milking parlor in the freestall dairy herd. In feedlots, arrange-

ments in the watering or feeding areas are necessary.

For the wet bath, either a 5 percent copper sulfate solution or a 2 to 5 percent formalin solution is recommended. If one prefers a dry bath (especially in cold weather), a mixture of one part powdered copper sulfate and nine parts slaked lime seems equally effective. These methods undoubtedly reduce the number of causative organisms.

Punctures, Quittors

Other direct causes of foot lameness would include nail or wire punctures or the presence of a mass of soft tissue growth between the toes referred to by some as a *quittor*. In the former, one should search the environment for the cause, such as a board lying on the ground or a floor with nails protruding from it.

In the latter, this growth was thought at one time to be hereditary and initially seemed to be present almost exclusively in the Hereford breed. Today, however, an abundance of the growths can be found in many older animals of all breeds.

The affected animal becomes lame either when the growth becomes so large it extends to the bearing surface

Common Causes of Lameness

(and then becomes injured) or when a foreign object (such as a stone) becomes wedged between the growth and one of the claws.

In the average case, removing the object and bandaging with an antiseptic ointment results in recovery. In the valuable brood cow or herd sire, complete surgical removal offers the best chance for permanent recovery.

Laminitis is an important foot problem in some herds and most frequently involves half grown to young adult animals. When this occurs, the laminae (sensitive vascular tissue between the hoof wall and the inner foot) become inflamed and very tender. Though all four feet may be involved, usually the animal is equally lame only in both front feet.

The animal prefers to lie down. When forced to move, it walks painfully with back arched and rear limbs tucked up under the body to carry most of the weight. In extreme cases, the animal may walk on its knees.

The cause is controversial, as is true in horses as well, but two incriminated contributory factors include an abrupt change in feed, particularly from a high fiber diet to a high protein and/or en-

ergy ration, or because the feet have dried out excessively. In the latter case in dairy cattle, this may happen due to changing the bred heifers from a mud lot or a pen with a deep manure pack to a dry bedded cement platform in a stanchion or tie stall barn after calving.

Treatment or prevention consists of eliminating the abrupt diet change and softening the feet with a moist pack such as bunk or manger sweepings. Antihistamines are thought by some to help reduce the inflammation.

Miscellaneous local causes of lameness are numerous and frequently unrelated. For example, in some confined dairy herds, several individuals may become lame from knee or hock injuries usually due to combinations of too short and/ or too narrow platforms with inadequate or abrasive bedding or protruding objects at the base of the stanchion or edge of the manger. By laceration or bruising, various organisms gain entrance to the joint capsule or joint and ultimately cause a septic arthritis and severe lameness.

Calving Effects

Lameness associated with calving sometimes occurs. If the birth was difficult, especially if due to an excessively large calf, nerves (such as the obturator) within the birth canal may become bruised or otherwise damaged. The result is that the mother loses the ability to keep her rear limbs in under her body. She becomes "spraddle-legged" and some cows will be unable to stand, especially if the footing is slippery as on wet, smooth cement floors.

Good nursing care is essential to prevent further injury (such as hip joint dislocation) and most recover in from 5 to 14 days.

Another lameness associated with calving is when the animal is unable to rise for a prolonged period of time after calving (such as in stubborn or repeated cases of milk fever) and begins to knuckle forward on one or both rear fetlocks.

The cause is bruising of the deep peroneal nerve at the region of the stifle from the weight of the cow being on that area for prolonged periods of time, especially if this area of the body is on the edge of the curb of a cement platform or a rocky area in the pasture or barnlot. Again, with good nursing care, the condition usually resolves within a one- to two-week period.

Trauma and slipping occasionally result in lameness from sprains, broken bones, or joint dislocation. Prevention includes providing good footing for the animals at all times and handling them in as quiet a manner as possible. Slippery cement floors are the most common offenders in an inside environment, while ice on a bare frozen ground surface may cause problems on the outside.

Lameness may be caused also by a disease or condition affecting the entire body. In such cases, lameness would be but one of many signs (results) of the specific illness.

Examples include the stilted gait or sawhorse position of tetanus, the painful gait and ultimate foot and limb deformities of fluorine poisoning, the occasional lameness involved with the mucosal form of bovine virus diarrhea, the extreme lameness with the affected limb(s) in blackleg, the lameness associated with ergot poisoning, and some cases affected with vesicular stomatitis.

As the name implies, it is logical to expect lameness to occur in the dreaded exotic viral disease, foot-and-mouth disease.

Common Causes of Lameness

Common Toxic Diseases

By Robert B. Hillman

Poisonings occur in domestic animals from many sources and under a great variety of circumstances. Most poisonings result from accidental ingestion of the toxic substance, and any dietary deficiency that leads to an abnormal appetite will increase the likelihood of eating toxic materials. Some conditions that might lead to ingesting abnormal materials include: Lack of salt, low calcium or phosphorus in the diet, lack of roughage (fiber), starvation, and boredom.

Lead is one of the most common causes of poisoning in farm animals. Lead-based paint ingested by licking or chewing old painted woodwork is the most frequent source of

---

Robert B. Hillman is Senior Clinician—Section of Theriogenology, New York State College of Veterinary Medicine, Cornell University, Ithaca.

the toxic material. Other common sources include painting materials (paint buckets, dropcloths), putty, old batteries, plumbing materials, gasoline, linoleum, and some fruit sprays.

Clinical signs include blindness, and nervous signs—which vary from extreme excitement with bellowing, frothing of the mouth and attempts to climb the walls, to dullness and depression with head pressing, falloff of appetite, and failure to respond to any external stimulus.

In suspected cases of lead poisoning a veterinarian should be consulted immediately. Treatment can save some animals if applied soon enough and if an overwhelming dose of lead has not been ingested.

Arsenic is another common cause of poisoning in livestock due to its many uses in agriculture. It has been employed in insecticides, anthelmintics, weed killers, sheep and cattle dips, and wood preservatives. Poisoning occurs when these products are used improperly or if animals are allowed to ingest them.

Large doses of arsenic lead to death so rapidly that the animal is never seen to be ill. With smaller doses, signs include intense abdominal pain (colic), staggering gait, diarrhea, dehydration, and shock. While the outlook usually is unfavorable, rapid treatment with specific agents and fluid support will result in saving a few of the less severely poisoned animals.

Copper, Fluorine

Copper also has many uses in agriculture and can produce animal poisonings. Copper sulfate is used in orchard sprays, for treatment of pastures to control liver flukes, and for a foot soak to prevent foot rot. Improper use or allowing animals to graze too soon after use of copper sulfate can result in poisoning.

Copper poisoning is seen most frequently in sheep but does occur in cattle and usually results when animals have ingested forage containing small amounts of excess copper for a considerable period of time.

At a time of stress (shipping, giving birth, etc.), the animal becomes acutely ill as the excess copper that has been slowly stored in the liver is suddenly released, resulting in destruction of the animal's red blood cells. The animal becomes weak, icteric (yellow), and has a dark brown urine. Supportive treatment with fluids and a change of diet may save some animals.

Fluorine poisoning usually follows contamination of forage with fine ash from manufacturing plants that process metals at high temperatures (aluminum, steel, etc.). Signs of fluorine poisoning include tooth lesions (discoloration and uneven wear), poor growth, weight loss and lameness. Treatment is aimed at removing the source of fluorine (change diet, reduce pasture contamination) and supportive care.

Urea is used as a feed additive in the diet of ruminants as a cheap substitute for more expensive protein sources. Properly used, it is safe and effective. When improperly used (improper mixing, added at too high a level, spilled), it can cause poisoning.

Signs of urea toxicity occur shortly after ingestion and include bloating, increased salivation, incoordination, increased urination, and difficulty in breathing. Prompt veterinary treatment of the rumen by relieving the bloat and giving acidifying agents and cold water will result in saving most cattle with urea poisoning.

Organophosphate pesticides are used extensively in agriculture as animal sprays, systemic insecticides, and as treatments for seed grains and soil insecticides. If these products are improperly mixed and applied, or if they are ingested, poisoning results.

Signs of organophosphate poisoning include constricted pupils, increased salivation, diarrhea, muscle twitching, incoordination, and death.

Treatment is aimed at removing the toxic material by washing with lots of water if the poisoning is due to improper spraying, or giving absorbents and laxatives if the toxic material has been eaten. Specific veterinary treatment to counteract the drugs is also essential.

Dangerous Plants

Many plants can produce toxicity in cattle. Cows do not normally eat poisonous plants but if forced to by overgrazing or attracted to them by some change in the environment, poisoning can occur. Poisonings frequently follow dumping of green hedge clippings or garden refuse into a pasture. Cattle are attracted to the "new" material and investigate by tasting.

Clippings from *Taxus* or Japanese yew are a common cause of death in cattle due to the presence of an alkaloid that impairs functioning of the heart. Other plants (such as Cherry, Sudangrass) contain glycosides which release cyanide upon digestion. Cyanide prevents oxygen from leaving the blood to enter the cells and results in very rapid death of the animal.

Another group of dangerous plants accumulates toxic levels of nitrates when grown under certain conditions (high fertilization, stunted growth). Some common weeds (pigweed, lambsquarter) and even some crops (oats, corn) will contain toxic levels of nitrate under these conditions. Nitrates are converted to nitrites in the rumen and they, in turn, combine with the blood—making it incapable of carrying oxygen. If untreated, these animals can die from lack of oxygen.

Other toxic plants (St. Johnswort, buckwheat) can produce photosensitization, which results in the white portions of the body becoming sensitive to sunlight. If ex-

Dairy and Beef Cattle

posed to direct sunlight, these unpigmented areas will become reddened and swollen and, if not protected from the sun, these portions of skin will die and peel off. Other plants can produce excessive bleeding (Bracken fern, sweet clover) when eaten for a period of time.

Good management practices—including providing ample palatable and nutritious forage, plus limiting exposure to toxic agents and plants—will reduce the chances of poisoning.

Foreign Diseases

By Edwin I. Pilchard

Freedom from over 20 diseases disastrous to beef and milk production in many parts of the world is enjoyed in the United States. Like most freedoms, this was hard-won and keeping it requires eternal vigilance.

Contagious bovine pleuropneumonia was the first livestock disease eradicated from the United States. The U.S. was declared free of it September 26, 1892, after completing a long campaign by the newly established U.S. Bureau of Animal Industry (BAI). The BAI was created in 1884 by a Congress faced with the refusal of foreign countries to buy U.S. cattle because of the widespread presence of the disease in this country.

Edwin I. Pilchard is a Principal Staff Officer, Veterinary Services, Animal and Plant Health Inspection Service.

Contagious bovine pleuropneumonia severely damages the lungs of infected cattle and water buffalo, often resulting in death. The microbe causing it, *Mycoplasma mycoides mycoides,* spreads slowly but surely from coughing, infected animals to others they live with or near. There is no effective vaccine or treatment. Prevention depends on keeping infected cattle from entering the country from Africa and the parts of southwestern Europe where it exists.

The last decade of the 1800's also saw a major breakthrough for disease prevention in general, when three U.S. Department of Agriculture scientists—Theobald Smith, Cooper Curtis, and Fred Kilbourne—proved that ticks spread Texas fever. Before that time, disease transmission by ticks and insects was unproven. A program of dipping cattle to kill carrier ticks

Dairy and Beef Cattle

eliminated the disease by 1943.

Significant as these early successes were, they seem overshadowed by the elimination of six outbreaks of foot-and-mouth disease, the last occurring in 1929. The fight to keep it out of the United States still goes on.

Between 1946 and 1954, over 1,500 U.S. veterinarians and scientists helped Mexico eliminate foot-and-mouth disease. Canada eliminated a small outbreak there in 1952. Each year hundreds of outbreaks of this disease are reported in other parts of the world, while nations free of the disease include the United States, Canada, Mexico, Central America, Australia, New Zealand, Japan, Great Britain, and the Scandinavian countries.

Foot-and-mouth disease in the nations that have it is costly in losses of meat and milk production. Added to this is the cost of over 2 billion doses of foot-and-mouth vaccine used each year in control efforts by affected countries throughout the world.

Foot-and-mouth disease virus spreads easily among cattle, swine, and other cloven-hoofed animals. Some pregnant cattle abort and some young ones die. But most of the disease damage is from the fever, sore mouths, feet, and teats that slow or stop milk production and make affected animals stop eating. Humans rarely are infected.

It would cost about $54 million each year to control foot-and-mouth disease in the United States if it were to gain entry here and spread to one of every 1,000 animals susceptible to it, before it was again eradicated.

Rinderpest is another virus-caused foreign disease worth special attention by cattle owners. It has been increasing in parts of Africa since 1979, after several years when it was kept low through widespread vaccination. Rinderpest also is reported regularly in Southeast Asia and the Middle East.

Once introduced in a herd by the addition of an infected animal, rinderpest spreads easily, producing severe, often bloody diarrhea, ulcers in the mouth and digestive tract, and high death rates in infected cattle.

Rift Valley fever affects not only cattle, but also sheep, and humans. Biting insects spread it, and several kinds of biting insects common in the United States are capable of spreading Rift Valley fever if

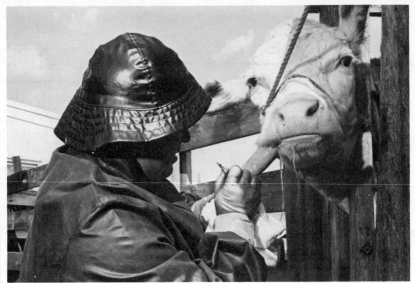

Each year hundreds of outbreaks of Foot and Mouth Disease are reported in other parts of the world, while the United States remains free of it. FMD virus spreads easily among cattle, swine and other cloven-hoofed animals. It would cost about $54 million each year to control FMD in the U.S. if it did gain entry and spread to one-tenth of one percent of the susceptible animals.

it should enter this country.

The disease causes high rates of abortion in pregnant cattle and sheep, and death of calves and lambs. Rainy seasons in the Great Rift Valley of Africa, and in some recent years in Egypt, bring renewed outbreaks there.

Heartwater disease— which gets its name from the large amount of fluid found around the heart in animals that die from it—has been discovered recently in some of the Caribbean Islands. The disease also exists in eastern and southern Africa and Madagascar.

Carried by Amblyomma ticks to cattle, sheep, goats, antelope and some other hoofed stock, the microscopic *Cowdria ruminantium* causing heartwater can produce violent convulsions that resemble strychnine poisoning, or stiffness resembling tetanus, and sometimes death. It also can be carried by normal-appearing recovered and resistant animals.

Diagnosis requires special methods and experience available in only a few laboratories. This fact, and ability of the causative agent to be carried in zoological animals, make heartwater potentially hazardous to cattle kept with or near these species.

'Summer Bleeding'

Another foreign disease of recent concern to cattle is parafilariasis or "summer bleeding." Caused by the microscopic worm-like parasite, *Parafilaria bovicola,* parafilariasis has been found in cattle in Africa, Sweden, and France.

Cattle get infected while grazing with carrier animals on summer pasture. Several months later small streaks of blood may be seen on the hair where the adult parasites have come out from the skin and muscle to lay their eggs. Flies feeding on this egg-laden blood spread the disease.

Although not fatal, parafilariasis is costly because as much as 25 percent of the best cuts of beef have bruise-like hemorrhages which must be trimmed away at slaughter.

Exotic bluetongue, melioidosis, and tick-borne fever also can affect cattle. These are briefly described in the foreign disease part of the section on sheep and goats.

The other foreign cattle diseases not described in this brief report include Akabane, petechial fever, ephemeral fever, Asiatic hemorrhagic septicemia, Ibaraki, lumpy skin disease (Neethling virus), schistosomiasis, theileriasis, East Coast fever, Wesselsbron, and African trypanosomiasis.

Even though trypanosomiasis often is considered the most destructive cattle disease in many parts of Africa, its dependency on the tsetse fly for transmission makes it unlikely to become established or spread in the United States.

Screwworms

Foreign insect pests also cause serious damage to cattle and other livestock in the countries where they exist. For example, the screwworm *(Cochliomyia hominivorax),* so named because of the spiral bands that give the maggots the appearance of wood screws, can make livestock raising unprofitable.

Attracted to any scratch or wound on warm-blooded animals, and to navels of the newborn, the adult screwworm fly lays its eggs. These hatch in a few days and the young maggots eat their way into the otherwise healthy animal, eventually resulting in death if not treated.

Chuck Herron, USDA-APHIS

John Kucharski, USDA-APHIS

Dairy and Beef Cattle

Fred Witte, USDA

A unique cooperative program between industry and government resulted in the eradication of screwworms from the U.S. The program involved the release of billions of sexuallly sterilized flies, collection of screwworm samples from infected areas and treatment of any fresh wounds to avoid infestation. The screwworm fly lays its eggs in wounds of warm-blooded animals. Once the eggs hatch, they develop into larvae that begin feeding on the host's flesh. Eradication of this pest from the United States resulted in an annual savings to livestock producers of $400 million.

Screwworms were eliminated from the United States in 1966 through a unique Federal program in which mil-

lions of sterile male flies were raised artificially and then released from airplanes flying over infected land. Once at ground level, the sterile males mate with females of the species. Female screwworm flies breed only once in their lifetime, and since the males dropped to them are sterile, the eggs they lay do not hatch.

The U.S. Department of Agriculture screwworm program has returned over $10 in benefits for every dollar expended. Now that the United States is free of screwworms, we are cooperating with Mexico in a program expected to virtually eliminate this pest from Mexico by the end of 1984.

Foreign Diseases

Preventive Medicine

By William C. Rebhun

As regards cattle, preventive medicine programs are called "herd health programs." Preventive medicine can include vaccinations, control of parasites, reproductive programs, nutritional programs, and mastitis control.

General guidelines for preventive medicine, or herd health programs, can easily be formulated but *each* farm needs to be considered individually when formulating an exact herd health program. The program should be formulated by a cooperative group that includes the owner, veterinarian, extension experts, and any other consultants necessary to aid with specific problem areas.

The following information

William C. Rebhun is Associate Professor of Veterinary Medicine and Ophthalmology, New York State College of Veterinary Medicine, Cornell University, Ithaca.

will present general guidelines for specific herd health programs but should not be interpreted as the "only way" to implement preventive measures.

Vaccines

Vaccination for respiratory diseases in northern climates is done usually in early fall to provide maximum protection during the fall and winter pneumonia season.

In beef cattle, regardless of geographic locality, respiratory disease vaccines are generally employed at least 2 weeks before shipment of animals destined for feedlots. This allows the cattle to develop protective antibodies prior to being shipped to a new location where they likely will encounter other cattle assembled from many farms.

The common respiratory diseases for which vaccines are available include IBR,

PI3, Hemophilus, and Pasteurella. Close attention should be paid to label directions and veterinary advice to ensure proper vaccination.

Vaccination against *Leptospira sp.* usually is performed once or twice yearly depending on the relative risk of this abortion-causing disease in certain geographic areas. In beef cattle and bull-bred dairy cattle herds, vaccination against Vibriosis may be necessary on a yearly basis to avoid reproductive failure due to this disease.

Vaccination against BVD is usually done in beef cattle and often done in dairy cattle that reside in infected herds or geographic areas with a high incidence of BVD. Vaccines for BVD may or may not be combined with vaccines against respiratory disease. Usually it is recommended that this vaccination be repeated yearly. The type of BVD vaccine to be used in a herd should be discussed with a veterinarian.

Vaccinations against blackleg, malignant edema, and tetanus are indicated for calves and young stock in some geographic areas. These diseases are caused by *Clostridium sp.* bacteria which are more common in some parts of the United States than in oth-

ers. Veterinarians and agricultural extension agents can be consulted regarding the value of these vaccines within a given locale.

Vaccines against calf diarrhea (calf scours) were discussed previously in the chapter on *Digestive Diseases* and they are indicated primarily for herds with this specific problem.

Calfhood vaccination against brucellosis (Bang's disease) is indicated for female calves in almost all areas. The heifer calves currently are vaccinated with a reduced dosage of Strain 19 type *Brucella* between 4 and 8 months of age. This age range must be strictly adhered to in order to avoid problems with blood testing at a later age. Bull calves must not be vaccinated. In some endemic areas where test and slaughter eradication of Bang's disease has been difficult, adult cows have been vaccinated—but generally this is not indicated.

Any discussion of brucellosis and vaccination techniques for this disease must include veterinary input.

Parasite Treatments

Wormers or anthelmintics, directed against endoparasites, coccidia, and lungworms should be used mainly in

Preventive Medicine

calves, feeder calves, and young stock of both dairy and beef breeds. In addition, where management conditions allow heavy exposure to parasites, adult cow treatment may be indicated.

Thiabendazole, levamisol, coumaphos, amprolium, monensin, and ivermectin are drugs used for various parasites. The exact choice of drug should be discussed with a veterinarian and will require consideration of age, sex, breed, and intended use of the animals. Management procedures that discourage exposure to parasites should be employed as well, and these include pasture rotation, removal of manure, and avoiding crowding where possible.

Ectoparasites such as lice, ticks, mange mites, and flies are treated by an assortment of sprays, pour-ons, dips, dust bags, pesticide additives in feeds that kill fly larvae, and ear tags. Once again the exact needs will vary from herd to herd.

Routine reproductive examinations at regular intervals are indicated in all herds to insure adequate reproductive performance. Most dairy herds have their veterinarian perform monthly reproductive checks to detect heats, determine pregnancy status, and treat problem cows that have uterine infections, fail to show heat, or have cystic ovaries. Beef herds have regular pregnancy checks to confirm pregnancies or determine open cows that might require treatment or culling.

Without a regular reproductive program, problems such as a prolonged calving interval or low calving percentage can easily develop. These problems are disastrous economically in either dairy or beef cattle systems.

Nutrition. Due to the tremendous diversity in feedstuffs and feeding programs in today's cattle industry, a great deal of attention should be directed to nutritional principles such as ration balancing and ration formulation for intended use of cattle on each farm. Energy, protein, mineral content and fiber all need to be considered.

A management team consisting of owner, veterinarian, and extension consultants may be best able to handle this problem. Maximum growth or production to increase profits is the desired result of any nutritional program.

Mastitis. Participation in a mastitis control program will often pay large dividends for a dairy farmer. Culturing quarters, performing regular somatic cell counts or white cell analyses, checking milking equipment regularly, teat dipping, dry cow therapy, and maintaining a clean environment for the cows are all essentials for the control of mastitis.

The veterinarian, dairyman, and State mastitis control experts are integral members of the management team when attempting to control mastitis.

Ideally, cows should be calved in a clean maternity area that can be disinfected after each use. If this is not possible, the cleanest area available should be used as a maternity area and should be well-bedded and free of mud and manure.

Newborn calves should have their navels dipped immediately with 2 percent iodine to discourage bacterial invasion of the navel. Colostrum should be provided within the first few hours after birth, and the calf should ingest colostrum equivalent to at least 10 percent of its body weight within the first 24 hours of life.

The calf's environment should be kept as clean as practically possible for the first few days of life to minimize exposure to pathogenic organisms.

Antibiotics in Feed

Feed additives or antibiotics that promote growth and maximize profits are used primarily in beef cattle such as feeder calves and in feedlot operations.

These products work several ways to maintain a healthy flora of organisms in the gastrointestinal tract and thereby allow maximum conversion of feed to weight gain. The products also may prevent low grade bacterial infections such as liver abscesses (sawdust livers) and rumenitis that deter growth or result in condemnation of various organs at slaughter.

Use of feed additives and antibiotics has been watched closely by regulatory agencies to ensure wholesome meat supplies, and the current additives are deemed safe products. These additives are tremendously important in maximizing efficient growth in beef animals. Without them, commercial beef operations would be unable to raise cattle without increasing the price of beef significantly.

Genetic Diseases

By Horst W. Leipold

Congenital defects or diseases are abnormalities of structure or function present at birth. In cattle many of these defects of either genetic, environmental, or unknown cause—or due to environmental-genetic interaction—have been identified. The genetically caused diseases are mostly due to homozygosity of a simple autosomal recessive gene, meaning that the animal has received one defective gene from each of its parents.

It is desirable to recognize congenital defects which are of significance to cattle owners and breeders. Not only is diagnosis important, but methods to control genetically induced defects should be available. The most frequently encountered defects seem to involve bone, brain, muscle and skin. In this chapter the more significant genetic diseases in beef and dairy cattle are reviewed.

Mulefoot. The single most common and economically important disease in Holstein, Angus, Chianina, Charolais and Simmental cattle is syndactyly (mulefoot). This is nondivision or fusion of functional toes. It affects most frequently the right front foot followed by the left, then right hind and all four feet. The cow is not adapted to the single hoof and walking is painful and difficult for mulefoot animals. Frequently they die due to stress.

Syndactyly is a simple autosomal recessive gene. It is common in various breeds in the United States and Europe. Other species affected are swine, sheep and dogs.

This ranks as the most important genetic disease in cattle in the United States.

Horst W. Leipold is a Professor in the Department of Pathology, College of Veterinary Medicine, Kansas State University, Manhattan.

Dairy and Beef Cattle

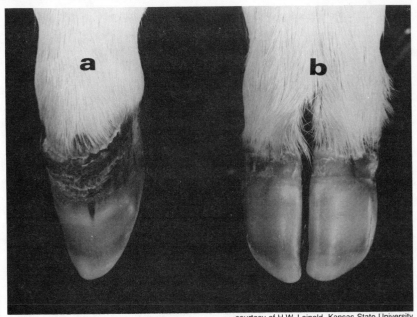

courtesy of H.W. Leipold, Kansas State University

Treatment is by control of carrier bulls in artificial insemination and natural breeding.

A method of early detection has been developed at Kansas State University. It combines superovulation, embryo transfer (two embryos for recipient), and early fetal cesarean section at 60 days of gestation—at which time the mulefoot condition can be easily recognized.

Cows may also be tested in this way: The cows are superovulated and then inseminated with semen from an affected syndactylous bull. The embryos are transferred to recipient cows (two per recipient) and then the fetuses are

Mulefoot (syndactyly) in a Holstein calf. Notice right front foot (a) is affected with syndactyly while the left front foot (b) is normal.

removed by cesarean section at 60 days of gestation. It takes 7 normal fetuses per cow or bull to declare the suspect animal clean (a non-carrier). As outlined above, prevention can be accomplished only by preventing the use of carrier animals in breeding.

Too Many Toes. Polydactyly, more toes than normal, also is a genetic disease—mostly in Simmental and Holstein cattle. It is transmitted as a polygenic (many genes with small effects). Usually

Genetic Diseases

195

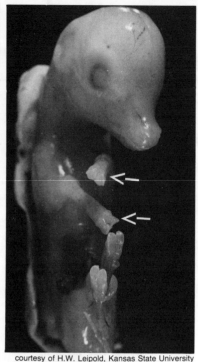

courtesy of H.W. Leipold, Kansas State University
H.W. Leipold

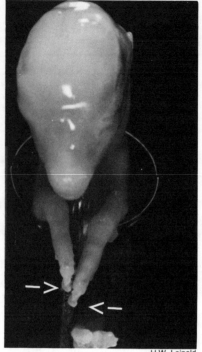

H.W. Leipold

Normal 60-day fetus. Note normal cloven foot (arrows).

A 60-day fetus affected with syndactyly (mulefoot). Note abnormal uncloven front feet (arrows).

Polydactyly (more toes than normal) in a calf. Notice three toes developed instead of normal two toes. Affected calves have difficulty walking.

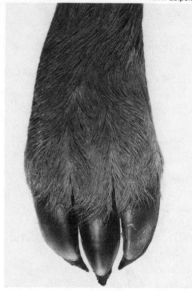

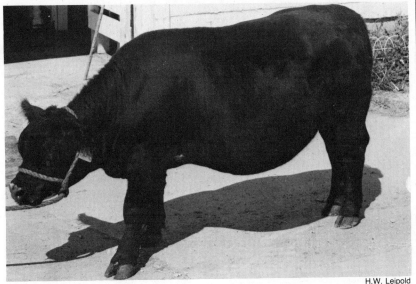

H.W. Leipold

one finds 3 toes on both front feet. The affected animals have difficulties in walking. Spread of this defect is by carrier bulls. There is no treatment. Prevention and control is only by carefully recording defective calves and removing carrier bulls from service.

Tibial hemimelia is a bone defect in the hind legs of Galloway calves. It is due to a genetic factor, a simple autosomal recessive (with one abnormal gene from each parent). Affected calves lack development of a bone in the hind leg, the tibia. Thus, the calves are unable to rise and nurse. Other defects accompanying this defect are brain and reproductive abnormalities. There is no treatment for

"Snorter" dwarf with typical saddle nose, short legs and bloated belly. Dwarfs are rare today but once were a serious threat to livestock industry.

the condition except to prevent its occurrence by eliminating carrier animals from breeding service.

Besides leg defects there are various other abnormalities including the bone of the head and spinal column. Cleft lip and cleft palate may be hereditary defects in cattle but they need more careful studies.

The entire skeleton is affected in dwarfism, bulldog calves (chondrodysplasia), and marble bone disease (osteope-

Genetic Diseases

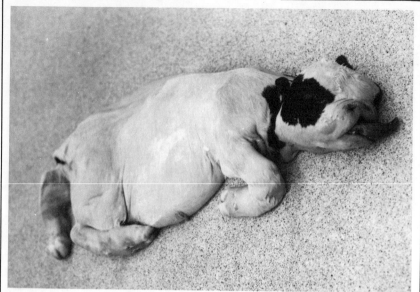

H.W. Leipold

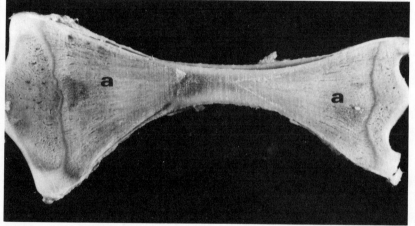

H.W. Leipold

"Bulldog" calf born dead. Notice abnormal face and short legs.

Leg bone split in half from calf affected with marble bone disease. Note lack of bone marrow cavity (a).

198   Dairy and Beef Cattle

trosis). All these defects are genetic in origin.

Dwarfism is characterized by small size and a snorting sound while breathing. That led to the condition being referred to as snorter dwarfism. At one time it was the single most important disease in U.S. beef herds. There still are occasional cases. It is inherited as a simple autosomal recessive. Prevention and control is by carefully controlled breeding programs.

Bulldog calves are seen in the Holstein breed and various beef breeds. They are small, have head deformities, and frequently are born early. The legs always are very short. Severe abnormalities involve bones of the legs.

Bulldogs have a genetic cause and more studies are needed to clarify the mode of transmission. Spread of the disease is via carrier animals which implies again that control may be accomplished by identifying carrier animals and eliminating them from breeding programs.

Osteopetrosis (marble-bone-disease) has been described in black and red Angus calves. Occasional cases have been observed in Simmental and Hereford cattle.

The disease is caused by homozygosity of a simple autosomal recessive gene.

This defect is characterized by small body size and weight. Calves are born 3 weeks prematurely and dead. There is a short lower jaw. All bones in the body of a calf affected with marble bone disease are hard and solid. There are no bone marrow cavities.

Spread of the disease occurs by carrier bulls and carrier dams. There is no treatment for this genetically transmitted disease. Control and prevention is only possible by diagnosing affected calves which identifies the sire and dam as carriers. Carrier animals have to be excluded from further use in breeding.

Muscle defects are next in importance. Crooked calf disease may affect any breed of dairy or beef cattle. Most commonly it has been diagnosed in the Charolais breed.

This defect is inherited as a simple autosomal recessive. A word of caution: plant poisonings such as lupine (silver or blue lupine) may cause a similar defect. However, a good veterinary examination usually can distinguish the genetic condition from the lupine problem.

Calves affected with the

Genetic Diseases

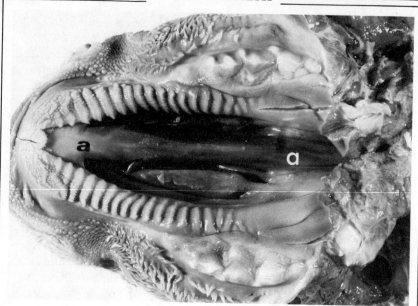

H.W. Leipold

Cleft palate in calf affected with "crooked calf disease" (arthrogryposis). Note that all the roof of the mouth (palate) remained open (a).

genetic form of "crooked calf disease" (arthrogryposis) have all four legs in a frozen position (contracture). The legs cannot be moved and may cause problems during birth. Almost always a cleft palate is present. The defect can be spread only by carrier bulls and dams. These animals should be identified and eliminated to prevent occurrence of the disease.

An important muscular disorder is "double muscling" encountered in most U.S. beef breeds. It is considered a genetic defect due to homozygosity of a simple autosomal recessive gene.

External appearance of double muscling varies, the most noticeable being a round outline of the hind quarters. Muscles of the shoulder, neck, back and hind legs are heavy and separated by deep creases. The tail is attached higher than normal. Many double-muscled animals stand in a stretched position. Reproductive organs are small.

Spread of the disease occurs by breeding animals carrying the gene for double muscling. Control and prevention of the disease is by eliminating carrier animals.

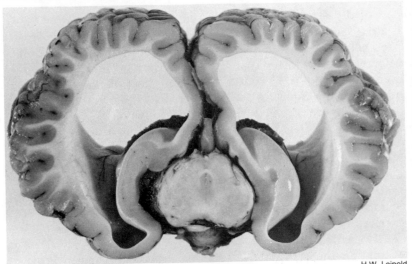

H.W. Leipold

Brain Defects

Congenital defects of the central nervous system are common and economically important. There is a lot of room for improvement of diagnosis and further studies are needed to arrive at a better understanding of these defects.

The single most important brain defect is internal hydrocephalus (water-on-the-brain), and occurs most commonly in beef cattle such as Herefords. Hydrocephalus is an inherited defect of simple autosomal recessive nature. It results from excessive fluid accumulation in the brain cavities.

The head may be domed or not. There are eye defects such as small eyes, and muscles are pale. Calves do not

Cross section of newborn Hereford calf affected with internal hydrocephalus (water-in-the-brain). Note markedly dilated internal compartments of brain. This feature led to term "water-on-the-brain" (hydrocephalus). Note also blockage of pathway of central nervous system fluid.

get up after birth and are unable to nurse. Some of the calves are soon dead or they die within a few days after birth. Spread of hydrocephalus is through using carrier bulls in herds where carrier dams are present. There is no treatment and control again is possible only by identifying carrier animals and eliminating them from breeding.

Congenital cerebellar disease is important in cattle. A disease afflicting a certain

Genetic Diseases

201

part of the cerebellum (a brain area deterioration) has been described in calves. It is referred to as abiotrophy and occurs in Holstein, Hereford and Charolais calves.

This appears to be a simple autosomal recessive. Calves lose control over their movements at an age of 6 to 8 months. Spread by carrier animals should be prevented by identifying and eliminating carriers.

Hereditary neuraxial edema, another brain disease, has been seen in Hereford calves. It is considered a simple autosomal recessive. Calves are born unable to get up and nurse. Hand clapping or touching the calves can send them into violent spasms. Calves ultimately die or are destroyed. The spread of neuraxial edema is by carrier animals and only their identification and removal from service prevents and controls this disease.

Spinal Cord Ills

Spinal cord diseases are just starting to emerge as genetic problems in calves. Further studies are needed to better understand and control them.

Spastic and paralytic diseases, common in cattle, are of genetic origin. Their spread, control and prevention can be accomplished only after further studies. Spastic paresis is characterized by one or both hind legs stiffening up and being kept off the ground, preventing afflicted animals from moving about.

An important brain and spinal cord disease afflicts Brown Swiss cattle between 6 to 8 months of age. It is referred to as the weaver condition. The disease most likely is transmitted as a simple autosomal recessive.

Calves become sick at about 6 months of age. Weavers then have an unsteady gait, will frequently stumble and fall to one side. The disease progresses during the next few months. Most cases are misdiagnosed as back injuries or arthritis. Weavers finally go down and die or have to be destroyed.

Spread of the weaver condition is via carrier animals. There is no treatment and control and prevention is by adjusting breeding programs.

Storage diseases of genetic nature are beginning to emerge in cattle. Material accumulates inside cells mainly in the brain.

One such disease has been identified in Angus cattle in the United States. Called mannosidosis, it is transmitted as a simple auto-

H.W. Leipold

Brown Swiss affected with weaver condition. Note sidewards sway.

somal recessive. Angus calves may be affected at birth but usually come down with the disease between 6 to 8 months of age. They quit growing, have difficulties walking, and die within the first 12 months of life.

This is due to an enzyme deficiency. Since the spread is by carrier bulls and dams, the enzyme deficiency can be used to detect carriers. Carriers have half the normal enzyme activity. This fact can be used to identify carriers and thus control and prevent the disease.

Eye, Skin Defects

The most common eye defects in cattle are lack of eyes or small eyes. This may be a genetic problem but needs much more study. A defect which is polygenic (many genes involved) accounts for the transmission and spread of feather-eyes (dermoid) in dairy and beef cattle; skin on the eye surface leads to partial or complete blindness. Feather-

Genetic Diseases

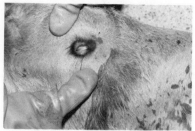

H.W. Leipold

H.W. Leipold

H.W. Leipold

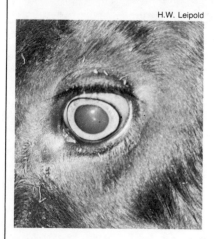

H.W. Leipold

Calf affected with anophthalmia (lack of eye development). Note lack of eye.

Feather-eye (dermoid) in Hereford calf. Note skin covering front of eye, causing blindness.

Albinotic color deficiency in Angus heifer. Note dilute coat color instead of deep rich black.

Albinotic color deficiency in Angus calf. Note white iris color.

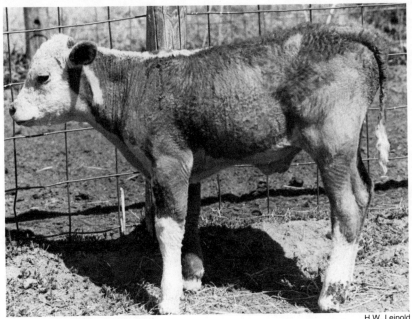

H.W. Leipold

Hereford calf affected with moderate degree of hairlessness (hypotrichosis).

eye, as well as any other defect of polygenic nature, can be controlled only by carefully keeping records of affected calves on a breed basis, thus identifying possible transmitters of the defect.

Genetic defects of the skin have not received enough attention and study. However, a few are important and are presented here.

Albinism has been diagnosed in various breeds of cattle. It always is genetic, usually a simple autosomal recessive.

A new albinotic color deficiency has been identified recently. It is inherited as a simple autosomal recessive.

The defect imparts to Angus cattle a brown hair instead of the typical black. The eyes are white, thus causing the animal pain and reduction of vision in bright light. Spread is again due to normal carrier animals which must be identified for control.

Skin fragility has occurred in various beef breeds. It is passed on as a simple autosomal recessive. The skin is very fragile and tears away from even slight injury. Hematomas (accumulation of blood) and infections are com-

Genetic Diseases

mon. Spread is by carrier animals.

A common skin defect is *epitheliogenesis imperfecta* in Holstein, Shorthorn and Angus calves. A simple autosomal recessive accounts for this defect. Areas of skin turn up missing on the legs and head, allowing infections to gain entrance. The calf usually dies in the first 3 weeks of life.

Use of carrier bulls and dams spreads this defect. Since the carrier animals are normal, only occurrence of the defect reveals the carrier status. Their removal from breeding prevents further cases.

Protoporphyria in Limousin cattle is really a metabolic disease but the main sign is sunburn. It is inherited as a simple autosomal recessive. Inflammation of the skin occurs on the head, neck and back. Skin of the ears and the muzzle are affected. Normal appearing carrier cattle may be detected by an enzyme test, and control instituted with this test.

Hypotrichosis (severe loss of hair) in Hereford calves is a genetic disease caused by homozygosity of a simple autosomal recessive gene. Hypotrichosis varies from mild to severe. Affected calves suffer from adverse weather condi-

tions and also are more susceptible to fungal and bacterial skin diseases.

The disease is seen throughout the United States and is spread by normal unaffected carrier animals. Control and prevention require identifying the normal carriers and eliminating them.

Internal organs such as the heart do not escape genetic defects. Much more research on these defects is needed to help establish their nature and significance.

The most important reproductive system defect in the United States is rectovaginal constriction (RVC) in Jersey cattle. RVC affects the anus and part of the reproductive system in Jersey heifers. These areas are inelastic and constricted, leading to difficulties during artificial breeding and problems with birth, usually leading to cesarean section. In addition, RVC cows frequently develop severe udder edema followed by mastitis. RVC is of considerable economic significance. Spread occurs by using normal and affected carrier bulls.

Identification by diagnosing affected offspring helps to control the disease. The bulls identified as transmitters (carriers) may be removed from service.

IV. SHEEP AND GOATS

USDA-APHIS

Preventive Medicine

By Brad R. LeaMaster and
D. Scott Adams

SHEEP

It is much more productive and economical to prevent disease than to treat sick animals. Flock health management is a program of cooperation between the owner and veterinarian and should blend with management procedures that occur throughout the year.

Early Spring Lambing.
Ewes should be separated in groups based on fullness of the udder (bagging). Increase their nutritional level during the last six weeks of preg-

---

Brad R. LeaMaster is with the U.S. Sheep Experiment Station, Agricultural Research Service (ARS), Dubois, Idaho. D. Scott Adams is with ARS at the Animal Disease Research Unit, Department of Veterinary Microbiology and Pathology, Washington State University, Pullman. He is chief editor/writer for this Yearbook section.

nancy. And they should be vaccinated for enterotoxemia types C and D, tetanus, and dewormed. Set up a record system for lambing.

Lambs must be castrated, docked and vaccinated shortly after arrival. Vaccinations vary depending on the geographical location, but enterotoxemia type D and tetanus should be considered. Routinely inspect rams for signs of pneumonia, epididymitis, foot rot, etc. After removal from the ewes, increase the nutritional level.

Late Spring Shearing.
After shearing, all animals—including lambs—must be treated for external parasites by dusting, dipping or spraying. Ewes and rams should receive clostridial vaccine, be dewormed, and have feet trimmed. Dry ewes can be culled.

Late Summer Weaning, and preparation for breeding.
Lambs are weaned and the

Marie T. Sebrechts

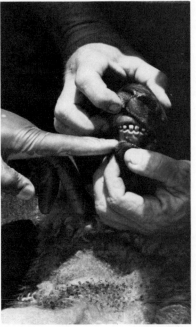
Kevin Shields

ewes' nutritional level reduced. All ewes should be examined and culled on the basis of mastitis, condition of teeth, age, and production. Replacement ram and ewe lambs should be kept separate from the adult sheep during the first year. Nutritional level of the rams should be increased.

Check Rams
Fall Breeding. Before breeding, rams should be checked for the presence of internal and external parasites and treated if needed. They must have their feet, legs, teeth, eyes and reproductive organs

Before breeding, the condition of animals should be checked. This includes examining their feet, teeth, legs and eyes.

examined. Special attention should be directed for the presence of epididymitis. A semen evaluation also is recommended.

Ewes also can be checked for the condition of feet, legs, teeth, eyes, and udder, and vaccinated for the common abortion diseases such as vibriosis and enzootic abortion. A leptospirosis vaccination also may be considered, depending on the area of the country. Three to 4 weeks be-

Preventive Medicine

Kevin Shields

Karen Rusinski, USDA-SCS

Pasture rotation and alternating types of deworming drugs can be helpful in control of internal parasites.

fore breeding, sterile rams can be introduced to increase cycling and conception rates.

Humid warm, high rainfall areas are ideal conditions for internal parasites, and you may need to deworm every 4 to 6 weeks. Pasture rotation and alternating types of deworming drugs may help.

Soils of the Pacific Northwest, Northeast and Southeast generally are low in selenium, and sheep should be supplemented by injecting or adding selenium to salt. Feedlot lambs should be vaccinated for enterotoxemia type D, dewormed, and implanted with Ralgro 2 days after arrival. At 2 weeks post arrival the lambs are shorn, and 3 to 4 weeks after arrival a second enterotoxemia booster should be administered.

GOATS
Seasonal Procedures. In summer, provide trace mineralized salt, shade, and plenty of fresh water to all animals. Prepare bucks for breeding season by examining genital organs, trimming feet, and increasing concentrate. Submit manure samples to your veterinarian for evidence of parasites, and perform deworming as indicated by the results.

In the fall all shelters should be thoroughly cleaned and good drainage established to prevent damp indoor conditions. Treat all animals for external parasites by dipping or dusting several times at 2-week intervals.

In winter, examine buildings for evidence of condensation. If found, remove the source of moisture and increase air exchange in the buildings. Hold drinking water above 45° to increase intake. Trim feet.

Kidding and Breeding. Navels of kids should be treated immediately with iodine, and kids given at least ½ pint of colostrum in the first 6 hours after birth. Check them for birth defects. Disbud kids at 3 days to 2 weeks of age, preferably with a hot iron made for that purpose. Castrate buck kids and remove accessory teats from doe kids.

Selenium/vitamin E shots should be given in areas where the deficiency occurs. Give immunizations for enterotoxemia and tetanus at 4 and 6 weeks of age. Anticoccidial drugs may be necessary in some herds. Start a record with health, reproduction, production, and disposition information on each kid.

Breed does at 7–10 months of age. Examine does bred 3 months earlier for

Marie T. Sebrechts

During summer months provide shade, plenty of fresh water, and trace mineralized salt to all animals.

pregnancy; if pregnant, does should be dried off. Intramammary antibiotics may be indicated at your veterinarian's instruction. Dip teats at least 3 days after drying off. Examine udders periodically for evidence of mastitis throughout the dry period.

When does are near kidding, they should have an increase in concentrates and decrease in calcium—but not be allowed to become too fat. Make sure they get exercise. Two to 4 weeks before kidding, give enterotoxemia vaccine and tetanus and selenium/vitamin E as indicated by the incidence of disease in your area. Give kidding does a clean, quiet pen. Consult your veterinarian if you suspect problems.

Watch milking does carefully at all times for evidence of mastitis. Inapparent mastitis may be detected with the California mastitis test. Milking equipment should be clean and in good order, milkers should be very careful not to overmilk does, and routine teat dipping with a non-irritating disinfectant should be carried out.

Give bucks all routine immunizations. Worm and deparasitize them at the same time as the does.

Respiratory Diseases

By D. Scott Adams

Respiratory diseases involving the nasal passages, throat, and lungs are common in sheep and goats, particularly among the young. Pneumonia, inflammation of the lungs, is the most common problem of economic concern.

Acute Pneumonia. This type of pneumonia occurs most commonly in lambs and kids but sometimes in adults.

Usually the disease is caused by interaction of a number of agents and factors which include viruses, mycoplasmas, bacteria, host genetics, environment, and management. Failure to receive enough colostrum (first milk) in the first few hours of life, and cold windy weather or hu-

D. Scott Adams is with USDA's Agricultural Research Service at the Animal Disease Research Unit, Department of Veterinary Microbiology and Pathology, Washington State University, Pullman.

mid barns with poor ventilation, also may lead to problems.

Signs include difficult, loud, or rapid breathing, and coughing. The head may be extended and the tongue protruded in severe cases. In all but terminal stages the animal will have a fever.

The viruses, bacteria and other infectious agents that may be involved in this type of pneumonia are spread by direct contact and through the air at relatively short distances.

If you have not previously consulted a veterinarian for this type of disease, it is strongly recommended that you do because a specific diagnosis is crucial to correct treatment. Antibiotics and rest are important, as well as other supportive treatment which your veterinarian may prescribe.

New born kids and lambs should receive adequate colostrum. Avoid overcrowding, high humidity and poor ventilation in shelters and unnecessary exposure of young animals to stress like transportation, and to outside animals.

Worm Pneumonia
Parasitic Pneumonia. This type of pneumonia is caused by several types of worms which invade the lung and cause damage to it. Sheep and goats grazing on infected pastures eat immature forms of worms.

Heavily infected young sheep and goats show difficult breathing, coughing, poor condition, weakness, and snotty noses. Submit manure samples and lungs of dead animals to your veterinarian for diagnosis.

Treatment—First obtain a specific diagnosis from your veterinarian, who then can prescribe the proper dewormer.

Life cycle of the worms can be interrupted by draining wet pastures and avoiding grazing those that cannot be drained. Periodic treatment with dewormers controls severe infections.

Progressive Pneumonias. These are infections of the lungs of adult animals and have a slow onset. The cause is several chronic bacteria and persistent viruses.

Adult animals are first observed having difficulty breathing during and after exercise.

The bacteria are spread from animals carrying abscesses to others through cuts and breaks in the skin. The viruses are transmitted mainly from the dam to the newborn through the milk and colostrum and through the air or direct contact, particularly when animals are crowded and have poor ventilation.

There is no treatment for the viruses, and response of the bacteria to antibiotics is poor.

The bacterial infections can be reduced by culling animals with abscesses and reducing the likelihood of cuts and abrasions, for instance at shearing. Good clean surroundings without excessive crowding may help reduce the number of new infections.

The viral diseases can be prevented if lambs or kids are removed from the dams at birth and raised on a safe source of milk. Consult your veterinarian for details.

Nose, Throat Ills
A wide variety of things may cause disease in this area.

Causes—nasal bots or larvae (maggots) of a fly which live in the nasal sinuses. Tumors in the nasal passages and throat. Abscesses, particularly from *Corynebacteria spp.*, in the throat area. Bluetongue virus.

Often sheep and sometimes goats get "snotty noses" from nasal bots and have noisy breathing. A similar picture is seen with tumors in the nasal passages. Abscesses in the throat may be seen on the outside of the neck but not necessarily, and if not they may cause difficult breathing. Bluetongue virus causes severe illness in sheep and goats with reddening of the nose and mouth, fever and rapid respiration. The tongue may become very swollen.

Spread—nasal bots are immature forms of a fly that lays its eggs in the nasal sinuses of sheep. The cause of tumors is thought to be a virus but is still not definitely determined. Abscesses are transmitted from infected animals to others through breaks in the skin. Bluetongue virus is spread by small biting flies mostly in the fall of the year.

Nasal bots can be treated with various insectides recommended for sheep and goats. If the other diseases are encountered, contact your veterinarian for advice.

Rotate Pastures

Nasal bots may be prevented by rotating pastures, since the flies do not travel long distances or live very long. Vaccination for bluetongue is of limited value but may help in some areas, and eliminating water where biting flies breed can provide some aid.

Digestive Problems

By D. Scott Adams

The number of potential problems in the digestive system is extremely large, but because of space limitations this chapter must be limited.

Colibacillosis is a disease of young lambs and kids which is manifest as diarrhea (loose stool, scours) in newborns and an infection of the blood in animals 2 to 6 weeks of age. The cause is certain strains of *Escherichia coli* (a bacterium or germ), which is the most common organism found in the intestinal tract of animals.

Lambs and kids 1 to 4 days of age develop diarrhea with a yellow or gray color which contains more water as the disease becomes worse.

D. Scott Adams is with USDA's Agricultural Research Service at the Animal Disease Research Unit, Department of Veterinary Microbiology and Pathology, Washington State University, Pullman.

Death occurs in 24 to 48 hours in many cases. In the other form of the disease, lambs and kids 2 to 6 weeks of age develop high fevers and may become dull, unable to see, incoordinate, unable to rise, and they may die.

The bacterium that causes it is shed in the stool and lasts for extended periods in the environment.

Lambs and kids of sufficient value should be treated under the supervision of a veterinarian. Fluids and appropriate antibacterial drugs are given.

Lambing and kidding on areas known to be seeded with the bacteria should be avoided if possible. If it is not, then areas should be thoroughly cleaned with disinfectant solutions, and ample clean bedding supplied. Contact between sick and well animals should be minimized.

Salmonellosis. This widespread disease of all ages of

216

sheep and goats often is precipitated by stress. The cause is *Salmonella spp.,* a genus of bacteria.

Signs are diarrhea, depression and fever. Blood often is seen in stools.

Infected animals shed the bacteria in their feces, which are consumed by others in contaminated feedstuffs. Certain Salmonella spp. can infect humans. Professional advice should be sought.

To treat animals, fluids and antibacterial drugs should be given under the direction of a veterinarian.

For prevention, use good sanitation procedures. Clean and disinfect contaminated pens, with several weeks of drying. Control rats, mice and birds which can carry the bacteria.

Enterotoxemia is a group of diseases caused by toxins of three different bacteria which inhabit the intestinal tract: Yellow lamb disease, hemorrhagic (bloody) enterotoxemia, and overeating disease (pulpy kidney).

Causes—yellow lamb disease is caused by *Clostridium perfringens* type A, hemorrhagic enterotoxemia by *Clostridium perfringens* type C, and overeating disease by *Clostridium perfringens* type D.

Signs—sudden death of previously healthy lambs and kids. Yellow lamb disease: Yellow lining of mouth and whites of eyes, fever, and red urine. Hemorrhagic enterotoxemia: Loose bloody stool. Overeating disease: The most common form occurs in lambs or kids, feeders (mostly), and adult goats in a more prolonged disease.

Acquired While Eating

The organisms persist in the soil and are acquired during eating.

There usually is no treatment, but antibiotics and antitoxins may be helpful. Consult your veterinarian.

Prevention—vaccination and dietary changes under direction of your veterinarian.

Parasitic Gastroenteritis is a very large category of disease caused by worms and single celled organisms which live in the stomach and intestines of sheep and goats and cause disease there.

Causes—stomach worms and worms of the small and large intestines; coccidia (single celled organisms) which infect the small and large intestines.

Signs are diarrhea, slow weight gains, poor hair coat, weight loss, anemia (thin blood) and death in severe cases. Bloody diarrhea and depression occur with coccidiosis.

Eggs of these organisms are shed in the feces and consumed as animals feed.

The most effective drugs for parasitic gastroenteritis of sheep and goats must be prescribed by a veterinarian.

Advice from your veterinarian is recommended so that a specific diagnosis, treatment and preventive program can be instituted. Regular checks for worms in fecal samples is a good way of determining the need for preventive drug therapy.

Bloat. This is a condition which results from accumulation of gas and frothy (foamy) material in the first stomach of the sheep or goat, and may result in rapid death because of pressure on the lungs.

The cause is lush legume (alfalfa, clover) pastures which produce froth, and objects like apples and potatoes. Signs are difficult breathing, lying down, and the left upper side of the animal may be greatly enlarged. This is not an infectious disease.

For treatment call your veterinarian. Mixtures of various detergents can be given orally and/or by insertion of a stomach tube by a qualified individual. Puncture of the first stomach under advice of a veterinarian should be attempted only in the most desperate situations.

Prevention—animals should be allowed only cautious access to legume pastures. Consult your veterinarian for advice on types of detergents which may be added to salt.

Genetic and Skin Diseases

By D. Scott Adams

Genetic diseases are those inherited by the lamb and kid from their dams and sires. They may be primarily structural (involve the way the body looks) or metabolic (chemical). While most result in early death of the fetus, some may not be particularly serious.

This chapter will discuss only conditions which affect productivity or survival. A great many more inherited problems are described in sheep than in goats.

Jaw Defects. The mandible (lower "jaw") is either too short or too long. **Rectal Prolapse.** The tissue inside the anus comes out. This condition is most common in black-

D. Scott Adams is with USDA's Agricultural Research Service at the Animal Disease Research Unit, Department of Veterinary Microbiology and Pathology, Washington State University, Pullman.

faced sheep. **Inverted eyelids (entropion).** Usually the lower eyelids turn in and cause the eye to be sore and runny. They may be surgically corrected.

Cryptorchidism. One or both testicles of male lambs and kids not present in the scrotum (sac) but retained in the abdomen. **Skin folds.** Wrinkled skin which lowers productivity and is associated with lowered fertility.

Face Covering. Ewes with fleece covering the face are less productive than those with short hair on the face. **Fleece Defects.** Several abnormal types of fleece can be inherited: Poor quality with a tendency to break, hairy or fuzzy lambs, and high belly wool.

Infertility

Infertility in Polled (hornless) Goats. Breeding of hornless bucks and does leads to hermaphrodism (intersex and

Marie T. Sebrechts

Horned or disbudded males should be bred to hornless females, since breeding of hornless bucks and does leads to hermaphrodism and small infertile testicles in male offspring.

infertile) and small infertile testicles in male offspring. Hornless females should be bred to horned or disbudded males.

Mannosidosis of Nubian Goats. Kids are born unable to rise and have flexed front legs and straight rear legs. **Myotonia Congenita of Goats.** Upon being startled the goats become very rigid for about 30 seconds.

Genetic diseases are caused by breeding animals carrying genes which when found together in the same offspring produce abnormal or undesirable characteristics.

These diseases are transmitted through certain types of breeding practices, particularly inbreeding. Breeding male offspring to their dams and dams to their sires are examples of inbreeding.

Very little can be done in the way of treatment in most cases, but a veterinarian should be consulted for advice.

For prevention, seek professional advice, avoid inbreeding when possible, and do not breed animals known to be carriers of genetic diseases.

Skin Diseases

The skin is the body's largest organ and first line of defense in many diseases. For these reasons, diseases which involve the skin and cause damage to it are many and varied. Generally speaking, conditions which affect sheep also occur in goats.

Parasitic skin diseases mostly are caused by insects—lice, ticks (keds), mites (mange and scabies), maggot infestations (fly strike).

Lice causing itching, loss of hair or wool, licking, biting at affected areas, and anemia (thin blood) in severe cases. The small insects can be seen on the affected areas and nits (eggs) can be found attached

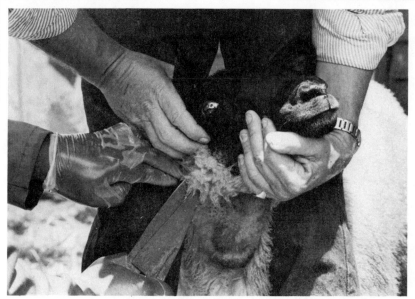

Marie T. Sebrechts

The skin is the body's largest organ and the first line of defense in many diseases. For these reasons diseases which involve the skin and cause damage to it are many and varied.

to hair and wool. Sheep keds are large (¼ in.), tick-like insects found mostly on sheep and in large numbers cause irritation.

Mange and scabies are contagious diseases which result in hair loss, intense itching, crusty scabs, and redness. Maggots are small rice-like worms hatched from eggs of blowflies which cause irritation, damage and holes in the skin under the wool—particularly around the anus and vulva.

Lice, keds, and mites are spread mostly by direct con-

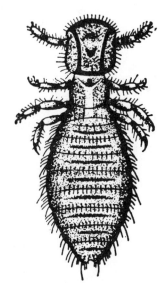

Female biting sheep louse.

Genetic and Skin Diseases

221

Scabies mites cause losses of wool and sometimes death if sheep are not treated.

USDA

Keds and lice can be better controlled by treating sheep after shearing.

Dr. Hans E. Nel, Aricultural Extension Service, Wyoming

tact, and strike is spread by blowflies. All can be treated with insecticides approved for use in sheep and goats. Consult your veterinarian for a specific diagnosis and treatment.

Prevention—lice and keds can be better controlled by treating after shearing. Animals with certain types of scabies must be quarantined and treated. The incidence of strike can be reduced by shearing the area around the anus and vulva.

Bacterial Diseases

Bacterial skin diseases are caused by microscopic organisms and occur in both sheep and goats. The causes are *Dermatophilus congolensis, Clostridium spp.*, and *Staphylococcus aureus.*

Signs are crusty scabs and hair. Wool pulls out easily with raw flesh beneath. Consult your veterinarian.

Spread usually is by direct contact, but some types of bacteria remain in the soil for long periods of time.

For treatment, consult your veterinarian. Antiseptic shampoo and antibiotics are recommended. For prevention, reduce contact with affected animals.

Fungal skin diseases are caused by organisms which are related to molds and often are called ringworm, although no worm is involved. The causes are several species of fungi.

Signs—grayish and generally circular areas of hair loss.

Spread is by direct contact with carrier animals. Some of these organisms can infect humans, especially children. Seek professional advice for prevention and treatment.

Prevention—ringworm usually is not a problem with good nutrition and plenty of sunlight.

Viral Skin Diseases

Viruses are the smallest infectious agent of disease. The most common viral skin disease of sheep and goats is contagious ecthyma (sore mouth or orf), a pox virus.

Signs are scabby, proliferative, reddened skin around the mouths of kids and lambs and udders of dams. Spread is through direct contact and virus that remains in the ground. The virus also will infect humans, and therefore professional advice should be sought.

For treatment of sheep and goats, consult your veterinarian. Vaccination is recommended only if contagious ecthyma is established in the flock.

Poisoning, Lameness

By Peter J. South and
D. Scott Adams

Most toxic diseases can be divided into those which result from consumption or exposure to toxic chemicals or poisonous plants. They can be prevented by limiting access to these chemicals and plants.

Copper Toxicity. Causes— (a) excessive copper ingestion, (b) absence of sufficient molybdenum in diet, (c) injury to liver tissue from plant alkaloids enabling the liver to store excess copper, (d) stress may trigger a hemolytic crisis (rapid anemia).

Signs are onset of anemia, extreme thirst, weakness. Skin and mucous membranes

Peter J. South is Extension Veterinarian, Department of Veterinary Science, University of Idaho, Moscow. D. Scott Adams is with USDA's Agricultural Research Service at the Animal Disease Research Unit, Department of Veterinary Microbiology and Pathology, Washington State University, Pullman.

turn dark brown in color. Animals go down, and most will die in 1 to 4 days.

For prevention and treatment, remove flock from suspected feed or forage. Treat daily with 50 to 100 mg ammonium molybdenate and 0.5 to 1.0 gm sodium sulfate per animal which can be sprayed on feed.

Lead toxicity is caused by eating or licking lead paint, battery plates, used oil, and certain automotive lubricants.

Signs—Acute: Colic, salivation, muscle tremors, twitching, grinding teeth, convulsions, coma and death. Chronic: Loss of appetite, dullness, diarrhea or constipation persists for several days.

Treatment—Epsom salts, mineral oil, and bismuth orally, and calcium EDTA subcutaneously (55 mg/kg b.w.) twice daily (for no more than 5 days).

Organophosphate Poisoning. Cause—improper dos-

Kevin Shields

USDA

Care should be taken to properly dose, spray and dip animals with worm medications, insecticides and parasiticides, in order to avoid organophosphate poisoning.

Poisoning, Lameness

225

ing, spraying or dipping, with worm medications, insecticides and parasiticides.

Signs are salivation, fast breathing, abdominal pain, muscle tremors, convulsions and death.

Treatment and Prevention—Protopam and atropine. Adhere strictly to manufacturer's directions on label.

Fertilizer Ingestion

Nitrate Poisoning. Cause—accidental ingestion of nitrate fertilizers, or plants rich in nitrates such as cereal crops, oat hay, lamb's-quarters, immature barley and wheat, and turnip, sugar beet and mangel tops.

Signs—sudden onset, difficult breathing, excitement, convulsions, and death.

Treatment—IV solution of methylene blue.

Prevention—have forage assayed for nitrate content.

Cyanide Poisoning. Cause: Ingestion of forages containing high amounts of hydrocyanic acid such as chokecherry leaves, arrow grass, sorghum, Bermuda grass, Sudan grass. Plants contain more cyanide following retardation of growth due to drought or application of herbicides.

Signs are respiratory distress, cyanotic or blue mucous membranes, muscle tremors, convulsions and death.

Treatment—sodium nitrite and sodium thiosulfate may be given intravenously.

Miscellaneous Causes. There are many more causes of toxicity for sheep and goats, which in some geographical areas may be more important than those mentioned. A few examples are moldy sweet clover, halogeten, lupine, western false hellebore, water hemlock, castor bean, oleander, and rubber weed.

Lameness

Lameness among sheep and goats is one of the most common problems faced by producers, and can lead to other complications if not treated and controlled.

Problems of Hooves. These involve horny areas of the foot and its associated structures.

Causes—bruising from rough ground or stones, punctures from sharp objects, laminitis (inflammation beneath the hoof wall) usually caused by stress or dietary changes, wet conditions, separations of the white line (white line disease), poor hoof trimming practices, foot rot-causing bacteria (*Fusobacterium necrophorum* and *Bacteriodes nodosus*), and various viruses

USDA

When hooves are not properly trimmed, the feet become distorted and misshapen and the foot develops pockets and crevices. If foot rot bacteria gets into the hoof, these pockets can harbor the infection for long periods. The excessively overgrown hoof shown here caused lameness in the sheep, but there was no sign of foot rot.

including foot-and-mouth disease virus.

Signs are unusual gait, limping on one or more legs, grazing on the knees, walking "on eggs", prolonged lying down.

Infectious causes like bacteria and certain viruses are introduced into the flock by addition of new animals, and then spread by both indirect and direct contact.

Treatment—examine the feet and diagnose the problem or seek veterinary advice. Depending on the cause, trimming, footbaths in disinfectants, antibiotics, and even vaccination may be indicated.

For prevention, avoid exposure of animals to sharp objects and wet conditions, and regularly trim hooves. If infectious causes have been diagnosed in your area, avoid additions of new animals when possible.

Problems Above Hooves. These problems can result when the bones, joints, tendons, ligaments, vessels, muscles and nervous system are affected.

Causes: Traumatic injuries (accidents) which break bones and sprain or dislocate joints; infections with bacteria and viruses (*Staphylococcus spp., Streptococcus spp., Co-*

Kevin Shields

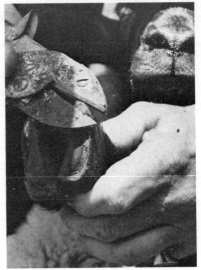
Kevin Shields

The best way to prevent hoof problems is to avoid exposure of animals to sharp objects and wet conditions and regularly check and trim hooves as necessary.

rynebacterium spp., Myco-
plasma spp., Chlamydia psittaci). Caprine arthritis-
encephalitis virus, which may
infect the joints themselves or
the spinal cord and brain. Deficiencies of essential vitamins
(vitamin D, and E) and minerals (selenium, calcium,
phosphorus, and copper) which
result in malformations and
degeneration of nervous tissue, muscles, tendons, joints
and bones.

Very often with traumatic
injuries the animal will be unable to bear weight on the

limb, particularly of course if
it is broken. Infections of the
joints by bacteria are more
common in lambs and kids
than in adult sheep and goats,
and often are associated with
navel infections (navel ill).
These young animals develop
enlarged joints, usually have
a fever, and become quite
lame.

Kids and lambs infected
with *Mycoplasma spp.* develop
very high fevers, and sometimes most in the flock will
become sick. *Chlamydia psittaci* (stiff lamb disease) is reported most often in feedlot
lambs as an epidemic.

Caprine arthritis-enceph-
alitis virus causes chronic arthritis in adult goats and
rarely in young goats. One or

several joints may be swollen and sore, and weight loss often is an aftereffect. When this virus affects young kids, they may become unable to stand.

Very similar signs are seen with copper-deficient (swayback) lambs and kids. Kids and lambs affected with selenium-vitamin E deficiency or white muscle disease often stand with the shoulder blades pointed outward or are reluctant to rise.

Rachitic Rosary
Calcium and phosphorus imbalances and vitamin D deficiencies usually are manifested in kids and lambs as bumps on the rib cage (rachitic rosary) and crooked legs, especially bowed front legs.

Diagnosis and control of these diseases can be very complex, so professional advice should be sought to minimize losses.

The bacteria that cause joint ill are carried by other animals and also persist for some time in the environment. Lambs and kids usually become infected through the navel and other body openings at or near birth.

Caprine arthritis-encephalitis virus most often is transmitted through milk and colostrum to the kid.

Neither *Chlamydia* nor *Mycoplasma* persist in the environment as long as some bacteria, and so are spread mainly by direct contact.

Initially, specific diagnosis and treatment are handled best by a veterinarian. Generally speaking, the bacterial, chlamydial, and mycoplasmal causes of arthritis can be treated with antibiotics but success depends on whether the right treatment is given early enough. There is no specific treatment for caprine arthritis-encephalitis.

Vitamin and mineral deficiencies often can be treated by correcting the deficiency, but this is not always successful in advanced cases.

Situations in which very traumatic events might occur should be avoided. Navel ill can be reduced by keeping lambing and kidding areas clean, using iodine on navels, and making sure that adequate colostrum is consumed by newborns.

Caprine arthritis-encephalitis can be controlled by separating kids from infected does, and providing a safe source of colostrum and milk. When outbreaks of chlamydial and mycoplasmal arthritis occur, separate affected animals from the normal ones. Consult your veterinarian for details.

Poisoning, Lameness

Metabolic Diseases, Mastitis, Abscesses

By Steven M. Parish and
D. Scott Adams

Metabolic diseases among sheep and goats are wide and varied. Most of the reported conditions occur in association with pregnancy, lactation and/or periods of stress. These disease processes are not contagious but can and do affect groups of animals.

Pregnancy toxemia or twin lamb disease is a condition of thin or overly fat ewes in the last third of pregnancy. Due to rapid growth at this time of the unborn lambs and often a declining plane of nutrition, the ewe may develop hypoglycemia or low blood

Steven M. Parish is Associate Professor, Department of Clinical Veterinary Medicine, Washington State University, Pullman. D. Scott Adams is with USDA's Agricultural Research Service at the Animal Disease Research Unit, Department of Veterinary Microbiology and Pathology, Washington State University.

sugar. Ewes carrying single lambs and ewes lambing for the first time rarely develop this disease.

Because of low blood sugar the ewe ceases eating, becomes uncoordinated and weak. Soon the ewe becomes unable to stand and neurologic signs such as blindness, muscular tremors, convulsions and coma appear, followed by death. Possible treatments include intravenous glucose, oral glucose precursors, vitamins, and possible induced abortion to relieve the ewe of the burden of pregnancy.

Prevention includes maintaining the ewes in moderate condition in early pregnancy, and then increasing the level of nutrition in later pregnancy as demands of the unborn lambs increase. This condition has been reported in goats but is not common.

Lambing Sickness
Low blood calcium (lambing

sickness, transport tetany) is associated with several conditions of sheep and goats. The cause is lack of available calcium for metabolism, or a sudden increased demand for calcium by the body which cannot be met.

The disease generally affects fat ewes and goats during the last 6 weeks of pregnancy and during the first week of lactation. It also can occur in rams and bucks and feedlot lambs following fasting and transporting.

Affected sheep and goats in early stages show stiff and incoordinated movements—especially in the hind legs—followed later by muscle tremors, muscle weakness and breathing problems. In late stages the animals are down, unresponsive and unable to rise. Soon they pass into a coma and die unless treated.

Treatment includes administering calcium products. Prevention includes maintaining adequate levels of calcium in the diet and preventing periods of stress without adequate feed and water.

Low blood magnesium (grass tetany) occurs when milking ewes and does are grazing early spring pasture. Most cases occur in females in the first 4 weeks after giving birth, although other classes of animals occasionally develop the disease. The animals become excited, uncoordinated, become recumbent, convulse, pass into a coma, and die.

Treatment includes administering magnesium-containing products. Prevention includes magnesium supplement in the diet of susceptible animals.

Mastitis

While a myriad of additional diseases may affect sheep and goats, only two additional ones will be discussed in this chapter—mastitis and abscesses.

Mastitis, inflammation of the mammary gland, can be caused by a variety of things, but most often results from bacterial infection in both sheep and goats.

In acute clinical (obvious) mastitis of dairy goats, milk production is reduced and the milk often is watery and contains flecks, pus, blood and chunks. The gland often is reddened and harder and warmer than normal. For every case of clinical mastitis, many cases of subclinical mastitis are present and may only reduce milk production.

Sheep with acute clinical mastitis acquire a hard, hot udder and often become very

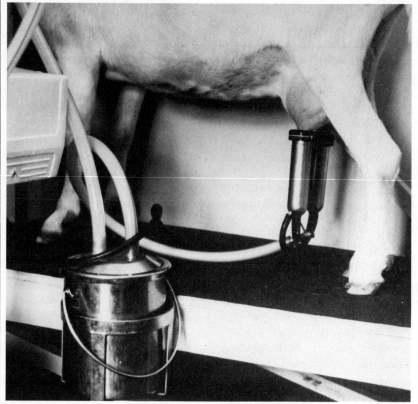

J.L. Carlson; photo from D.S. Adams

Milking equipment should be clean and in good order, both to assure a sanitary product and as one step in preventing mastitis in your goats.

ill with a high fever. In severe cases the udder may become cold and bluish (gangrenous), and death often results.

Most forms of mastitis are spread by contact with the organisms that may be present on milkers' hands, milking equipment, and bedding. Nursing lambs and kids also may transmit the causative organisms. Avoid anything including faulty milking equipment that may damage the udder.

Antibiotics often are helpful. Professional veterinary advice should be sought.

Prevention: In goat dairies, keep milking equipment clean and in good working condition. Good milking practices also will help. Dry treatment with antibiotics, and teat dipping may be advisable. Close observation and reduction of grain and water at weaning of lambs will reduce mastitis in ewes.

Abscesses

These are pus-filled cavities usually seen as external lumps under the skin, particularly around the head and neck. They also may be found in virtually any internal location.

Causes: Many different bacteria and foreign bodies but *Corynebacterium pseudotuberculosis* (ovis), the cause of caseous lymphadenitis, is the most common.

Abscesses under the skin appear as lumps from less than one to several inches in diameter. The signs caused by internal abscesses are highly variable.

Corynebacterium pseudotuberculosis is spread by infected animals and remains in the environment for months. It enters the body through cuts and scrapes. It may infect human beings.

For treatment, consult your veterinarian. Abscesses may be opened, drained and flushed with disinfectants like hydrogen peroxide and organic iodine preparations.

Separate infected animals from the others when abscesses are open, as a preventive measure. New additions to the flock should be carefully screened for abscesses. Avoid anything that causes cuts and scrapes to the skin. Disinfect contaminated areas.

Foreign Diseases

By Edwin I. Pilchard

More than 14 foreign diseases and arthropod pests are important threats to the $615 million sheep and $375 million goat enterprises of the United States.

Three of these diseases were once present, but were eliminated through industry and State cooperation in Federally organized eradication programs. The last outbreak of foot-and-mouth disease was eradicated in 1929, screwworms in 1966, and sheep scabies (*Psoroptes ovis*) in 1973.

Both sheep and goats are susceptible to some of the foreign diseases—for example, foot-and-mouth disease, heartwater, screwworm myiasis, babesiosis *(Babesia motasi* and *B. ovis)*, contagious agalactia, Borna, melioidosis, Nairobi

---

Edwin I. Pilchard is a Principal Staff Officer, Veterinary Services, Animal and Plant Health Inspection Service.

sheep disease, peste des petits ruminants, tick-borne fever *(Rhipicephalus phagocytophilia)*, and exotic types of bluetongue disease. Foot-and-mouth disease, screwworms, and heartwater are discussed under Section II on cattle.

Exotic types of bluetongue and Rift Valley fever deserve special attention because of their potential to become established if they should emerge in the United States. Also, although five types of bluetongue virus have been reported in the United States, 15 others are foreign and therefore subject to regulatory efforts to keep them out.

Bluetongue disease in sheep usually produces fever accompanied by difficult breathing; purplish-red discoloration of the muzzle, lips, ears and tongue; and many deaths in infected flocks.

In cattle, signs may resemble those seen in sheep, with the development of raw

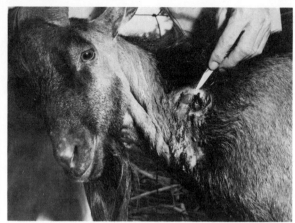

Both sheep and goats are susceptible to a variety of foreign diseases, including screwworm, foot-and-mouth disease, heartwater, Rift Valley fever and exotic types of bluetongue.

USDA

areas on the muzzle in some individuals. However, many may show little or no outward sign of sickness. Lowered fertility may be seen in some affected breeding herds.

Rift Valley fever causes high rates of abortion and death of lambs in infected flocks. It is described more fully under Section III.

Pox Viruses

Certain foreign diseases of sheep do not affect goats. These include sheep pox, louping ill, and nematodiasis.

Sheep pox is caused by a virus that differs in its immunizing characteristics from the virus of goat pox. It produces a high fever, and many sheep in affected flocks die showing typical pox lesions on unwooled areas of skin. Conversely, goat pox virus causes a disease in goats similar to that described in sheep with sheep pox.

Louping ill, a nonfatal tick-borne viral disease of sheep, is seen as a peculiar leaping gait, difficulty in coordinating the legs and body while walking or standing, and exaggerated movements when touched or frightened. This disease also has been reported in cattle and other animal species and humans.

Nematodiasis, caused by *Nematodirus battus* in Great Britain and parts of Europe, is an intestinal parasitism that produces profuse diarrhea, severe dehydration, and deaths of lambs 6- to 12-weeks old.

Babesiosis destroys red blood cells in animals on which carrier ticks have fed, producing severe anemia, yellowish discoloration of the

Foreign Diseases

white parts of the eyes and other tissues (jaundice), and sometimes death.

Agalactia

Contagious agalactia of sheep and goats, caused by the bacteria-like microbe *Mycoplasma agalactia,* produces sudden and profound swelling of the udder, swollen leg joints, abortion, and sensitivity to bright light which causes affected sheep to seek shade or darkened shelters.

Contagious caprine pleuropneumonia in goats closely resembles contagious bovine pleuropneumonia in cattle as described in Section III. However, cattle are not susceptible to the virus of caprine pleuropneumonia.

Borna disease, caused by an unclassified virus, has a prolonged course in which affected sheep and goats progressively lose control of their muscles and sense of balance. The loss of muscular control often allows the tongue to protrude from the mouth.

Melioidosis can affect sheep, goats, cattle, horses, and certain wildlife. The bacteria causing this disease, *Pseudomonas pseudomallei,* can produce a variety of signs ranging from an acute, fatal pneumonia, to arthritis, loss of muscular control, and

death. Many affected animals have lumps or swellings under the skin caused by swollen lymph nodes.

Peste des petits ruminants (French), or plague of small ruminants (English), resembles rinderpest, described under Section III on cattle. However, the virus causing it does not produce disease when injected into cattle.

Tick-borne fever of sheep, goats, and cattle, caused by a microbe called *Rickettsia phagocytophilia,* is seen as a fever with stiffness of the body, neck, and limbs, and lameness accompanied by weight loss, with abortion in pregnant ewes or does. Few deaths are caused by this disease in fully developed animals.

Prevention of foreign diseases of sheep and goats requires compliance with Federal import laws by all who import animals or unsterilized animal products from affected countries. Prevention also requires that no one brings or sends prohibited animal products or souvenirs into the United States.

Section I gives more details on the prevention of foreign animal diseases, and a brief description of the way foreign diseases are found and eradicated.

Reproduction

By W. Duane Mickelsen

SHEEP

Effective management of reproduction is essential to profitability in the sheep business. Thus, knowledge in this area is very important.

Estrous Cycle: Most ewes are seasonal breeders, with peak fertility in the fall (September–November). Duration of the breeding season varies with breed, geographical location, climate and nutrition. Average length of the estrous cycle is about 17 days and estrus (heat) about 36 hours. Ovulation occurs near the end of estrus.

Lambs born early in the spring usually will have their first cycle and conceive at 6 to 8 months. Those born late in the spring may not cycle until the next fall.

W. Duane Mickelson is Associate Professor, Department of Veterinary Clinical Medicine, Washington State University, Pullman.

Gestation period in the ewe averages 150 days in length.

Birth: The fetus releases hormones from the brain which in turn cause the release hormones from the ewe that start uterine contractions. Normal second stage labor lasts for 30 to 60 minutes.

If no lambs are born after 1½ hours of active labor, or no progress is made within 30 minutes after appearance of the water bag or a fetal extremity, veterinary assistance may be required. Single lambs, or lambs over 12 pounds at birth, are more likely to cause dystocia (abnormal birth).

Animal Selection: Select ram lambs with large testicles for breeding because they produce higher pregnancy rates and sire ewe lambs which mature at an early age and ovulate more ova. Ewe lambs that were born twins should be selected for the breeding flock.

Reproduction

Although it is often assumed that sheep are relatively fertile animals, according to USDA figures in 1982 there were 8.8 million ewes of reproductive age in the United States and yet only 8.5 million lambs were weaned. This amounts to .97 lambs per ewe exposed from a species that is capable of weaning at least 1.5 lambs per ewe.

Infertility in Ewes

Early and late (before October and after November) in the breeding season, fertilization failure is more common in sheep. Early embryonic death (EED) has a higher incidence in young ewes, with increased ovulation rates and with nutritional and environmental stress.

With high humidity and rapid growth, forages such as certain clovers, birdsfoot, trefoil or alfalfa cause depressed ovulation and cystic degeneration of the uterus which results in failure of the embryo to implant.

Many infectious diseases can cause abortion in ewes, such as vibriosis, chlamydiosis (enzootic ovine abortion), salmonellosis, brucellosis, leptospirosis, and toxoplasmosis.

The two most common causes are vibriosis and chlamydiosis. Both cause abortion during the last 4 to 6 weeks of gestation when the fetus is growing rapidly. The abortion rate may be as high as 60 percent when first introduced into a flock but is more commonly 5 to 10 percent. The fetus and placenta are both important for diagnosis and should be saved for your veterinarian. These two diseases can be prevented by vaccination.

Most infectious causes of abortion can be prevented by proper management, such as keeping feed off the ground and clean water sources.

Ram Infertility

Epididymitis is the most important reproductive disease in the ram. The primary cause is *Brucella ovis*, although other bacteria also have been shown to cause the disease. The incidence in the Western United States is 15 to 40 percent. The infection is spread by sodomy from older rams to young rams.

Diagnosis may be accomplished by feeling the testicles, isolating the organism from the semen, and serological testing. Control is by culling affected rams and keeping young rams separate from mature lambs or any ewes that the mature rams have mated.

Marie T. Sebrechts

Marie T. Sebrechts

Proper management, including keeping feed off the ground and providing clean freshwater sources, will help prevent most infectious causes of abortion.

Reproduction

Care of Newborn

Since scours and pneumonia are more common in lambs born early in the year when climatic conditions are poor—and fertility is higher among ewes bred in October and November—lambing is recommended in March and April.

Place lambs in clean, well-bedded and roomy box stalls with their dam. The lambs should be allowed to nurse colostrum as soon as possible following birth so as to obtain disease resistance from the immunoglobulins present in this first milk.

Navels of the newborn lambs should be dipped in iodine solution, and lambs should be kept warm to prevent overexposure to adverse weather which is the leading cause of lamb death in many areas.

Most ram lambs are castrated by using an Elastrator, a rubber ring which is placed around the neck of the scrotum above the testis, or by a sharp knife and incising the scrotal sac followed with removal of the testical by pulling straight away.

GOATS

Goats like sheep are seasonal breeders with peak fertility in the fall. The estrous cycle for goats is 20 to 21 days in length. The duration of estrus (standing heat) is 32 to 40 hours, and ovulation occurs spontaneously at the last part of estrus.

In the United States the trend is toward small herds of does separate from the buck which in many cases may have to be transported to the male. This increases the importance of estrus detection, return to estrus and pregnancy diagnosis.

Does actively seek a male when in estrus. The odor of a buck seems to be significant for estrous does. The presence of a buck may initiate and even synchronize the cyclic activity of does early in the breeding season.

Signs of estrus in does includes tail wagging, bleating, and urination near the buck. There is some swelling of the vulva and mucous discharge.

Does, unlike ewes, will occasionally stand for mounting by other does. But the level of homosexual activity, unlike cows, is relatively low.

Gestation: 150 days. Dairy goats, like cows, need a 6 to 8 week dry period for best milk production during the following lactation.

Birth: As normal parturition approaches, the udder fills. The vulva also enlarges. The expectant doe is restless

USDA

Karen Rusinski, USDA-SCS

Place lambs in clean, well-bedded and roomy box stalls with their dam. The lambs should be allowed to nurse colostrum as soon as possible following birth so they obtain disease resistance from the immunoglobulins present in this first milk.

USDA

Sheds or barns for use during lambing are useful on any size operation. Whether lambing takes place indoors or outside, it is important to have a series of small pens—called "jugs"—in which to put a ewe and her lambs for a period of two or three days after birth.

and may hollow out a nest. When parturition is imminent, the doe should be placed in a clean, well-bedded and roomy box stall.

The expectant doe is restless, and duration of labor is the same as for ewes (see sheep reproduction). After parturition, she licks the kid(s) and may eat part of the placenta. The kid usually is on its feet in 10 to 30 minutes.

Select bucks with large testicles because they have higher fertility rates and daughters that reach puberty earlier. Also, these bucks have a tendency to have higher pregnancy rates because of the increased capacity to produce more spermatozoa.

The intersex condition, or hermaphroditism, is a common cause of infertility in polled goats. The affected animals are genetically female. If one parent is horned the offspring will almost never be intersexed. Horned and polled animals can be differentiated at birth. A whorl of hair precedes the hornbuds in the newborn kids.

Angora goats which are inbred, with selection for quality and density of hair coat, will repeatedly abort. Inbreeding should not be accomplished. Cull these aborting

does from the breeding program.

Infertility in Does

Anestrus or failure to come into heat during the normal breeding season may be due to the intersex condition, failure to observe heat, pregnancy, pseudopregnancy (see below), hydrometria, nutritional deficiencies or parasitism.

Metritis is a pathological condition in which the uterus is inflamed. It is often caused by inserting hands into the uterus. Under the direction of your veterinarian, administer injections of penicillin until the placenta has dropped and the appetite of the doe has returned to normal.

Pseudopregnancy (hydrometra or water in the uterus) frequently occurs in the goat and is referred to as a "cloudburst". After a normal gestation, the doe discharges a large volume of cloudy fluid. She may produce milk in small quantity. The cause of this condition remains obscure.

Cystic follicles on the ovaries may result in nymphomania. If persistent or irregular estrus is observed from October to December, cystic follicles are a possibility. Cause of this condition may be hereditary or due to excessive estrogen treatment.

Abortion, loss of the fetus before normal birth, may be a result of: Ingestion of toxic plants such as locoweed, broomweed and false hellebore; worm medications including phenothiazine and tetramisole when administered in late gestation; vitamin A deficiency and manganese deficiency; infectious diseases such as listeriosis, a bacterial infection, and toxoplasmosis. Seek veterinary advice for control of these diseases.

Failure of the buck to produce offspring may be due to several causes. See earlier chapter on genetic diseases for intersex and cryptorchidism. Testicular degeneration results in testes reduced in size as much as one half, changes in shape, and consistency (either soft or firm). Replace bucks with any of these disorders.

Care of Newborn

See the first chapter in this section, on preventive medicine.

Most dairy goat owners separate the kids from the dams at birth. If this is done, then colostrum must be fed with a pan or bottle.

Colostrum is very important for disease resistance in the neonatal kid. But keep in mind that you may want to control diseases such as caprine arthritis-encephalitis and mycoplasmosis (see chapter dealing with lameness). Colostrum from an older doe on the premises should be frozen in ice cube trays and stored in plastic bags as an emergency source.

Dip the navel of the newborn kid in iodine solution. Then place the kid in a warm, partially covered box. The doe will be less agitated if she can see the kid, even if nursing is not allowed.

If nursing of the doe is to be allowed, there is a critical period of about 2 hours after birth during which time the doe must be exposed to her kid. Licking for 5 to 10 minutes usually is adequate for acceptance.

If castrated, a male kid that is being raised for meat or as a pet can be kept with the rest of the herd without fear of undesired matings. Young kids are castrated as described for lambs. Tetanus vaccination is imperative following castration.

Nutrition

By Jan L. Carlson

Nutritional management should be of primary concern to the livestock producer. A properly nourished animal is better able to withstand environmental stress and challenge by disease-causing organisms. The main categories of nutrients are energy, protein, vitamins, minerals and water.

Energy is the fuel used by animals to carry on all life functions including metabolism, activity, growth, lactation and gestation. A low energy diet may result from an inadequate amount of feed or from an unlimited amount of poor quality feed.

Protein is essential for all functions but is especially important for growth, weight

---

Jan L. Carlson is Research Associate, Department of Veterinary Microbiology and Pathology, Washington State University, Pullman.

gain, and in the late stages of gestation.

Ruminants are able to synthesize vitamin C and the B vitamins. Other vitamins usually are readily available in feeds with the possible exception of vitamin A, which may be absent in dry roughage that was improperly cured. Vitamin D is not a problem unless animals are maintained in an area where they are not exposed to sunlight.

Most of the minerals required by sheep and goats can be provided by giving the animals free-choice trace mineralized salt. This salt should be in the form of loose salt since sheep and goats prefer to chew the mixture rather than lick it from a block.

Certain areas of the country are deficient in minerals such as selenium, copper, manganese, cobalt and iodine. State or county agricultural extension services will have

Nutrition

Karen Rusinski, USDA-SCS

Nutritional management should be of primary concern to the livestock producer. A properly nourished animal is better able to withstand environmental stress and challenge by disease-causing organisms.

Marie T. Sebrechts

information about areas that may be deficient. Ideally, the calcium to phosphorus ratio should be 2 parts calcium to 1 part phosphorus, but up to 4 to 1 is acceptable. If the ration consists mainly of legumes, a phosphorus supplement may be necessary.

Sheep and goats prefer clean, fresh water and quite often will not drink contaminated water. Animals in confinement or drylot situations should have access to water at all times. Animals on lush, green grass will require less water but should be watered at least once a day. Dairy animals require more water and if the water supply is limited, production also will be limited.

Types of Feed

Feeds are divided into two main classifications: Roughages and concentrates. Roughages consist of the entire plant and are higher in fiber than concentrates, which for the most part are cereal grains. Concentrates are high energy feeds and are not needed in a maintenance diet unless the roughage is of very poor quality.

Most feeds may be categorized as either a grass or a legume. Examples of legumes are alfalfa, soybeans, peas,

vetch and clover. Legumes are higher in protein than grasses and make excellent feeds, especially for growing or high producing animals.

Grasses can provide adequate protein and energy if they are fed at the vegetative stage. As plants become more mature, most of the energy is put into seed production, which is why the cereal grains (seeds) that are produced are high in energy. Examples of grasses are oats, barley, timothy, wheat, corn, and pasture grasses.

The poorest quality roughages are obtained when a cereal grain crop is harvested and the remaining plant material (straw) is used for feed. This type of feed must be supplemented just to meet maintenance requirements.

Nutritional requirements of sheep and goats vary greatly, depending on the function and life stage of the animal. A maintenance ration is the amount of nutrients required by an adult animal to stay alive. Additional nutritional requirements are needed for milk production, growth, weight gain, and the late stages of pregnancy.

Basic Ration

A basic ration for mainte-

Kevin Shields

Marie T. Sebrechts

Animals in confinement or dry-lot situations should have access to water at all times. Water requirements for dairy animals are high and if the water supply is limited, production also will be limited.

Sheep and Goats

nance of an adult sheep or goat would be 3½ pounds of legume hay or 4 pounds of good quality grass hay per head per day.

During the early stages of pregnancy, sheep and goats require no more than maintenance ration. But during the last two months of gestation they require a 12 percent protein diet and 50 percent more energy than maintenance. This may be accomplished by feeding a roughage that is at least 12 percent protein and supplementing with 1 pound per day of concentrate.

An increased protein level is important in a growing animal, and the younger the animal the higher the requirement. Early-weaned kids and lambs should receive a ration totaling 14 percent protein. By the time they are 6 months of age 12 percent protein should be adequate until they reach maturity.

A lactating animal will require two times the maintenance level of energy. Energy usually is the limiting factor in a high producing dairy animal's diet, and quite often a doe will lose weight in the peak producing months of her lactation because she cannot eat enough feed to sustain that level of production. This is why the ration provided to

a dairy animal should be of the highest quality.

A rule of thumb is to provide all the good quality roughage a doe will eat, and supplement with a half pound of concentrate per pound of milk produced.

If good spring and summer range are available for ewes and lambs, lambs can reach market weight directly from grazing alone. But if the pasture is marginal, it is wise to supplement the lambs by providing a creep feeder in which a concentrate ration is fed.

Lambs that do not make market weight at weaning time can be fed in a feedlot. In this situation the lambs are switched gradually from a ration that consists primarily of roughages to one that is primarily concentrate. The lambs are kept on this concentrate ration until they are sent to slaughter.

Doelings being raised as replacements for the dairy herd should not be fed a fattening ration but rather a ration that will let them achieve the maximum growth without allowing them to become overfat. Lots of high quality roughage will provide the protein required for growth and will encourage development of rumen capacity. A small

Nutrition

Karen Rusinski, USDA-SCS

A basic ration for maintenance of an adult sheep or goat would be 3½ pounds of legume hay or 4 pounds of good quality grass hay per head per day.

amount (about ½ pound per day) of concentrate is all that's needed.

Disease Problems

Nutritional diseases of sheep and goats include a wide variety of problems which may result from too much or too little of a particular nutrient. Most problems can be avoided with a balanced diet as outlined earlier in this chapter and with particular strategies at certain times (see chapters in this section dealing with preventive medicine, poisoning, and metabolic diseases).

Some common diseases which were not mentioned in the other chapters and their clinical signs include the following:

Copper deficiency—fading black fleece, poor wool crimp and growth, weight loss, anemia, and swayback (see chapter dealing with lameness). Iodine deficiency—enlarged thyroid glands (goiter) in the neck. Cobalt deficiency— weight loss and anemia.

Urolithiasis (kidney stones, bladder stones, water belly)—stones in the urinary tract block the tract of male animals, cause dribbling and straining, and may result in death. The stones are caused by high protein and concentrate diets with imbalances of calcium, magnesium, and/or phosphorus. Urolithiasis can be controlled by acidifying the ration or adding salt to it.

Consult with your veterinarian if signs of nutritional diseases occur in your flock.

Handling, Housing and Sanitation

By Jan L. Carlson

SHEEP

The operational needs of a sheep business vary greatly depending on the type of operation, climate, feed availability, and a host of other factors. There are at least three basic types of sheep enterprises: Farm flock, range operation, and feedlot.

A farm flock can vary in size from a few ewes to several hundred and its main characteristic is that the sheep usually are maintained on the land belonging to the farm.

A range sheep operation consists of one or more bands of sheep consisting of approximately 1,000 ewes and their lambs herded together by a sheepherder. Range bands of

sheep seldom are maintained under fence but are moved often to areas of optimum grazing throughout the year. A range operation usually owns only a small amount of land to house the "lambing camp". This is an area where the sheep are brought to lamb and to be fed during the part of the winter when no grazing is available.

In a feedlot, lambs are fed to market weight and then sent to slaughter. In some cases, farm flock or range sheep owners also maintain a feedlot, but usually the feedlot owner buys lambs from these producers. Besides these three types of management, a wide combination of systems is possible but each should take advantage of the resources available.

Generally, adult sheep need not be housed inside for any reason. Quite often, especially in a smaller flock, the sheep are given access to shel-

---

Jan L. Carlson is Research Associate, Department of Veterinary Microbiology and Pathology, Washington State University, Pullman.

Marie T. Sebrechts

USDA-SCS

There are at least three basic types of sheep enterprises: Farm flock, range operation and feedlot.

Karen Rusinski, USDA-SCS

Sheep and Goats

ter or are fed inside a barn. This reduces stress on the animals in extreme weather and often is more convenient for the people doing the feeding.

"Jugs" for Lambing

Sheds or barns for use during lambing are useful on any size operation. If lambing takes place in a warm climate or during the warm months of the year, buildings are not absolutely necessary. It is important to have a series of small pens, called "jugs," in which to put a ewe and her lambs for a period of two or three days after birth. These jugs should be four feet square.

The lambing jugs may be placed outside in warm weather, or a barn or shed may be fitted with portable jugs made from panels fastened together. The panels may be taken apart and stored when not needed, thus freeing barn space for shearing, feed storage, or feeding and housing the sheep.

Mixing pens are an important part of a lambing operation. These are small pens that can hold from three to ten ewes and their lambs. The pens are used to group ewes and lambs into small lots directly from the lambing jugs and before they go into the main band of sheep. This is done to avoid the possibility of lambs getting lost from their mothers.

Permanent fences for sheep are best when made of woven wire that is at least four feet high. Fences should be kept in good repair to hold small lambs and discourage predators. Many sheep producers make use of unfenced temporary grazing areas by employing woven wire and metal stakes to construct a temporary fence that may be moved.

Portable panels have many uses on a sheep operation. A selection of panels 4 feet high and of lengths from 6 to 14 feet can be made into working corrals, chutes, alleyways or various sized pens. The advantage to the panels is that they can be used for one function at one time of the year and become part of another structure in a different season.

Quite often the profitability of a sheep enterprise depends upon availability of inexpensive grazing land. Federal and State lands, aftermath grazing from cash crops, and grazing of fall regrowth can cut feed costs. In these cases, the sheep are moved to a new area once the feed is gone.

Charles O'Rear, USDA

Parasites can be a problem in areas where sheep are pastured continually. Pasture rotation and deworming the sheep in spring before they are turned onto pasture can help reduce this problem.

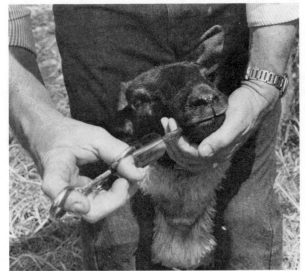

Kevin Shields

Pasture Tips

When pasture is used, take care to rotate the grazing. The available pasture should be cross fenced so the animals can graze one area of grass while the other areas are allowed time to regrow.

Parasites can be a problem in areas where sheep are pastured continually. The sheep shed parasite eggs in their manure, which contaminate the pasture. Then the sheep reinfest themselves while grazing.

It is important to try to break this cycle. Deworming the sheep in spring before they are turned onto the pasture is a good idea. Pasture rotation also helps to reduce the problem since the areas that are grazed down will be exposed to sunlight which dries up some of the parasite eggs.

Another way to break the parasite's life cycle is to allow other species of animals such as cattle or horses to graze the area. Sheep parasites will not live in another type of livestock.

When grass is not available and sheep must be fed dry roughage, it is advantageous for health and economic reasons to feed in bunks or troughs. County extension services can provide information about the types of feeders recommended and the amount of feeder space required.

Hoof trimming should be done at least twice a year for sheep maintained under normal grazing conditions. Sheep that spend part of the year in dry, sandy, or rocky soil may wear down their feet enough so they will not need trimming.

Recordkeeping is important for the success of a sheep enterprise. To record the data from individual animals it is necessary to identify each animal. Methods by which this may be done are ear tags, ear notches, tattoos and paint brands.

GOATS

The majority of goats in this country are dairy goats and they are managed much the same as dairy cows. They require milking twice daily and the usual length of lactation is 305 days. This allows a 60-day dry period for the doe to replenish her body stores of nutrients before the next lactation. When a doe kids, or "freshens," it is common practice to remove the kids and raise them separately from their dams.

Goats require protection from the elements. The shelter provided need not be elab-

The majority of goats in this country are dairy goats and they are managed much the same as dairy cows.

Marie T. Sebrechts

orate but it must keep the animals clean and dry and away from drafts. During the summer months, it is important to provide a shady area with adequate air circulation for the goats and to control flies.

Adequate space is essential for housing dairy goats to prevent aggressive does from monopolizing feed bunks and limiting production of timid does. Each doe should have 15 square feet.

Feeders should be designed to discourage animals from wasting feed, and to prevent feed from being contaminated with manure. Provide enough space for all animals to eat at one time. Outside, each doe should have at least 30 square feet of drylot for exercise area if pasture is not available.

Dairy goats can make use of many types of pasture and browse to supplement their diets during the grazing season. Goats often prefer to eat brush and weeds rather than grasses, so quite often an area is improved after being grazed by goats. However, they sometimes kill young trees. High producing dairy goats should receive supplemental rations when on pasture to maintain

Sheep and Goats

the level of nutrition required to sustain production.

Fencing, Gates

Goats require good fences. Woven wire (2″ × 4″) that is 5 feet high should be adequate. If four foot wire is used, it is advisable to put two strands of barbed wire along the top. One strand of electric wire along the inside of the fence line at about goat nose height will keep goats away from the fence and save on maintenance. All gates should be fitted with goat-proof latches. A simple hook and eye will not fool a goat for long.

Kevin Shields

Goats require good fences and gates which are fitted with goat-proof latches. A simple hook and eye will not fool a goat for long.

An average dairy goat will give about six to ten pounds of milk a day, and should be milked twice a day at approximately 12-hour intervals. A milking parlor or an area away from the main barn is needed for this purpose. Commercial sale of milk must be licensed by the State department of health. Contact your State sanitarian to obtain the health codes for each individual State. The basic equipment needed to obtain milk for home use is a milking stand, stainless steel pail, sanitizing solution, teat dip, and a milk strainer.

To avoid mastitis, does should be milked in an area free of dust and insects. Wash and dry each doe's udder thoroughly, using disposable paper towels. Milk the first few squirts of milk into a strip cup to check for abnormal milk. Use a teat dip on the doe's udder after milking.

Screen for mastitis with the California mastitis test, and treat any positive animals immediately. Milk any does with mastitis last, and discard the milk. Any doe that has chronic mastitis is quite likely to infect other does and should be culled.

After the does have been milked, the milk should be

run through a stainless steel strainer fitted with an approved milk filter. Then it should be chilled to 50° F or less within 30 minutes of milking and held at that temperature until use.

Feeding Kids

Most dairy goat kids are taken from their dams at birth and bottle fed. The first meal for a newborn kid should be colostrum. This is the first milk that a doe produces and it contains antibodies to protect the young kid from infection until its own immune system can take over. Quite often, goat raisers simply let the kids nurse their dams for their first meal. The milk a doe produces for three days after freshening is not acceptable for commercial use.

Kid goats may be raised on goat milk, cow milk, or commercial milk replacer. A kid should be started on 5–6 oz. three times a day. Within three weeks they should be able to consume a pint three times a day.

Kids can be weaned as early as six weeks of age if they are eating other feed well. They will start to nibble at hay leaves by about one week of age if hay is available to them. They should be offered a very palatable concen-trate ration after about three weeks of age.

Sometimes does are allowed to raise their own kids. In this situation, the does should be checked daily to make sure their udders are being emptied of milk. If not, the doe's udder may become lopsided or she may be in danger of contracting mastitis. Some producers lock the kids up at night, milk the does in the morning, then turn the kids back in with their dams during the day to reduce bottle feeding and milking.

FURTHER READING

Management and Diseases of Dairy Goats. S.B. Guss. Dairy Goat Journal Publishing Corp., P.O. Box 1808, Scottsdale, AZ 85252. $19.00.

Diseases of Sheep. R. Jensen and B.L. Swift. 2nd Edition. Lea and Febiger, Merchandising Department, 600 South Washington Square, Philadelphia, PA 19096. $35.00.

The Sheepman's Production Handbook. G.E. Scott. Sheep Industry Development Program, Inc., 200 Clayton Street, Denver, CO 80206. $20.00.

Sheep and Goat Production. Elsevier Science Publishing Co., 52 Vanderbilt Avenue, New York, NY 10017. $121.50.

The Veterinary Clinics of North America, Volume 5, No. 3, Symposium on Sheep and Goat Medicine. W.B. Saunders Co., 210 West Washington Square, Philadelphia, PA 19105. $19.50.

Raising Sheep the Modern Way. P. Simmons. Garden Way Publishing, School House Road, Pownal, VT 05261. $7.95.

V. SWINE

Tim McCabe

Swine Herd Health

By LeRoy G. Biehl

Preventive medicine or swine herd health is an important part of overall swine management. A low level of disease in the swine herd may limit top performance and result in lower profits. A severe disease outbreak can cause heavy death loss and serious economic losses.

The well-managed, predetermined swine herd health program can minimize either type of disease problem by preventing exposure to disease organisms and by increasing a herd's immunity against known diseases. A sound herd health preventive program includes excellent sanitation, isolation of herd replacements, good nutrition and housing,

LeRoy G. Biehl is Swine Extension Veterinarian, College of Veterinary Medicine, University of Illinois, Urbana. He is chief editor/writer for this section of the Yearbook.

genetic resistance and vigorous parasite control.

Since swine management systems may range from a small pasture herd to the large commercial, complete confinement operation, no single preventive medicine program will work for all farms.

Some swine farms close their herds to new additions of breeding stock, and rigidly control traffic of outside personnel. They rely on strict isolation and sanitation to prevent introduction of disease agents.

Open herds that bring in new breeding stock and allow human traffic on the farm will need a more complete immunization schedule as part of their preventive medicine program. If the herd is likely or known to be exposed to diseases, these disease agents will be included in the immunization program.

The swine farm's immunization program will be accom-

Tim McCabe, USDA-SCS

plished either by injecting a vaccine or by exposing the pig to disease agents during a period in the production cycle when no harm will be done. Most swine producers use a combination of vaccination and planned exposure.

When determining which type program is best for the individual farm, consult the local swine veterinarian. All the vaccinations are neither practical nor feasible for all farms, but the local vet is familiar with what diseases are in the area and which ones are most likely to strike the herd. The veterinarian and the herd owner can also discuss what type of vaccines are available, along with when and where to administer them.

Since swine management systems may range from a small pasture herd to a large commercial, complete confinement operation, no single preventive medicine program will work for all farms.

Breeding Stock
A healthy swine herd begins with selection of healthy breeding stock. When new breeding stock is brought onto the farm, numerous diseases can be introduced into the herd by carrier animals which show no signs of disease. Some of these diseases include: External and internal parasites, leptospirosis, brucellosis, rhinitis, pneumonia, arthritis and scours. Virus diseases spread by herd additions are parvovirus, pseudorabies, TGE and influenza.

USDA

Negative blood tests for brucellosis, pseudorabies and leptospirosis should be required when purchasing a boar or gilts.

Several routes are available when adding new animals. Specific pathogen free (SPF), artificial insemination and embryo transfer are methods that will reduce the risk of introducing new diseases.

When purchasing a boar or gilts, discuss herd disease history with the breeder or his veterinarian. A negative blood test for pseudorabies, leptospirosis and brucellosis should be required.

Although the seedstock producer has a responsibility to sell clean animals, the buyer also has certain responsibilities to minimize disease spread once the animal reaches the farm. A 60-day period to isolate, observe, test and help the animals become accustomed to new surroundings should be instituted before new animals are admitted to the herd.

Upon arrival, the new boars or gilts should be placed in isolation for 30 days in a separate building at least 100 feet from other swine. Observe for signs of dysentery, arthritis, salmonellosis and respiratory diseases. At this time treat for lice, mange and

Swine

worms, but do not treat with antibiotics because the antibiotic treatment may mask symptoms of any disease the animal may be harboring.

Retests, Vaccines

Thirty days after arrival, the animals should be retested for pseudorabies, brucellosis, leptospirosis and any other diseases the local veterinarian deems important for the herd. Vaccinations against parvovirus and other diseases at this time are optional, depending on the advice of the vet.

If blood tests are negative and no disease symptoms have been observed, the second 30 days of new farm adaptation can begin. Manure from the isolation area is scattered in the pens of open sows and gilts. In addition, manure from the adult breeding herd should be placed in the pens of the new animals so that the new additions can develop an immunity against common viruses (SMEDI) that would kill the embryos if exposed after breeding.

This manure exposure should be completed 30 days prior to breeding. No pregnant animals should be exposed to new additions or their manure.

Once the 60-day observance and adaptation period is

USDA

Hog louse. While in isolation upon arrival, new boars or gilts should be treated for lice, mange and worms. Antibiotics should not be administered at this time, however, because they may mask symptoms of any disease the animal is harboring.

over, the new animals can be admitted to the herd with little risk of disease problems occurring.

Ideally, gilts should be selected from good-milking sows that wean large litters free of genetic defects.

Soon after selection, reduce the gilt's feed intake to about 6 lbs. per day until bred. Parvovirus, leptospirosis and erysipelas vaccines usually are administered 3 to 4 weeks before breeding. In order to develop common natu-

Swine Herd Health

ral immunity against SMEDI viruses of the herd, gilts should be exposed to older animals as described earlier when new animals are purchased.

Microscopic examination of a manure sample by a veterinarian will determine if the gilts are infected with worms, and the type of dewormer needed. If necessary a broad spectrum dewormer should be used 2 to 3 weeks before breeding and again 7 to 10 days before farrowing.

All breeding stock should be treated for lice and mange before breeding and prior to farrowing.

Effectiveness of Dewormers

	Roundworms	Nodular Worms	Whipworms	Lungworms	Kidney Worms
Dichlorvos (Atgard)	99-100%	95-100%	90-100%	0	0
Hygromycin (Hygromix)	95-100%	95-100%	85-100%	0	0
Levamisole (Tramisol)	99-100%	80-100%	60-80%	90-100%	83%
Piperazine	75-100%	50%	0	0	0
Pyrantel (Banminth)	96-100%	99-100%	0	0	0
Fenbendazole (Safeguard)	100%	99-100%	99-100%	99-100%	100%

Source: North Carolina Agricultural Extension Service Bulletin.

Swine

Energy Intake

During the breeding period, the energy intake is increased to 6 to 9 lbs. and the gilts are moved to fenceline contact with the boars. Better litters result if the gilt is not bred during the first heat (estrous) cycle but delayed until the second or third estrous cycle.

As soon as mating has occurred, daily feed intake should be reduced to about 5 lbs. per day until the last month of pregnancy, when feed intake is again raised to 6 lbs. Gilts should gain between 70 to 100 lbs. and sows 50 to 75 lbs. during pregnancy.

Depending on the farm, several vaccinations may be considered for gilts prior to farrowing. *E. coli, Clostridium perfringens,* TGE, and atrophic rhinitis require two injections—with the first injection 5 to 6 weeks before farrowing and the second 2 to 3 weeks before. At the next farrowing only booster injections are required, at 2 to 3 weeks before farrowing.

The farrowing house should be thoroughly cleaned and disinfected. Gilts and sows are washed with a mild detergent before being placed in a clean farrowing crate or stall.

If someone can be present

Kevin Shields

Before placing gilts or sows in farrowing crates or stalls, the farrowing house should be thoroughly cleaned and disinfected.

at farrowing time, often several additional pigs can be saved. Dry the weak pigs off and make sure they nurse or are given a glucose electrolyte solution by mouth. To avoid chilling it is important for newborn pigs to find their way to a supplemental heat source such as a heat lamp or mat.

Swine Herd Health

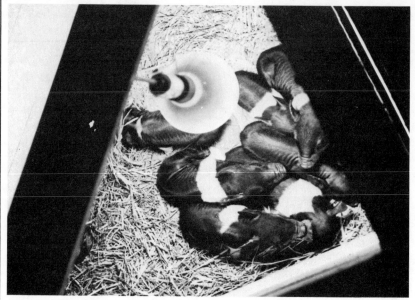

USDA

To avoid chilling it is important for newborn pigs to find their way to a supplemental heat source such as a heat lamp or mat.

Kevin Shields

Twelve to 24 hours after birth, pigs need to be identified by ear notching, and have their needle teeth clipped. In addition, they should have their navel cord cut and treated with disinfectant solution.

Swine

"Processing"

Several common procedures called "processing" are performed on young pigs. Twelve to 24 hours after birth, pigs need to: Be identified by ear notching, have their needle teeth clipped, have their tails docked, be castrated, and have their navel cord dipped in a disinfectant solution, usually iodine.

At the same time, iron is administered by injection or orally. If atrophic rhinitis is a problem on the farm, pigs need to be vaccinated against the disease within the first week of life.

Pigs are weaned at 3 to 6 weeks of age and placed in a warm, dry pen that can be kept clean.

Antibiotics often are added to the ration of weaned pigs to prevent diseases. Young pigs fed antibiotics usually gain faster because the disease-producing organisms are suppressed and the pigs remain healthy.

The advantage in feeding antibiotics to finishing hogs is slight, and usually the practice is halted at about 120 lbs. In addition most antibiotics must be withdrawn from the feed several days before the animals are slaughtered..

Since each feed additive has a different withdrawal time, the owner should be familiar with that time before swine are marketed for slaughter. Proper observance of withdrawal times is important to prevent residues of antibiotic feed additives in the meat.

Pigs should be treated at weaning for lice and mange with an approved insecticide. Pigs farrowed on perforated floors are less likely to be worm-infected at weaning. If pigs are worm-infected, a dewormer should be selected that is effective against the specific worm diagnosed.

Erysipelas and Hemophilus pneumonia are vaccinations to consider at weaning if these diseases are a problem on the farm.

During the growing-finishing stage of production, the owner should carefully observe the pigs for signs of disease such as diarrhea, lameness, coughing or labored breathing. Any unusual activities or signs should be reported early to the attending veterinarian for diagnosis so control measures can be taken before a severe disease outbreak occurs.

Nutrition

By LeRoy G. Biehl

Excellent nutrition in all phases of the swine production cycle is the key to top performance and feed efficiency. Although the pig's diet can vary tremendously in the kind and amounts of feedstuffs, certain basic nutrient requirements must be met if reproduction and growth are to occur.

Nutrients in swine diets can be divided into five classes: Water, energy, protein, minerals and vitamins.

Water is an essential part of the diet, and absence of water will cause death sooner than if the diet lacks any other nutrient. Clean water should be provided free choice at all times.

Energy in swine diets usually is made up of carbohydrates or fats. In the United States, corn is the major source of energy in swine rations. Other sources include wheat, oats, barley and fats such as tallow or vegetable oil.

Protein is the building block for muscle and is added to swine diets as a supplement. Soybean meal is the most common source of protein supplement, although cottonseed meal, fishmeal and tankage are additional protein sources. Low protein diets result in unthriftiness in growing pigs and poor milk yield in sows.

Minerals usually are divided into two classes, macrominerals which are required in relatively large amounts and micro or trace minerals which are required in small amounts. Calcium, phosphorus, sodium and chlorine are the macrominerals added to the common grain-soybean meal ration.

LeRoy G. Biehl is Swine Extension Veterinarian, College of Veterinary Medicine, University of Illinois, Urbana.

USDA

Excellent nutrition in all phases of the swine production cycle is the key to top performance and feed efficiency.

Marie T. Sebrechts

Water is an essential part of the diet in any hog operation, and clean water should be provided free choice at all times.

Depending on the stage of production, calcium and phosphorus should be added at recommended levels for maximum growth and good bone development. The calcium/phosphorus ratio should never exceed 2:1 with the optimum ratio near 1.2:1.

Supplements Vital

Adequate calcium-phosphorus supplementation is especially important to gestating-lactating sows and gilts. Bone growth of the fetus and milk production deplete the mother's supply of calcium and phosphorus from her bones.

Deficient diets can result in broken legs and spines. These usually occur immediately following weaning. Affected sows are unable to rise and frequently die. Excellent mineral supplementation of the ration during pregnancy and lactation will prevent these losses.

Sodium and chlorine are added to the ration in the form of salt. Usually 0.35 percent or 7 lbs. per ton of feed for all animals is adequate for all stages of production. Excessive salt without adequate water can cause convulsions and rapid death as a result of sodium ion poisoning. Water deprivation for 12 to 24 hours can cause "salt poisoning" to occur, even in pigs consuming normal rations.

Iron, zinc, manganese, copper, iodine, and selenium are microminerals commonly added to swine diets. Magnesium and potassium are required by the pig but traditional swine rations usually have them in sufficient quantity.

Vitamins are essential for enzyme and cell metabolic function and are added to swine rations for maximum production. The typical grain-soybean meal ration should be supplemented with vitamins A, D, E, K, riboflavin, niacin, pantothenic acid, choline and B_{12}. Biotin, folic acid, and pyridoxine are required by the pig but adequate amounts usually are provided in natural feedstuffs and do not need to be added to the diet.

Feeding Life Cycle

Swine require different concentrations of nutrients and amounts of feed depending on the stage of production. This is often referred to as the "life cycle of feeding" and is divided into: Gestation, lactation, starter, grower and finisher.

Feed intake must be limited in gestating sows to prevent them from becoming overweight. Four to five pounds of

USDA

Bone growth of the fetus and milk production deplete the mother's supply of calcium and phosphorus from her bones. Therefore, adequate calcium-phosphorus supplementation is especially important to gestating-lactating sows and gilts.

USDA

USDA

Vitamins are essential for enzyme and cell metabolic function and are added to swine rations for maximum production. The single pig is suffering from choline deficiency. The two pigs, which were litter-mates, show the importance of adequate nicotinic acid. No supplemental nicotinic acid was added to the diet of the pig that is now smaller, and which displays definite deficiency symptoms.

Nutrition

271

properly fortified feed is adequate for the pregnant sow, although during colder weather additional feed may be needed. Adding fat to the diet in late gestation may save more of the smaller pigs by increasing the energy stores in the baby pig and the fat content of the sow's milk.

Lactation diets are fed free choice and need to be high in energy and adequate in minerals to minimize the sow's weight loss and bone mineral depletion.

Prestarter and starter rations are the most highly fortified and complex of swine diets. For optimum performance, milk products frequently are added to prestarter diets. Addition of antibiotics to starter and grower diets increases growth rate and feed efficiency of the growing pig. This improvement is less noticeable in finishing pigs.

Growing-finishing pigs are allowed to eat the fortified diets free choice. Grinding and mixing just before feeding improves intake, but fine grinding may result in stomach ulcers.

To reach the recommendations of the five phases of production, the ration must be balanced with the correct amounts of each feed ingredient.

Nutrient Recommendations for Swine

	% Protein	% Lysine	% Calcium Min.	% Calcium Max.	% Phosphorus Min.
Gestation[1]	12	.50	0.85	1.00	0.65
Lactation[2]	14	.65	0.80	1.00	0.60
Starter					
10 to 20 lbs.	20	1.15	0.75	0.90	0.60
15 to 30 lbs.	18	.96	0.75	0.90	0.60
Grower (30 to 120 lbs)	16	.75	0.65	0.80	0.55
Finisher (120 lbs to mkt.)	14	.60	0.60	0.70	0.50

[1] 4.0 lbs. feed/day provides: Min. 15 g Ca and 12 g P.
[2] 12.0 lbs. feed/day provides: Min. 43 g Ca and 32 g P.

Source: University of Illinois Department of Animal Science

Swine

Kevin Shields

Nutritional Disorders

Generally, simple nutritional deficiencies are seldom observed in today's well-fed pigs. Deficiencies that develop are usually the result of mixing errors, ingredients that interfere with absorption and metabolism of nutrients, or disease conditions that may increase dietary requirements. Nutrient deficiency symptoms

Generally, simple nutritional deficiencies are seldom observed in today's well-fed pigs.

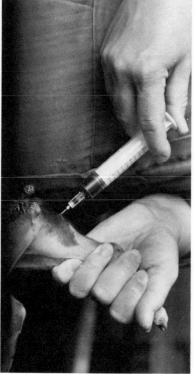

Kevin Shields

Kevin Shields

Baby pigs that do not have contact with the soil require supplemental iron to prevent anemia. Producers raising hogs in confinement administer iron either orally or by injection to baby pigs at 1 to 3 days of age.

of major ingredients have been discussed earlier in this chapter.

Anemia. Iron is required for formation of hemoglobin in the red blood cells and thus for the prevention of anemia. Baby pigs that do not have contact with the soil require supplemental iron. Producers raising hogs in confinement administer iron either orally or by injection to baby pigs at 1 to 3 days of age.

Injection of 100 to 150 mg of iron provides adequate iron for 2 weeks, at which time an additional injection is provided or an oral iron feed mixture free choice. Pigs raised on dirt or provided the oral iron mixture from birth seldom develop anemia.

Plump, fast growing pigs

devoid of supplemental iron develop anemia at about two weeks of age. They may breathe rapidly and have a doughy appearance with wrinkled skin. White pigs look pale. Death occurs quickly if the pigs are not treated with iron injections.

Anemia also can be caused by deficiencies of copper or vitamin B_{12}.

Parakeratosis can result when dietary zinc is inadequate or when dietary calcium is high. Symptoms of parakeratosis are a thickened crusty skin beginning on the abdomen and inner thigh. Addition of zinc to the ration will treat and prevent parakeratosis.

Selenium-Vitamin E Deficiency. An interrelationship exists between selenium and vitamin E in maintaining healthy cell membrane functions. Grain sources from the Midwest generally are deficient in selenium, and artificial drying may destroy some of the natural vitamin E.

Sudden death in growing-finishing pigs is the most common clinical sign of selenium-vitamin E deficiency. Dead pigs may reveal hemorrhages throughout the heart muscle (mulberry heart) or a discolored liver *(hepatosis dietetica)*. Pale muscles or stomach ulcers also may be found. Pigs born from selenium-deficient sows may die suddenly following routine iron injections.

Injections of selenium-vitamin E or the addition of selenium to the diet will halt death losses and prevent further problems. The Food and Drug Administration (FDA) controls selenium supplementation of feeds. Approval has been given by FDA for adding 0.3 ppm of selenium to starter swine feeds and 0.1 ppm to other feeds. Selenium toxicosis can occur if the ration contains more than 5 ppm selenium.

Rickets

Pigs raised indoors devoid of sunlight can develop rickets if vitamin D is not added to the diet. Vitamin D is required for calcium metabolism, and a deficiency results in demineralized bones. Unthriftiness, lameness, crooked or broken bones and tetany are clinical signs of vitamin D deficiency.

Vitamin K deficiency is unlikely unless an antagonist or mold is present in the diet. Navel bleeding or death due to hemorrhage at castration are the most prominent signs of vitamin K deficiency. Listlessness, off feed and visible bruising are additional signs.

Adding vitamin K to the diet will aid in preventing

Nutrition

bleeding problems as a result of moldy feeds or a vitamin K deficiency.

Vitamin A deficiency during a sow's pregnancy can result in the birth of dead pigs or pigs with birth defects (abnormal eyes, blindness, cleft palate). Young animals may show spasms because of spinal cord degeneration. Since swine often are unable to convert carotene in yellow corn to vitamin A, the vitamin should be added to swine rations.

Riboflavin deficiency can occur if feeds are stored for long periods. Impaired reproduction with lack of heat cycles or with stillbirths are symptoms of riboflavin deficiency.

Other vitamins and trace minerals when deficient can cause generalized symptoms of unthriftiness, but are unlikely to be deficient under practical feeding conditions.

Recommendations for Trace Mineral Concentrations in Swine Diets

	PPM Iron	PPM Zinc	PPM Manganese	PPM Copper	PPM Iodine	PPM Selenium
Gestation	80	50	10	5	.14	.10
Lactation	80	50	10	5	.14	.10
Starter (10-30 lbs.)	150	100	5	6	.14	.30
Grower (30-75 lbs.)	90	75	4	5	.14	.15*
Developer (75-125 lbs.)	75	75	2	4	.14	.15*
Finisher (125-Mkt.)	50	50	2	4	.14	.15*
Boars, Replacement Gilts	80	50	10	5	.14	.15*

*FDA allowance is 0.10 ppm.

Source: University of Illinois Department of Animal Science

Respiratory Diseases

By James McKean

Respiratory diseases of swine cause major economic losses. In many cases, respiratory disease losses are not recognized because death losses are low and reduced feed efficiencies are the primary effect.

The major infectious organisms currently associated with swine pneumonias are *Mycoplasma hyopneumoniae, Pasteurella multocida, Bordetella bronchiseptica, Hemophilus pleuropneumoniae, Hemophilus parasuis,* swine influenza and pseudorabies viruses. Other disease conditions such as salmonella, streptococcus may cause pneumonia as a secondary problem. Roundworm and lungworm migration may intensify the severity of pneumonia by

James McKean is Swine Extension Veterinarian, College of Veterinary Medicine, Iowa State University, Ames.

their movement through lung tissues.

A brief description of the major swine pneumonia diseases will be given. Each disease will be treated as a singular event, but the diseases usually occur together—producing a more severe problem than when alone.

Mycoplasma pneumonia of swine (MPS), also known as virus pig pneumonia (VPP), or enzootic pneumonia is a chronic disease of growing finishing swine. The causative agent, *Mycoplasma hyopneumoniae,* is a small bacteria found only in swine. Exposure to this organism is estimated as high as 65 to 80 percent for all U.S. swine.

Clinical signs are a dry, persistent cough, labored breathing and slow or uneven growth. Pigs are infected by aerosol transmission (fine misty particles as a result of breathing, sneezing, coughing) from their mothers or by other

Kevin Shields

Respiratory diseases of swine cause major economic losses in the form of reduced feed efficiencies. A key to preventing respiratory diseases is clean, dry housing with adequate ventilation and air space per pig.

pigs when grouped at weaning. Severity of signs may depend on the presence of secondary infectious agents and environmental conditions.

Treatment of mycoplasmal pneumonia is centered on reducing the effects of secondary bacterial infections and reduction of lung lesion development. Tylosin, lincomycin tiamulin, sulfonamides and tetracylcines—administered either by injection or orally—will reduce lesion development. Control of economic losses involves feeding growth-promoting levels of the above drugs and improving environmental conditions.

Prevention requires a complete break between infected and uninfected herds. Movement of swine between herds is dangerous. The specific-pathogen-free (SPF) management scheme, embryo transfers, and artificial insemination are all relatively safe methods of adding breeding stock to MPS-free herds.

Pasteurella Infections

Pasteurella pneumonias are common secondary pneumonia infections following MPS, Bordetella, influenza and environmental stresses. *Pasteurella multocida* occurs in apparently healthy swine but is rarely the initiating factor in pneumonia. Spread is by aero-

Swine

sol transmission from pig to pig.

Cold, damp, poorly ventilated, drafty, or overcrowded conditions make Pasteurella infections more serious. Clinical signs of pasteurellosis include a sudden onset of coughing, fever of 104° to 107° F, labored breathing and poor growth affecting a large percentage of the group.

Tetracyclines and sulfonamides in feed or water will reduce clinical severity of an outbreak. Individual animal treatment by injection may be needed for severely affected pigs.

Control of Pasteurella infections involves improved environment, reducing dust and aerosol bacterial contamination, treatment of visibly affected pigs, reducing stocking rate, adequate nutrition, and parasite migration control. Vaccines currently available may reduce the severity of lesion development but do not prevent disease.

HPP or *Hemophilus pleuropneumoniae (parahemolyticus)* causes a sudden to chronic pneumonia in pigs generally from 30 lbs. to adult. When it is first introduced into a group of swine, common signs are sudden death without signs of coughing, labored breathing, high temperatures—104° to 107° F, listlessness and loss of appetite. Some pigs die with a bloody froth coming from their mouth. Mortality can range from 5 to 50 percent of a group.

As the disease becomes more chronic, the sudden deaths are reduced but the chronic cough, labored breathing, slow growth and lung adhesions become more prominent. Sudden changes in temperature or management can cause a reappearance of the acute form. Spread of infection is by aerosol droplets from infected swine.

Treating Acute HPP

Treatment of acute HPP requires immediate action. The bacterium generally is susceptible to penicillin or tetracyclines injected at the higher treatment levels. Besides medical treatments, efforts should be made to increase ventilation rates, reduce numbers of pigs/air space, and avoid adding new animals until the disease is controlled.

After the sudden deaths are controlled, high levels of sulfas or tetracyclines given orally may help increase feedlot performance. Preventive measures including vaccination or oral medication are indicated.

Hemophilus parasuis is a common bacteria of the respiratory tract. It has been identified as producing inflammation of the lung cavity lining (pleuritis), intestinal cavity lining (peritonitis) and the joints.

Occasionally, infections of the brain lining result in meningitis. This infection, known as Glasser's Disease, is found in pigs from 25 to 100 lbs. and generally follows a stressful situation. *Hemophilus parasuis* is also recognized as important organism in swine pneumonias and rhinitis.

Use of tetracyclines, sulfonamides and penicillin by injection have resulted in reduced losses. Preventive techniques generally are not economically feasible because of the sporadic recurrence of the disease.

BB and Cats

Bordetella broniseptica (BB) is an important swine respiratory disease cause. Historically, BB has been identified as a major cause of atrophic rhinitis. Of increasing importance is its role in the pneumonias of pigs 1 to 6 weeks of age.

BB is spread by aerosol transmission from infected to uninfected pigs. Other animals also may spread this organism to pigs and to each other. Cats are recognized as particularly capable carriers because of their desire to cuddle with suckling pigs, under a heat lamp.

Sudden onset of severe coughing, elevated temperature and poor performance are clinical signs of infection. Recovered pigs may show persistent coughing and poor weight gains.

Treatment is by injections of tetracyclines, sulfas, tylosin or lincomycin. Prefarrowing vaccination of sows with Bordetella vaccines may provide colostral protection to the pigs.

Swine influenza virus occurs throughout the year but is most common during the widely changing weather of spring and fall.

Clinical signs in swine are similar to human symptoms. Rapid onset of muscle soreness, lack of appetite, high temperature, hacking cough, and weight loss in a group of growing-finishing swine are the most common signs. Mortality is low unless secondary pneumonias are triggered by this infection.

Treatment of influenza virus is not practical. No vaccines are available. Supportive treatments with sulfa

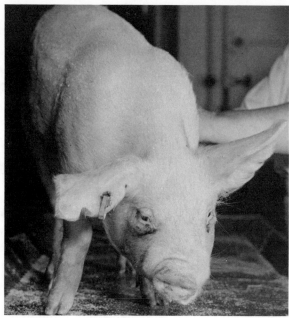

Atrophic rhinitis is a major economic problem for swine producers, since infected pigs may grow much slower than uninfected pigs. Loss of turbinates (atrophy) may also make it easier for bacteria and dusts to move into the lungs.

USDA

drugs and tetracyclines accompanied by electrolyte solutions can be used to treat secondary infections.

Types of Rhinitis

Rhinitis is an inflammation of the lining of the nasal cavity. There are three distinct clinical rhinitis problems—necrotic rhinitis, inclusion body rhinitis, and atrophic rhinitis.

Necrotic rhinitis (bull nose) is an uncommon disease in modern hog production units. It is caused by invasion of the skin or mouth cavity from *Fusobacterium (Spherophorus) necrophorus*. This organism enters a wound or

skin break and produces a large abscess area in the jaw.

Treatment of these abscesses generally is not successful. Prevention is by improved sanitation, reduction in skin abrasions from sharp flooring material, clean instruments in clipping teeth, and reduction of fighting whenever possible.

Inclusion body rhinitis (cytomegalic virus rhinitis, IBR) of swine is an infectious viral disease. Incidence of the disease is sporadic and quite low.

Clinical signs are respiratory distress caused by plugging of the nasal cavity with a thick, stringy material. Suckling pigs most often are infected and may be seen breathing from the mouth. Affected pigs cannot breathe or suckle normally and may die of starvation.

Treatment generally is ineffective. Removing the nasal plugs may give temporary relief. Injectable antibiotics may help reduce secondary infections in the nose and lungs. Because of the sporadic incidence of IBR, preventive measures are not economically feasible.

Atrophic rhinitis is an infectious, chronic inflammation of the nasal turbinate bones. The turbinates are tiny scroll-like bones in the nasal cavity that filter and warm air entering the lungs.

The principal infective agent is *Bordetella bronchiseptica* (BB). Other organisms—including *Pasteurella multocida, Hemophilus parasuis,* and IBR virus—have been identified as intensifying agents.

Major Problem

Atrophic rhinitis is a major economic problem for swine producers. Infected pigs may grow much slower than uninfected pigs. Loss of turbinates (atrophy) may also increase the opportunity for bacteria and dusts to move into the lungs.

Reduction in growth rate is most notable during the period when turbinate atrophy is occurring. After turbinate destruction stops, growth rate between infected and uninfected pigs may be similar, but infected pigs never regain the lost growth.

Organisms causing turbinate atrophy are spread by aerosol from adults to pigs and by pig to pig transfer.

Treatment of pigs with atrophic rhinitis will not reconstruct the severely damaged turbinate bones. Prevention of atrophy by a combination of vaccination, medication and improvement of environmental management is the best method.

Antibiotic feed additives are used to suppress secondary infections and to improve overall health of the pig. Vaccination of pigs or sows or both to increase immunity has been attempted. Vaccines have reduced, but not eliminated, Bordetella-caused atrophy.

All in, all-out farrowing and nursery management, maintenance of small groups of similar aged pigs and control of concurrent disease will help reduce the significance of swine atrophic rhinitis.

Other Common Ills; Molds, Chemicals

By James McKean

Agalactia

A common disease of swine is the MMA (Mastitis, Metritis, Agalactia) syndrome. This problem generally occurs at or several days after farrowing. Incidence of reduced milk flow (hypogalactia) or complete milk stoppage (agalactia) will vary between herds and between farrowing within herds.

Agalactia may be a primary disease or be secondary to a disease or environmental problem. Clinical signs in sows include depression, reluctance to eat or drink, high temperature, rapid breathing, and reluctance to move around or allow pigs to nurse. Affected pigs are hungry, weak, and appear restless. The entire udder or individual glands may be affected. Affected glands are usually

James McKean is Swine Extension Veterinarian, College of Veterinary Medicine, Iowa State University, Ames.

warmer, firmer and more sensitive than normal glands.

There is no specific cause for agalactia or hypogalactia. Bacterial endotoxins, hot environmental temperatures, constipation, poor sanitation, weak nursing action by sick pigs, hormonal imbalances, genetic predisposition, secondary effects of other infectious diseases, and management techniques contribute to MMA signs. Because of this diversity of causes, no treatment is uniformly successful.

Oxytoxin should be administered at 2 to 4 hour intervals to stimulate milk letdown and "milk out" diseased fluid. An injectable antibiotic and possibly anti-inflammatory drug should be administered to the affected sow. Milk replacer should be offered to pigs to supplement milk received from the mother.

Prevention must be based on determining the cause on each farm. Careful investiga-

Other Common Ills

Clean, dry farrowing crates or stalls will result in less mastitis.

Kevin Shields

tion by the producer and attending veterinarian should yield indications for preventive actions. Ration or feeding changes may be needed to reduce sow constipation. Laxative feedstuffs or additions of chemical laxatives to lactation feedstuffs may be beneficial. Temperatures above 80° to 85° F where the sow lays will reduce milk flow. Clean, dry farrowing crates or pens will result in less mastitis.

E. coli, Streptococcus, Staphylococcus sp. and, occasionally, *Klebsiella* are bacteria commonly found in affected glands. Very few cases of agalactia are the result of uterine infections (metritis). Routine use of uterine douches or infusions, intrauterine pills or boluses should be resisted unless a herd metritis problem is diagnosed by the attending veterinarian.

Some herds have a higher resistance to MMA than others. Whether this resistance is due to a genetic strength or to the absence of an immune-suppressing bacteria or virus is unknown.

Strep Infections

Streptococcus organisms are identified in several swine diseases. Besides their activity in the MMA syndrome, *Streptococcus sp.* have been associated with arthritis, jowl abscesses, meningitis, and pneumonia.

Streptococcus arthritis is discussed later, in the chapter dealing with lameness.

Jowl abscesses and puncture wound abscesses were once a major swine disease problem. With confinement rearing and better sanitation, these problems have been reduced greatly. But because pus from a swollen jowl abscess can contaminate feeders and waterers and infect normal swine, strict equipment sanitation and infected animal segregation must be practiced. The strep organisms can survive on the tonsils for long periods before producing abscesses.

Until recently, meningitis was an uncommon effect of strep infections. In the past 3 to 4 years, however, a strain of streptococcus—*Strep suis Type II*—has been identified in an increasing number of swine meningitis cases. Incidence of this disease has been predominantly in confinement situations, although a few outbreaks have been found in open air systems.

Clinical signs are sudden onset of depression, convulsions, involuntary paddling, coma and death. Pigs from 3 to 12 weeks are affected most commonly. They generally have just been through a stressful situation such as movement, weaning, commingling, overcrowding or poor sanitation conditions.

Most pigs in a group are infected but only a few develop meningitis. Without prompt treatment, mortality will approach 100 percent. The organism is probably spread by "aerosol" transmission (via breathing, coughing, sneezing) and spreads very rapidly.

Treatment consists of injecting large doses of effective antibiotics. All animals in an affected group should be treated initially. Treatment of pigs already exhibiting meningitis signs is generally not successful.

In herds with a persistent problem, medication and vaccine usage may be required for prevention. Reduction of stresses will help reduce incidence of the problem.

Pseudorabies or PRV

Pseudorabies (Aujeszky's Disease, Mad Itch, *Herpes suis*, PRV) is a herpes virus infection of swine and other mammals. Pseudorabies is completely different from rabies, but derived its name pseudo (false) rabies because of signs of mouth frothing, teeth grinding, changes in temperament, a choke-like spasm of the esophagus and other signs which may be seen with both diseases.

Swine are the reservoir host for this virus and may exhibit mild to severe signs when infected. All other mammals, except humans and horses, are susceptible to the virus.

In almost all cases of non-swine disease, death occurs soon after signs appear. Sheep, dogs and cats are the domestic animals most easily infected by PRV. Cattle are less readily infected. Raccoons, skunks and opossum are easily infected wildlife.

Swine pseudorabies may show mild signs of appetite suppression, fever and general reluctance to move for 3 to 4 days; or have more severe signs with abortions, high rates of stillbirths, weak pigs at birth, rhinitis and pneumonia in sows. Shaking, convulsions, coma and death are clinical signs in young pigs.

Generally, severity of death loss is age-related. Pigs under 4 weeks of age are most susceptible. Young pigs are more likely to be affected with convulsions and other central nervous signs, while older pigs may develop respiratory disease.

Recovered swine are the primary host and the most common method of spread to new farms. Aerosol transmission is the primary route of infection. Consumption of internal organs from infected wildlife by swine may lead to infection. Non-swine carriers can mechanically carry virus-containing material from farm to farm locally.

Carrier Detection

Treatment of pseudorabies is unrewarding because antibiotics will not affect the virus. Vaccination of swine before exposure can give good protection.

Recovered swine have antibodies to PRV for long periods, perhaps lifelong. High levels of protective antibodies can be passed in colostrum. Vaccines produce similar antibodies but do not last as long as natural infection. Currently a blood test is used to identify carrier swine by detecting the presence of PRV antibodies.

In herds experiencing an outbreak, vaccination of breeding herds offers protection from PRV economic losses, but does not prevent virus from entering the herd.

Semiannual vaccination should be maintained in a herd once vaccination starts. Federally licensed modified-live and killed vaccines are available and provide good

Murray Lemmon, USDA

protection from clinical disease when used correctly. In herds experiencing PRV-induced respiratory signs, vaccination of weaned pigs may be necessary to give protection through finishing stages.

Eradication of PRV from U.S. swine is a possibility, since there is adequate scientific information to begin an eradication program.

Pseudorabies can be a self-limiting disease in small herds, but in larger intensive operations virus circulates

Regulations controlling swine movement between States have helped keep the number of PRV infected herds from rising, since swine must test negative or originate from negative-tested herds before being allowed to move interstate.

Other Common Ills

through the unit. This means that total depopulation of the herd may be the only successful eradication method in large units.

The percentage of infected herds is not continuing to rise as it did in the late 1970's. This is partially due to the control of swine movement between States. Swine must test negative or originate from negative-tested herds before being allowed to move interstate.

Some States have instituted more stringent requirements for movement into and within their borders. Several States are operating pilot PRV-eradication programs which should provide valuable experiences about how pseudorabies can be eradicated.

Mycotoxins

Swine are exposed daily to hundreds of molds in feedstuffs and the environment. Most are harmless but a few produce small quantities of potent chemicals. These chemicals, called mycotoxins, are produced by specific mold species when relatively high temperatures and humidity conditions are present.

The southern and southeastern United States have more problems with aflatoxin contamination, while the Midwest has a higher incidence of *Fusarium sp.* mycotoxins—vomitoxin and zearalenone.

Aflatoxin is a potent carcinogenic toxin which can affect liver function, reduce performance, and suppress immune response to disease. Young pigs are more susceptible than older swine. At high levels, severe performance reductions and death are possible.

Grains which are severely weather-stressed (such as by drought or by hail) or damaged by handling or harvest are more likely to be contaminated with aflatoxin. Levels of 100 to 200 ppm may cause poor animal performance and eventual death. Levels of 500 to 1,000 ppm may cause sudden death. In both cases aflatoxin or aflatoxin metabolite residues in meat may occur.

The Food and Drug Administration (FDA) has set aflatoxin level guidelines in feeding of market swine. This level is low enough to result in no danger to the swine or to meat consumers.

Zearalenone is a mycotoxin formed by *Fusarium sp.* molds. It has a hormonal effect on swine similar to estrogens. Gilts fed zearalenone-containing feeds may have enlarged vulvas, protruding nipples and appear to be "in heat". Abortions, increased stillbirths, small litter size and reduced fertility have all been associated with feeding zearalenone-infested feeds.

Occur in Field

Unlike aflatoxin, which primarily is a storage mycotoxin, the *Fusarium sp.* mycotoxins generally occur in the field during wet, hot and humid conditions for the late growing season. The infected ears may have a pink to reddish colored growth on the husks and grain before harvest.

Harvest drying and storage may remove mold growth but leave the mycotoxins on the grain. Thus the grain looks to be of good quality even though potentially infested.

Vomitoxin, feed refusal factor and T-2 toxin are other *Fusarium sp.*-based mycotoxins which can cause problems for swine producers. These mycotoxins cause vomiting and feed refusal when fed at relatively low levels. A secondary effect of the toxins is the retarded growth rate of pigs attempting to consume these rations.

Ochratoxin and citrinin are mycotoxins which cause damage to kidneys and livers of pigs but are rarely seen in the United States.

Ergot poisoning in swine is relatively rare but can occur when rye and cereal grains are fed to swine. Ergot may cause signs that appear similar to MMA syndrome, but will not respond to treatment. Removal of infested grain will allow a rapid return to lactation.

Mycotoxins are an ever-present danger, and the only way to identify specific mycotoxins is by chemical analysis. If in doubt, have the feed tested or place several recently weaned pigs on the suspect feed and observe them for several weeks. Other mycotoxins, currently not known, may be the cause of feed-related toxicosis.

Several plant toxins can occur in swine, depending on the geographic location. Pigweed, cocklebur and nightshade are examples.

Pigweed toxicity is most commonly found in late summer or early fall. Clinical signs occur about 5 to 10 days after pigs are turned into a pasture containing the weed.

Affected pigs have muscle weakness, trembling and incoordination. Body temperatures are normal and the pigs remain alert for 48 hours or more. As the disease progresses, they enter a coma and die from kidney failure.

Digestive System Diseases

By Alex Hogg

Diseases of swine that affect the digestive tract (stomach, small intestine, and colon) include colibacillosis, transmissible gastroenteritis (TGE), rotavirus, swine dysentery, and clostridial enteritis. The general signs of these enteric diseases are scours or diarrhea.

Colibacillosis (baby pig scours, white scours or milk scours), is caused by the bacterium *E. coli*. Colibacillosis usually strikes 3 age groups of pigs: 1 to 4 days old, 3 weeks old, and again at weaning time.

In 1 to 4 day old pigs, the clinical signs include listlessness, diarrhea (scours), followed by dehydration, emaciation (becoming very thin), and

Alex Hogg is Swine Extension Veterinarian, Department of Veterinary Science, University of Nebraska, Lincoln.

a rough hair coat. The tail and skin around the rectum become wet with fecal material and the base of the tail becomes reddened. Death rate is generally very high in 1 to 4 day old pigs but less severe in 3 week old and 5 week old pigs.

Treatment is with injectable or oral antibiotics. In an outbreak, mass treatment of all pigs soon after birth with an effective antibiotic will control the disease and reduce losses.

Colibacillosis is prevented by improving sanitation; keeping pigs warm, clean, and dry; and vaccinating sows twice before farrowing with *E. coli* vaccines.

TGE (transmissible gastroenteritis) is caused by a virus and has been reported in most of the major swine producing countries.

The signs of acute TGE are vomiting, watery diarrhea, and severe dehydration.

A typical outbreak affects baby pigs, growing-finishing pigs, breeding sows, and boars that are not immune from a previous infection or immune due to vaccination.

Mortality is high in pigs under 2 weeks of age and decreases among older pigs. Pigs over 4 weeks of age seldom die. Sows may vomit, lose their appetite, have diarrhea and fever, and stop giving milk. TGE is more frequent during winter months, usually December to April.

In addition to pig carriers, TGE can be spread from one farm to another by dogs, foxes, starlings, and human traffic.

If a TGE outbreak occurs, pregnant sows that are more than 3 weeks from farrowing should be exposed immediately to the virus. Infected sows will develop an immunity and protect their pigs through antibodies in the milk.

Uninfected sows that will farrow in less than 3 weeks should be isolated and an attempt made to prevent infection with TGE virus until the pigs are at least 3 weeks old.

Endemic TGE

Continuous farrowing practiced in large units tends to make TGE a year-round prob-

lem rather than the winter-spring problem observed in classical TGE.

The clinical signs in this condition differ from those seen in classical TGE because some immunity develops in the sows, which partially protects the pigs. Diarrhea is usually observed at 10 to 12 days of age or after weaning. Not all litters or all pigs in the litter develop diarrhea.

Death loss in endemic TGE averages about 10 percent. To prevent TGE, sows should be vaccinated 6 weeks and 2 weeks before farrowing. A 3-month farrowing schedule to break the disease cycle will help prevent endemic TGE.

Rotavirus causes a mild type of scours, usually at about 10 to 14 days of age. Rotavirus also can affect pigs after weaning.

Clostridial enteritis (enterotoxemia, hemorrhagic enteritis) is a form of scours affecting young pigs that has been reported worldwide. This disease is caused by a bacterium, *Clostridium perfringens, Type C.* The disease usually affects piglets during the first week of life, but nursing pigs up to a month old can be affected.

Clinical signs are a watery, yellow scour that may contain traces of blood. Af-

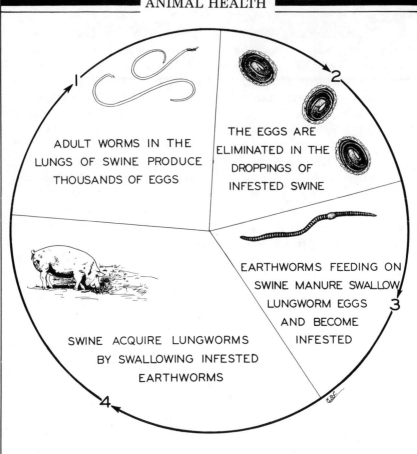

1 ADULT WORMS IN THE LUNGS OF SWINE PRODUCE THOUSANDS OF EGGS

2 THE EGGS ARE ELIMINATED IN THE DROPPINGS OF INFESTED SWINE

3 EARTHWORMS FEEDING ON SWINE MANURE SWALLOW LUNGWORM EGGS AND BECOME INFESTED

4 SWINE ACQUIRE LUNGWORMS BY SWALLOWING INFESTED EARTHWORMS

USDA

Life cycle of lungworm.

fected pigs may die in a few hours to 2 days.

Once clinical signs appear no treatment is effective, but injections of Type C antitoxin given to the newborn pigs as soon after birth as possible will help prevent the disease.

Injections of Type C tox-oid to sows 10 weeks and 3 weeks before farrowing will protect the nursing pigs.

Swine Dysentery

This disease also has been called black scours, bloody scours and vibrionic dysentery. Swine dysentery is reported worldwide, and is increasing rapidly in the U.S. Corn Belt. Dysentery is seen most frequently in 8 to 14 week old pigs. Older pigs and adult animals can be affected and are carriers of the disease.

A bacterium, *Treponema hyodysenteriae*, is considered the primary causative agent of swine dysentery.

The first signs of bloody dysentery usually appear 5 to 12 days after exposure, but an incubation period of 3 to 4 weeks sometimes is encountered in field cases.

A bloody, mucous diarrhea is the most prominent early sign and is accompanied by dehydration and weight loss. The bloody feces may be red and resemble tomato ketchup, or may have a black, tarry appearance. Affected pigs may be wobbly in the hind quarters and have evidence of abdominal pain.

Effective drugs and management practices are used to treat and control swine dysentery. Management practices that help control the disease include isolating affected pigs, maintaining pigs on a concrete floor which is washed down daily, or reducing exposure by putting the pigs in large pastures.

To prevent and control swine dysentery, don't purchase breeding stock from herds that have had swine dysentery within the past 2 years. All new swine brought to the farm should be isolated and treated with an effective drug for 30 days before being allowed contact with the main herd.

If prevention and drug control fail, the herd should be depopulated. Pens and equipment should then be thoroughly cleaned with soap and water and disinfected. Restock the farm with healthy animals 30 days after cleanup is completed. Depopulate only during hot dry weather.

Internal Parasites

Worms or internal parasites are a major cause of diseases of the digestive system.

The common worms that infect pigs are: Roundworm, threadworm, whipworm, nodular worm, stomach worm and lungworm.

Worms are controlled by making a diagnosis from postmortem examination or fecal examination. Once a diagnosis is made, start a deworming program with an effective medication for the species of worms identified. Use sanitary procedures that will prevent exposure to worm eggs passed in the feces.

Lameness in Swine; Genetic, Skin Diseases

By Alex Hogg

Four common causes of lameness in swine are: Infectious arthritis, nutritional deficiencies or imbalances, trauma or injury, and genetic. The economic impact of lameness in a given herd can vary from minor to severe.

Most of the arthritis that occurs in swine is caused by bacterial infections. The usual signs of infectious arthritis are lameness and swollen joints.

Four infectious bacteria commonly are involved in swine arthritis: The streptococcus species, erysipelas, mycoplasma (formerly PPLO), and *Corynebacterium pyogenes*.

Strep arthritis, sometimes called navel ill, occurs from birth to 3 weeks of age. It is

Alex Hogg is Swine Extension Veterinarian, Department of Veterinary Science, University of Nebraska, Lincoln.

caused by navel infections or breaks in the skin. Prevention includes cleanliness and strict sanitation in the farrowing house.

Erysipelas is caused by the bacterium *Erysipelothrix rhusiopathiae*. Erysipelas arthritis affects pigs from 3 weeks old through adulthood. Anti-erysipelas serum and penicillin are the treatments of choice and must be given early. Sows should be vaccinated 3 weeks before farrowing and pigs when about 6 to 8 weeks old. It may be necessary to repeat the vaccination on problem farms when pigs are 100 to 125 lbs.

Mycoplasmal Arthritis. This arthritis is caused by two species of mycoplasma. *M. hyorhinis* affects 3 to 10 week old pigs and adult swine, while *M. hyosynoviae* affects 10 to 20 week old swine and adults.

Clinical signs of M. hyorhinus are abdominal pain and

USDA

labored breathing, a temperature of 104° to 107° F, inflamed testicles, arthritis and lameness. In severe cases the pig is unable to arise and there is evidence of severe pain.

Clinical signs of *M. hyosynoviae* are sudden onset of lameness and little joint swelling. Hocks may show "puffiness". The acute stage lasts 3 to 10 days. Affected animals may pick up the affected leg, indicating severe pain. Adult pigs may be unable to stand.

Injectable tylosin or lincomycin should be injected during the first 24 hours of the

Erysipelas arthritis affects pigs from 3 weeks old through adulthood.

acute stage and repeated daily for 3 days. An injection of a corticosteroid may be given once at the time of the first treatment to reduce pain. Oral lincomycin may be a useful treatment.

Nutritional Lameness. The major cause is calcium-phosphorus imbalances or deficiencies which were discussed earlier—in the second chapter, on nutrition, in this section.

Lameness Due to Injuries. A good deal of lameness

Lameness, Genetic and Skin Diseases

is caused by injuries to the feet and legs. This is especially true in confinement-reared swine where rough floors or defective slatted floors take their toll.

Osteochondrosis, a lameness in rapidly growing pigs that are 5 to 8 months old, is fairly common. To control it, avoid selecting replacement boars and gilts that have the conformation related to osteochondrosis.

Genetic Defects

Congenital defects are those present at birth in animals. The most common in swine are:

—Anal atresia, the lack of an opening from the rectum. This defect occurs in both males and females but is more common in the male, and is perhaps the most common defect observed in swine.

If the blind intestine is just beneath the skin, it may be possible for a veterinarian to surgically repair the defect. Most are not repairable, with the pig dying at 2 to 3 weeks of age.

—Splay legs, paralysis of the hind legs. This genetic defect is more common in certain strains or breeds.

Pigs with milder signs of splay legs can be saved by taping the legs together with wide adhesive tape applied in the form of a figure 8 around the outside of one hind leg, crossed between the hind legs and then around the opposite hind leg so as not to cut off the blood circulation to the lower legs.

—Scrotal hernias, ruptures into the scrotum. This defect should be guarded against at the time of castration. Pigs having the appearance of a large testicle, usually on the left side, should be castrated by a veterinarian who will be prepared to repair the hernia during the castration procedure.

—Cryptorchidism, failure of a testicle to descend into the scrotum. During development of the male pig before birth, one or both testicles may not descend from their original position in the abdominal cavity to the scrotum, resulting in a cryptorchid.

—Inverted nipples, nipples or teats which tend to be short and flat. The center of the teat is depressed, making it impossible to milk the sow. Prospective gilts or boars to be added to the main breeding herd should be examined for inverted nipples to prevent this defect from becoming established in a herd.

An attempt should be made to eliminate all genetic

defects. This is best done by identifying all litters in which one or more pigs have a defect. No animals should be selected for breeding that are from a litter with any of the listed genetic defects.

Skin Diseases

Many conditions can affect the skin of pigs. The more common of the skin problems are briefly described:

Sunburn. White pigs are more severely affected. Sunburn is the result of moving pigs that were raised indoors to outside pens without providing shade.

Photosensitization occurs in white breeds or the white skin of partially colored pigs. It results from exposure to sunlight and access to certain plants such as rape. In these animals, the white skin becomes red and begins to slough off. Photosensitization is prevented by removing exposure to sunlight and eliminating access to the offending plant.

Greasy Skin Disease is caused by infection from staphylococcus species of bacteria. The skin becomes dry and scruffy, and a brownish black coating soon covers the affected areas of skin—which can include the entire body.

Treatment is by antibiotic injections and dipping the piglets in certain disinfectants. Thorough cleaning and disinfection between groups of pigs also is required to control and prevent greasy pig disease.

Skin Erysipelas is a form of erysipelas that differs from the acute and joint forms. It also is called "diamond skin disease" because of the diamond shape of the skin lesion. In later stages, the skin sloughs off in patches. Skin erysipelas can be prevented by vaccination.

Sarcoptic Mange is caused by a very small (1/50th inch long) mite that burrows in the skin. Itching is intense, and affected pigs do a lot of rubbing and scratching. Small bumps can be observed on the belly of affected pigs. Later the skin becomes thickened and wrinkled. Treatment is by spraying or dipping with an approved insecticide solution.

Ringworm is a fairly common skin disease caused by a fungus, *Microsporum nanum.* Lesions often start behind the ears of sows. Later, large wet areas that collect dirt appear on the sides and sometimes on the udder. Ringworm differs from mange in that the pigs don't seem to rub and scratch with ringworm. Treat with sulfurized mineral oil.

Foreign Diseases

By Edwin I. Pilchard

The United States is free from more than nine devastating diseases that make pork production far less profitable in many other countries. Foremost among these are African swine fever, hog cholera, and foot-and-mouth disease.

The list also includes swine vesicular disease, porcine babesiosis, Japanese encephalitis, Teschen disease, melioidosis, screwworm myiasis, and exotic types of vesicular stomatitis.

African swine fever is caused by strains of a virus that vary widely in their disease-producing ability.

Some strains—particularly those found in parts of Africa—can cause high fever; hemorrhages in the skin, and in the spleen and other internal organs; and death of nearly all infected swine. However, strains found in recent years in Southwestern Europe, Italy, Malta, South America, and the Caribbean area produce a more prolonged disease showing difficult breathing, accumulations of fluid in the body cavities, and survival of many unthrifty virus-carriers.

The virus can be transmitted readily by direct contact, contact of swine with virus-contaminated items, and the bite of certain infected soft ticks (Ornithodoros) if the virus is in the ticks.

These ticks can get African swine fever virus either by feeding directly on diseased swine, or by hatching from eggs produced by infected ticks.

There is no successful vaccine for African swine fever. Its eradication from Cuba, the Dominican Republic, Haiti, Malta, and France

Edwin I. Pilchard is a Principal Staff Officer, Veterinary Services, Animal and Plant Health Inspection Service.

Chuck Herron, USDA

required the destruction and safe disposal of all swine in the affected geographical area.

The disease has persisted for many years in Africa, Portugal, and Spain, and also may exist in several countries in which past outbreaks were reported. To help reduce the threat of this disease, the United States, Canada, and Mexico assisted the Dominican Republic and Haiti in their successful African swine fever eradication campaigns, 1978-1981.

Hog cholera was eradicated from the United States in 1978, following systematic diagnosis, quarantine, destruction of infected herds,

Hog cholera was eradicated from the United States in 1978, following systematic diagnosis and destruction of infected herds. Before eradication the annual cost of hog cholera exceeded $60 million, including vaccination for its control.

safe disposal, and cleaning and disinfection of affected premises.

Before eradication the annual cost of hog cholera exceeded $60 million, including vaccination for its control. It has been estimated that $5.1 million would be needed to eradicate even a small outbreak of hog cholera in the United States.

Foreign Diseases

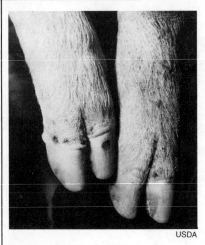

USDA

Foot-and-mouth disease virus causes fever, and blisters (vesicles) of the feet and sometimes the snouts, mouths and tongues of infected swine.

Caused by a virus that infects only swine, hog cholera spreads easily among swine of all ages, causing high fever, weakness, reddening of the skin, and high death rate in infected herds. Some strains of the virus have low virulence, and produce prolonged sickness which may resemble the pneumonia and intestinal disease common to swine raised in unsanitary facilities.

Vesicular Diseases

Foot-and-mouth disease virus causes fever, and blisters (vesicles) of the feet and sometimes the snouts, mouths, and tongues of infected swine. These vesicles usually break, leaving raw ulcers that ordinarily heal after several days.

Most of the losses from foot-and-mouth disease are caused by slow weight gains, delays in reaching market weight, secondary infections, and death of very young animals. More details on this disease and its costs are given in Section II on cattle.

Swine are susceptible to three other vesicular diseases: Vesicular stomatitis, swine vesicular disease, and vesicular exanthema.

Vesicular stomatitis is caused by a family of viruses, some members of which occasionally are found in the United States. These affect not only swine, but also cattle, sheep, horses, and sometimes humans.

In contrast, only swine are affected by swine vesicular disease. This caused serious problems to swine production in parts of England from 1974 to 1982, and has appeared in Italy, Germany, France, Japan, and Hong Kong. It is particularly resistant to eradication efforts and may go unrecognized in countries affected also with foot-and-mouth disease.

Although not foreign to the United States, vesicular exanthema is mentioned because of its economic impor-

Swine

Vesicular Diseases of Swine and Other Animals

Species Affected	Foot-and-mouth disease	Vesicular stomatitis	Swine vesicular disease	Vesicular exanthema
Swine	+	+	+	+
Cattle	+	+		
Sheep	+	+		
Horses		+		
Humans	(rarely)	+		
Marine Animals				+

Host species indicated by +

tance and similarity to foot-and-mouth disease. It has been reported only in the United States, where it was eradicated in 1959.

Controversy continues over the possible risk of more outbreaks of vesicular exanthema in swine, because viruses identical to it have been isolated from both marine and land-living animals in some States bordering the Pacific Ocean.

Prevention of foreign diseases of swine depends upon basic principles discussed under Section I. Any unusual sickness or losses in swine, es-pecially when the signs discussed here are seen, should be promptly reported to the State or Federal veterinarian.

Swine producers, their veterinarians, and veterinarians who work in diagnostic laboratories are most likely to be the first to notice a foreign disease that has just entered the country. It is their responsibility to swine producers and consumers not to delay seeking assistance in getting an accurate diagnosis that will either relieve the suspicion, or permit disease eradication to be completed with the least possible loss.

Reproduction

By Al Leman

Boars reach puberty at about 6 months of age. They should not be used for regular mating until they are at least 8 months old. The quality and quantity of the sperm generally increase until the boar reaches about 12 to 15 months of age, after which it plateaus.

The useful life of a boar in a herd is from about 8 to 30 months of age. If boars are kept in a herd longer there is the possibility of father-daughter matings. This in-breeding can increase the rate of genetic defects and cause a loss in hybrid vigor.

Ten billion sperm cells or more are needed for optimal fertilization. Mature boars produce at least 10 billion sperm a day, while young

boars may require several days to produce this amount. Boars from 8 to 12 months should be used 2 to 3 times a week, while older boars can be used 4 to 6 times a week. Most herds need 1 boar for every 20 to 25 females.

Boars affect the conception rate, litter size, pig survival, growth rate, and carcass quality of their offspring. Since boars comprise half the genetic basis of a herd, producers should select them with appropriate care. The following is a list of generally accepted standards for boars.

–The underline should contain 12 or more evenly spaced, well developed teats

–They should be free from lameness and have generally free and easy movement

–Boars should attain 230 pounds at an age of 155 days or less

–During their test period of about 60 to 230 pounds, boars should require not more

Al Leman is Swine Extension Veterinarian, College of Veterinary Medicine, University of Minnesota, St. Paul.

than 2.75 pounds of feed per pound of gain

–Daily gain during the same test period should be at least 2 pounds per day

–Backfat at 230 days should be 1 inch or less

Gilt Development

Gilts usually are selected on their body conformation, weight for days of age, and an estimation of backfat. Gilts usually reach puberty between the fifth and seventh month. The exact time of puberty is influenced by the breed, season, growth rate, exposure to boars, amount of daylight, pen space, and the number of animals per pen. When all these factors are optimal, 90 percent of the gilts should have had their first estrous cycle when 8 months old.

Estrous cycle of the pig averages 21 days, and most fall within 19 to 23 days. Estrus or sexual receptivity ranges from 1 to 3 days. Ovulation occurs just prior to the termination of estrous behavior. The optimum time for mating is 5 to 10 hours before ovulation or sometimes into the second half of the sexual receptivity period.

There are two generally accepted forms of mating. One is called pen mating, where

the boars are mixed and housed with the females and mating occurs unmonitored and whenever there are receptive females.

The other type of mating is called hand mating where producers attempt to detect estrus in females and pen the estrous females together with the boars. The mating is observed and generally recorded for a future reference to the time of farrowing.

Pregnancy, Birth

Usual ovulation rate for the gilt is 12 to 14 eggs, while older sows may ovulate 15 to 18 eggs. Most of these eggs are fertilized. Embryonic losses soon occur, however. By day 25 after mating only about 75 percent of the fertilized eggs still remain viable.

Gestation in the pig is usually 114 to 116 days. A generally accepted standard for the industry is that 80 percent of the mated females should farrow a litter. The very best farms in highly controlled mating programs sometimes exceed 85 percent.

Animals that do not farrow may have never become pregnant, may have returned to heat normally or abnormally (that is, after day 25), or they may have resorbed their litter and come back into

Reproduction

heat perhaps at day 40 to 50. Abortions also are possible. Up to a 2 percent annual abortion rate is generally accepted as being normal.

Farrowing begins with restless behavior by the sow. The sow's instincts cause her to attempt to build a nest. In certain confinement situations without bedding, however, this nesting is not possible.

Once the active process of farrowing starts, the sow usually finishes in about 2 to 4 hours. Average interval between the birth of 2 live-born pigs is about 20 minutes. The interval between a live-born and a subsequent deadborn pig is about 45 minutes.

About 40 percent of the pigs are born tailfirst, and about 60 percent headfirst. Last pigs in the litter to be born are the most likely to be stillborn, since most stillbirths result from insufficient oxygen during the birth process.

Within minutes after birth the baby pig is on its feet and searching for the mammary gland of the sow. The first milk is called colostrum and is very high in antibodies, which help protect the pig against the diseases likely to be encountered.

The biggest pigs at birth seem to have a strong survival advantage. They mi-

grate toward the front mammary glands which usually yield the most milk.

Litter Size

Average litter size of U.S. sows is about 10 total pigs including about ½ to ¾ pigs per litter dead at birth or stillborn. First litter females generally have the smallest litters. Litter size increases as these sows have their second, third and fourth litters.

The third to sixth litters generally produce the most pigs, after which litter size begins to drop somewhat. As sows get older, litter size drops slightly but there is a major increase in the stillbirth rate.

Average live-born litter size is about 9.3 pigs and the average litter weaned throughout the United States is about 7.4. Some well managed farms are doing much better, but this national average has remained unchanged for many years.

Lactation The only source of nutrition for the baby pig during the first two weeks of life is the sow's milk. Sows can produce up to 20 pounds of milk a day. To do this, they must consume high amounts of energy and protein. There is considerable variation between the quality and quan-

Marie T. Sebrechts

The only source of nutrition for the baby pig during the first two weeks of life is the sow's milk. Pigs have a very strong nursing order and once they establish themselves on one of the teats they are likely to stay there until weaned.

tity of milk from the different mammary glands on the same sow.

Pigs have a very strong nursing order. Once they establish themselves on one of the teats they are likely to stay there until weaned, even for a pig that attaches to a mammary gland producing very little milk. This pig will not grow well and will be a runt.

In the United States, about 20 percent of all live-

Reproduction

born pigs fail to reach weaning age. Death can result from: Crushing or overlaying by the sows, starvation, chilling, or a variety of baby pig diseases.

The control for these diseases is to provide the baby pig with a warm, clean environment and a good supply of milk. When these things are in place, natural defense mechanisms of the pig usually suffice to fight off diseases.

Weaning. Peak milk production in sows is usually in the third to fourth week after farrowing. The average weaning age for pigs is probably between 4 and 5 weeks, although some pork producers now are trying to wean at 3 weeks.

Weaning pigs at 3 weeks, when they weigh between 10 and 13 pounds, requires an excellent nursery facility and high quality nursery feed for high survival and performance. Weaning at 3 weeks of age as compared to weaning at 4 weeks will result in a slightly smaller litter the next time the sow farrows.

Common Diseases

Leptospirosis is a bacterial disease that can cause late term abortion, stillborns, and weak pigs. It is best controlled by vaccination. Vacci-

nation is common throughout the United States and the disease appears to be less important than it was 10 or 20 years ago.

Brucellosis can cause swine reproductive failure, although the disease is very uncommon. There are attempts to eradicate brucellosis from U.S. swine because it is a potential human health hazard, especially to workers at slaughterhouses.

Porcine parvovirus is the major viral reproductive disease of swine. It once was classified under the SMEDI syndrome which stands for stillbirths, mummified pigs, embryonic death and infertility.

This virus is widespread, and present on almost every farm. The animals at risk are those that do not become naturally infected and immunized prior to mating. On most farms this amounts to only 10 to 20 percent of the animals. New vaccines appear helpful in controlling parvovirus and in creating immunity in the animals that were previously at risk.

Another reproductive disease is pseudorabies. This disease is discussed in the fourth chapter of this section. It is capable of causing an abortion in sows.

Swine Production Systems

By Al Leman

Historically, pigs were reared in a pasture setting with individual farrowing hutches for each sow. For the past 30 years in the United States, the trend has been toward confinement.

First, sows were moved into a central farrowing house. The early confinement systems utilized a pen for the sow and her litter. Around the outside of the pen, guardrails reduced the number of crushed pigs.

These soon gave way to farrowing crates, which are commonly 2 feet wide by 7 feet long. The sow is restrained in the crate so she is less likely to crush her baby pigs. At first, sows were taken from the crate twice a day for feeding and watering.

Al Leman is Swine Extension Veterinarian, College of Veterinary Medicine, University of Minnesota, St. Paul.

Today, however, sows spend their entire lactation period in a farrowing crate, often with automatic feeding and watering. The trend toward confinement has continued, until now an estimated 75 percent of the pigs are reared in some kind of confinement. The term "total confinement" refers to the entire life cycle of the pig being inside buildings. Sow housing may feature pens of sows or sows in individual stalls or tethers.

Nursery housing for pigs begins after they are weaned, commonly from 4 to 10 weeks of age or when pigs weigh 15 to 50 lbs. The growing phase of production is commonly from about 50 lbs. until about 100 lbs., and the finishing stage is commonly from 100 to 220 lbs. or market weight.

Slotted Floors

In the past 20 years it has become common practice to rear

pigs on slotted floors to allow urine and manure to pass through the floor to a pit or gutter system below. The attempt, of course, is separation of the pig from its fecal material.

Two types of common finishing facilities are called totally slotted or partially slotted, depending on the flooring in the building. The partially slotted floor usually consists of a ⅔ solid floor with a ⅓ slotted floor.

Abrasion-free floor surfaces help promote normal hoof development and wear, lessening the chance of damage, infection and lameness. Floors made of expanded metal and wire mesh offer an excellent opportunity for baby pigs to be born in a manure-free environment.

Besides floor surfaces, other factors influence transmission of pathogens. Solid partitions between pens help reduce nose-to-nose contact and disease transmission. Solid walls help separate groups of pigs and encourage all in, all-out production.

All in, all-out production is an effective, yet underused, method of disease control. It encourages age separation of pigs and facilitates cleanup between groups. All new building and housing systems should be designed with this concept in mind. Existing facilities often can be improved by partitioning pigs into smaller groups.

Fresh Air

With the trend to confinement, providing fresh air to swine becomes a vital part of reducing disease. Fresh air helps dilute the concentration of microbes, harmful gases and dust. It promotes healthier respiratory tissue, which in turn reduces the dose of microbes that get deep into the lung tissue.

The amount of fresh air is a function of the ventilation system, animal density, volume of space per animal, and the waste management system. There is evidence that pigs with about 4 cubic yards or more of air volume have fewer lung lesions at slaughter than pigs with less air volume.

Current winter ventilation systems in fully slotted barns over a full anaerobic pit do not support optimum performance. Future pork production will feature aerobic waste systems, or more air movement than currently is being provided.

VI. KEEPING FISH HEALTHY

Gordon, USDA-SCS

Growing Fish Field Creates Big Splash

By Douglas P. Anderson

Fishing is a national recreation, fish are a nutritious and staple food, and raising fish as pets and for display is a delightful hobby for millions of Americans. Clean streams and lakes are sources of healthy foods and places to escape and relax from our busy social and work-a-day world.

We use more fish for sport and food than nature can provide; therefore, growing fish on farms, called aquaculture, is developing into a multibillion-dollar business. Raising fish interests entrepreneurs and established farmers who search for new ways for making profits and seek to diversify by expanding into little-

---

Douglas P. Anderson is Chief, Immunology/Biologics, National Fish Health Research Laboratory, U.S. Fish and Wildlife Service, Kearneysville, W.Va. He is chief editor/writer for this section of the Yearbook.

used marginal river lowlands or other clean water sources.

The National Aquaculture Development Plan prepared by a Joint Subcommittee on Aquaculture and edited by the U.S. Departments of the Interior, Agriculture, and Commerce, reports that catfish farming is the largest aquaculture industry with over $120 million invested at the beginning of the 1980's. Raising baitfish is second in value with over $100 million, and trout farming third at $48 million. The value of tropical fish farms is probably underestimated at $20 million. A rapidly growing industry is Pacific salmon culture, often done in sheltered marine bays. It is valued at over $4 million.

Pollution Effects

Keeping fish healthy and their waters clean are major concerns of all Americans. Pollution from cities, indus-

Keeping Fish Healthy

USDA

James L. Bilyou, USDA-SCS

The fact that we use more fish for sport and food than nature can provide is the main reason aquaculture is developing into a multibillion dollar business. Catfish farming is the largest aquaculture industry with over $120 million invested at the beginning of 1980.

tries and agriculture affects our Nation's waters. Reports of fish kills due to spills of chemicals into the water are not uncommon.

From long term environmental research studies we now realize that the slower, insidious effects of lingering, low concentrations of chemicals such as pesticides, fertilizers, and industrial exhausts may result in the gradual deterioration of fish health. Acid rain can kill small plants and animals on the lower part of

Growing Fish Field

A. Hawk, USDA-SCS

"Fish"—this word brings smiles to the faces of millions of Americans with memories of an enjoyable day of fishing on the water . . . the sport and anticipation of a possible freezer full of fish for some, a livelihood and business for others . . . and hours of enjoyment with a pet for the rest.

the food chain, indirectly affecting fish populations. The effect of some pollutants may supress defense mechanisms, causing the fish gradually to be more susceptible to infectious diseases.

Infectious diseases of fish are similar to those of other wild and domestic animals. Fish may harbor, or be exposed to, parasites and pathogenic disease-causing agents during much of their life.

Most healthy animals are able to resist or at least accommodate their microscopic enemies. But when fish are domesticated and raised under intensive conditions, the magnification of environmental conditions can make them more susceptible to disease.

Humans can easily upset the delicate balances of the ecological web. Once interrupted, the interactions of aquatic animals, disease agents and their environments are difficult to repair; sick fish rarely get well. There's a cynical saying by fish culturists, "A sick fish is a dead fish," and it's often true. To prevent and cure diseases, veterinarians and pathologists are developing better management techniques, stricter import and transportation regulations, new chemicals for disinfection, stronger drugs, potent vaccines and genetic breeding methods to build up and maintain healthy fish stocks.

Unique Aspects

Raising fish presents unique differences from culture of other animals. Each farm, pond and tank is an isolated environment with its own particular advantages and problems. Variations in temperature, oxygen supply and water quality must be recognized by the supervisor and special care taken. Prediction of disease outbreaks and patterns is difficult; indeed, a disease occurring in one local pond for some unexplained reason may not spread to another. Other times, an epidemic is uncontrollable.

Management for individual fish farms, hatcheries or aquariums has to be specifically designed. In addition, species of fish we cultivate are so different from one another that treatment of diseases of trout held in cold water, for instance, may not resemble those treatments used in eel culture or warm water household aquariums.

Recognizing diseases and their causes in individual fish

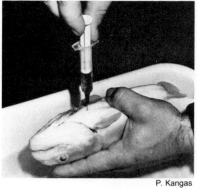

P. Kangas

Growth of aquaculture has resulted in increased efforts by veterinarians and pathologists to develop better management techniques and more effective fish vaccines and medications. Here a blood sample is taken from an anesthesized albino rainbow trout. The blood will be tested for antibody which indicates that the vaccination worked.

and large populations is important to prevent spreading to other ponds by early treatment. There are various ways of recognizing and identifying diseases: the simplest level is the observation that includes noting mortality patterns. If there is a sudden increase in deaths, the farmer might begin to look for unusual behavioral signs. The fish may be "off feed," and showing irregular growth patterns—for instance, big and little fish occurring in a pond of fish that are all the same age. There may be individual darkened

P. Kangas

A sterile needle is used to take a kidney tissue sample from a diseased fish. The sample will be smeared on agar media to observe for bacterial growth for diagnosing a bacterial disease.

fish swimming at the end of the pond, gills may appear pale, or lesions and ulcers may occur on the fish.

Diagnosis, Control

The next stages of disease recognition may have to be done by highly trained professionals, who are veterinarians or fish pathologists certified to do this work. If a viral disease is suspect, tissue samples of fish are taken and processed in a diagnostic laboratory. Identification of bacterial diseases often requires taking a kidney sample and streaking the piece on an agar plate to check for growth of the pathogen.

Disease control requires continual vigilance. Many chemicals and drugs have been used in the past with various success; today only a few of the drugs are approved for use in food fish. Whenever treatments are used on fish, careful management of effluents is necessary. Major advances have recently been made in controlling disease by immunization. Fish can be given baths of vaccine to build up immunity against diseases.

Fighting changes in the aquatic environment and keeping diseases from reducing production is a continual process for the fish farmer and aquarist. The following chapters discuss some of the special problems you may face in raising fish and keeping them healthy.

Managing a Fish Farm

By George W. Klontz

Food fish farms in America come in many sizes and shapes. Although no two are alike in layout, there are major similarities: all of course have fish, utilize water, have ponds to retain the water, use either natural or commercially prepared feed, and incorporate some degree of management.

Each of these major categories has several physical, chemical, and biological factors which can, and often do, affect productivity of the fish farm. These factors must be considered by the fish farmer for the farm to be economically profitable.

Nutritional, environmental, and behavioral requirements of the fish are the most important factors to be considered. Fish are perhaps the

most diverse of all creatures. There are fish which live in waters of nearly 100° F (46° C), others live in waters of nearly 32° (0° C). Each species has its preferred temperature; its growth potential will be reduced if required to live in waters outside its temperature optimum.

Dietary preferences of fish range from those which are herbivores (plant eaters) to those which are carnivores (meat eaters). Some fish can utilize both plant and animal proteins. These are omnivores. Behavioral tendencies of fish range from those which are sedentary and territorial to those that roam in schools.

It is essential that these major insights about fish be taken into account when one manages a fish farm. All the other factors of pond style, water quality, and nutritional quality (and quantity) are predicated on meeting needs of the fish.

George W. Klontz is Professor of Fishery Resources, University of Idaho, Moscow.

Managing a Fish Farm

Product Definition

Managing a fish farm can be very complex or relatively simple, depending upon the nature of the farm. No matter what the degree of management is, the process begins at a common point—the product definition. That is, what is to be produced in terms of size, quality, number, and season.

Good management embodies matching fish-water-pond interactions with the product definition. The nutritional component is like the throttle on an automobile. The more the fish are fed, up to a point, the faster they will grow.

Product definition is established first, then the management process is initiated with the purchase of eggs or fry. This stage in life of the fish is fraught with all sorts of disaster potentials.

Dissolved oxygen and ammonia levels can become critical quite rapidly. Also, uneaten feed and accumulated fecal solids can reach dangerous levels in a matter of hours. Any of these overloads is deadly for the fish and quite expensive for the farmer.

The usual mortality occurring from the fertilized egg through a 2-inch fish is 15 to 20 percent, just from improper management practices.

Economics of producing

AVERAGE LOSS DATA FRESHWATER FOOD FISH INDUSTRY		
	Fish food production	
	Loss	Number
Green eggs		1,000,000
Eyed eggs	7%	930,000
Hatch-out	5%	883,500
Swim-up	6%	848,160
Grow-out	1%	839,678
Processing	25%	629,759
Distribution	5%	598,271

food fish dictate the need for sound management practices. Perhaps the single most inadequately applied practice is record keeping. This is really the drudge work of fish farming. Still, the farmer must know how many fish of what size are in the pond in order to feed them appropriately and economically. In addition, the farmer must know how rapidly these fish are growing in order to determine at some point in the future when carrying capacity of the system will be exceeded.

Computer Role

Keeping records and predicting when the fish will be a certain size is done with computers, the most recent development to assist the fish farmer. One standard personal

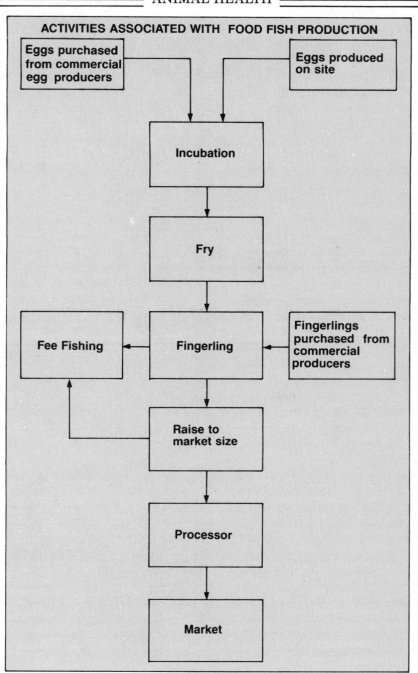

ACTIVITIES ASSOCIATED WITH FOOD FISH PRODUCTION

Eggs purchased from commercial egg producers

Eggs produced on site

Incubation

Fry

Fee Fishing

Fingerling

Fingerlings purchased from commercial producers

Raise to market size

Processor

Market

In any high density fish pond, dissolved oxygen and ammonia can reach critical levels quite rapidly. A portable aerator is used in this catfish pond to replenish the oxygen supply.

Tim McCabe, USDA-SCS

computer can store and evaluate the collected data from virtually any fish farm. Besides saving time for the farmer, the computer also can reduce day-to-day mortality by providing a warning that a pond is near the danger point for the fish.

Continuing education is another frequently overlooked aspect of fish farm management. This aspect can take many forms: reading one or more of the many fish farming magazines, attending fish farming association meetings and conventions, attending short courses. They all cost money and take time, but there is no easy way to keep up to date on new technological developments in fish farming.

M. Stuckey

Easy-to-use kits are available for sampling water quality, including oxygen levels and particulate matter.

Transporting Fish or Fish Eggs

By Peter G. Walker

Transporting fish or fish eggs from one place to another always carries with it the risk of spreading diseases. Thus as the science of fish pathology has developed, so too has a maze of State and Federal regulations designed to minimize these dangers.

Available treatments for some fish diseases are expensive and often only partially effective; for others such as the viral diseases, no known cure exists. Once a virus has been introduced to a site, a fish culturist has two options: live with the problem or take the station out of production, disinfect and start over with disease-free stock. Either choice is very costly. The alternative is to take the necessary precautions to avoid diseases in the first place.

Peter G. Walker is Fish Pathologist, Fish Disease Control Center, Colorado Division of Wildlife, Fort Morgan.

Fish diseases of State and national concern were, until quite recently, almost entirely those that affect species of the trout and salmon family. Now there is increasing concern in some areas for protection from certain serious diseases and parasites of warm water fishes as well.

The most serious fish diseases are responsible for grave financial losses wherever they occur. Fortunately, wise fish health management assisted by adequate fish importation legislation can effectively minimize spread of these diseases from one area to another.

Legal restrictions faced in transporting fish or fish eggs can vary a great deal, depending on the locale. Federal regulations prohibit importing members of the trout and salmon family (alive or dead) and their eggs unless they have been certified free of two serious disease-causing

Fish and Wildlife Service-POF

Since transporting fish or fish eggs from one place to another carries with it the risk of spreading diseases, a variety of legal restrictions or certification requirements exist to protect fish health. Before any anticipated transfer or importation of fish or eggs, the local fishery agency should be contacted to determine what regulations exist.

agents. Individual State fish importation laws, however, range from very strict to none at all. In addition, there is a growing trend towards integrated fish health management of entire watersheds spanning two or more States or Canadian provinces.

It therefore pays to check with authorities before importing or transporting fish and eggs.

Advantages of Eggs
Shipping fish eggs offers some

advantages with regard to preventing disease transmission. While viral diseases and at least one bacterial disease are passed from parent to progeny within the egg (vertical transmission), most of the bacterial diseases and virtually all the higher parasitic diseases can be removed from outside surfaces of trout and salmon eggs with an iodine disinfectant.

Two major salmonid viral diseases are endemic to North America: Infectious hematopoietic necrosis (IHN) has, until recently, been largely confined to salmon and trout hatcheries along the Pacific slope; infectious pancreatic necrosis (IPN) is especially devastating in cultured brook trout.

Another serious viral disease, viral hemorrhagic septicemia (VHS), has been con-

Keeping Fish Healthy

fined to European trout farms to date. It is of special concern to salmonid fish culturists everywhere since, unlike other viral diseases, it often breaks out in market-sized fish and thereby causes grievous financial losses. VHS is one of the two diseases that is included under Federal Title 50 regulation, a legislative mandate requiring certification on salmonid importations into the United States.

Main State Action

State regulations regarding bacterial fish diseases are most often confined to furunculosis, enteric redmouth disease and bacterial kidney disease. All three pose an economic threat to salmonid growers.

Furunculosis and enteric redmouth disease are caused by *Aeromonas salmonicida* and *Yersinia ruckeri* respectively; both pathogens can be effectively disinfected from egg surfaces. *Renibacterium salmoninarum*, the causative agent of bacterial kidney disease, is transmitted vertically within the egg and should therefore be given special consideration when planning shipments.

Among the higher parasites, the myxosporidian protozoan *Myxosoma cerebralis*,

causative agent of whirling disease, is often considered the most serious danger from fish importations. Endemic to Europe, this internal, cartilage-destroying parasite became established in the United States in the late 1950's and has since spread to a number of States, although in most cases those with enforced importation laws have successfully remained free of the organism.

M. cerebralis is the second pathogen (along with VHS virus) for which inspection is required by Title 50 regulation before importation into the United States. Some other serious parasites frequently specified in interstate or interdrainage shipment requirements include the myxosporidian *Ceratomyxa shasta*, digenetic trematode blood flukes of the genus *Sanguinicola* and the Asian tapeworm *Bothriocephalus opsarichthydis*.

Certifications

Agencies requiring fish health certificates usually maintain lists of recognized fish health professionals qualified to perform inspections and certifications. Such individuals usually are employed by various colleges and universities, State agencies, the U.S. Fish and Wildlife Service, or private aquacultural and consulting firms. The U.S. Fish and Wildlife Service maintains an up-to-date list of fish pathologists from both the United States and foreign countries from whom Title 50 certifications may be obtained.

Professional standards for certifying fish health inspectors have been set up by the Fish Health Section of the American Fisheries Society (FHS/AFS) as well. A few State agencies now require that inspections be performed by FHS/AFS certified inspectors. As the number of these individuals grows, this program may become an increasingly important factor.

The technology of fish health inspections is being upgraded continually. Generally recognized standards for these inspections are maintained by the Fish Health Section of the American Fisheries Society in a volume titled "Procedures for the Detection and Identification of Certain Fish Pathogens," but more commonly known as the "Blue Book." Similar, sometimes more stringent procedures also are given in the "Fish Health Protection Regulations Manual of Compliance" of the Canadian Department of Fisheries and the Environment.

Advance Steps

Well in advance of any anticipated importation or transfer of fish or eggs, the local fishery agency should be contacted to determine legal restrictions or certification requirements. In many instances, officials may be concerned with the species or strain of fish involved, as well as the health status. For an international importation, the U.S. Fish and Wildlife Service must be notified as well.

Regardless of legal constraints, for one's own protection it is always wise to obtain both current health inspection data and past disease history of any source of an intended shipment. Give consideration to whatever pathogens are already present at the receiving facility and surrounding watershed. In addition, identifying the greatest potential threats beforehand can be of considerable help in making decisions whether or not to allow shipments.

Quarantine facilities help to further reduce the risk of bringing diseases to a fish cultural station. Such facilities are considerably removed from the production units, have independent water supplies and outlets and, ideally, effluent treatment.

Fish and Wildlife Service-POF

Maine Dept. of Inland Fisheries and Wildlife

Transporting fish requires some very important precautions to prevent disease introduction from one location to another. It is important to make sure all equipment and vehicles are cleaned and disinfected before entering a farm. Fish are being loaded into a truck and released into a pond. This truck, specially equipped to transport fish, has double-walled insulated aluminum tanks that are electrically aerated.

Transporting Fish or Fish Eggs   323

All implements such as nets, buckets and scrub brushes as well as the attendant's boots and gear remain at the site. Anyone traveling between the quarantine and production units must observe strict sanitation and disinfection procedures. A quarantine facility permits observation and examination of incoming lots of fish for several weeks or months before their actual introduction to the main station.

Treating Eggs

Incoming salmonid egg shipments pose less risk since only the viral agents and the causative agent of bacterial kidney disease are known to be transmitted within the egg. By treating the eggs before they are brought into the hatchery in a bath of 100 parts per million (active ingredient) iodophore disinfectant (for example, Betadine, Wescodyne) for 10 minutes, any pathogens on the outside of the eggs can be effectively eliminated.

Fish and egg transfers are by no means the only vectors that threaten disease introduction to a fish culture facility. Through carelessness in day-to-day operations, fish culturists can accidentally bring in disease organisms on equipment, implements, and trans-portation vehicles contaminated at other sites. These dangers can be minimized, however, by awareness and strict adherence to sanitation procedures.

The first and most obvious way to avoid disease is to minimize the use of gear from other sites or loaning of gear. This is not always possible, especially in use of fish transportation trucks which must routinely make contact with other waters. So disinfection of all incoming fish culture gear before it enters the facility should become a strict practice.

A soak of several minutes in 200 parts per million sodium hypochlorite (HTH, "chlorine") is effective, although corrosive to certain materials. Wherever the harshness of chlorine is a consideration, the quaternary ammonium disinfectant, Roccal, at 600 parts per million (active ingredient) is frequently the compound of choice. Take extreme care to rinse thoroughly all disinfected items before use to avoid harming fish. Rinsing can take place on station and, in any event, should be performed with water from one's own station or a clean source to avoid recontamination.

Salmon and Trout Diseases

By Stephen G. Newman

It is only in relatively recent times that coldwater fish, in particular salmon and trout, have been intensively reared, and the science of aquaculture came into existence. Along with the birth of this new area of agriculture came profit-limiting diseases. As with all other animals, these diseases are caused by various viruses, bacteria, protozoa and other parasites. The more important of these diseases are the subject of this section.

Viruses are extremely small infective agents capable of growth and multiplication only in living cells. Several of the viruses produce disease in epidemic proportions in hatchery-reared fish. They significantly impact commercial production and Government mitigation efforts.

Stephen G. Newman is Director, Microbiology Research, BioMed Research Laboratories, Inc., Seattle, Wash.

Infectious Pancreatic Necrosis (IPN) is an acute, highly contagious disease, affecting primarily juvenile salmonids. Fish less than two inches long usually are the most susceptible. The disease has been reported in most species of trout, Atlantic and coho salmon, and several species of char. It has been reported in most trout-producing areas of the United States as well as Canada, Europe, and Japan.

Typically, affected fish whirl, become dark in color, and have bulging eyes, swollen abdomens, and hemorrhaging. Losses may occur at all water temperatures normally encountered in rearing trout.

IPN is transmitted from fish to fish by contaminated feces, urine, and ovarian or seminal fluid. There is no way to treat the disease once it occurs. IPN can be controlled by improving husbandry tech-

Salmon and Trout Diseases

niques—including disinfecting eggs, eliminating carrier females, destroying infected animals, and possibly selective breeding.

Sockeye Disease

Infectious Hematopoietic Necrosis (IHN) is also an acute, highly contagious disease affecting primarily juvenile (less than two inches long) salmonids. Known variously as Oregon Sockeye Disease, Sacramento River Chinook Disease, Columbia River Sockeye Disease and Leavenworth Sockeye Disease, IHN is a disease of Pacific salmon affecting chinook, and sockeye salmon in addition to rainbow trout.

IHN has been reported throughout the United States, Canada and Japan. It causes massive destruction of the blood-forming organs. Affected fish hemorrhage under the skin and at the base of the fins. They have protruding eyes, swollen abdomens, and darkening of skin. Unlike IPN, IHN outbreaks occur mostly at 45 to 55° F (8 to 13° C) with some evidence that the incidence may be reduced at temperatures above 58° F (15° C).

IHN is transmitted from fish to fish by contaminated feces, urine, and ovarian or seminal fluid. As with IPN,

survivors become carriers.

IHN cannot be controlled once the disease occurs. Control is best by avoidance. Disinfecting eggs, separating brood fish from fry, disinfecting contaminated facilities, destroying infected animals— all are possible means of control.

Several other viral diseases—including Viral Hemorrhagic Septicemia (VHS), Viral Erythrocytic Necrosis (VEN), and *Herpesvirus salmonis* (HS)—also may significantly impact coldwater fish. VHS is a severe problem in Europe but has never been found in the United States, Canada or the Far East. Both VEN and HS, though responsible for severe disease, are of minor impact compared to IHN and IPN.

Bacteria are microscopic organisms living in soil, water, organic matter, plants or animals responsible for a wide variety of essential functions. They also are responsible for a wide range of diseases in all living creatures. Fish are no exception. In most cases, stress plays a role in predisposing fish to these bacterial diseases. Five of the most severe bacterial pathogens affecting coldwater fish in the United States are briefly discussed.

Vibriosis

Vibriosis is a severe disease caused by strains of *Vibrio anguillarum* and *Vibrio ordalii* affecting net pen reared salmon. All species of salmon reared in salt water are subject to infection. Vibriosis is worldwide, reported in the Americas, Europe, and the Far East. Large bloody lesions appear in skin and musculature. Hemorrhaged gills, eyes and fins also may occur.

Losses can occur at a wide range of temperatures, though the greatest generally take place at temperatures over 50° F (10° C). The disease is spread through the water column by infected fish or sediments, or by ingestion of infected materials.

Vibriosis can be prevented by immunization with commercially available bacterins (a type of vaccine). Bacterins have substantially reduced impact of this once devastating disease. The disease, when it does occur, usually responds to antibiotic treatment, although antibiotic resistance and failure of ill fish to eat are problems.

Furunculosis is another acute bacterial disease of cultured salmonid populations. Most species of salmonids and many species of non-salmonids reared in fresh, brackish and salt water are susceptible.

Furunculosis has been reported in most areas where fish are reared. As with other bacterial infections, symptoms vary somewhat with the fish's age and the severity of the disease. Chronically infected fish often display characteristic furuncles—dark, raised fluid-filled bumps—which ulcerate. Other signs include darkening, and loss of appetite.

The disease occurs at a wide range of temperatures and is transmitted through the water by diseased and carrier fish. Preventing contamination by carrier fish, and conscientious husbandry techniques, will help prevent spread of the disease. Sick animals may respond to treatment with antibiotics.

Rainbow Trout

Enteric Redmouth Disease (ERM) is a severe disease of commercially reared rainbow trout. The disease occurs largely in rainbow trout and has been reported throughout the United States and recently in Europe. Symptoms are like those in other bacterial diseases with a notable lack of lesions and a characteristic hemorrhage around the mouth and along the lateral line.

Salmon and Trout Diseases

G. Camenisch

White spots in the kidney of a rainbow trout may be a sign of infection by Bacterial Kidney Disease (BKD).

ERM occurs primarily at temperatures above 50° F (10° C) and is transmitted through the water by diseased and carrier fish. The disease can be prevented by immunization and controlled by improved management. Treatment with sulfonamides and tetracycline has been found effective.

Bacterial Kidney Disease (BKD) is a systemic bacterial disease of salmonids. Its total impact on aquaculture is uncertain. BKD has been diagnosed in a wide variety of salmonids and has been reported in the United States, Canada and Europe. External signs are similar to those reported accompanying other systemic bacterial diseases: enlarged abdomens, bulging eyes, small cutaneous ulcers, and reddened fin bases.

The disease appears to be transmitted by infected fish and through the eggs. Susceptibility to BKD is controversial with evidence that water hardness, blood mineral and vitamin levels, and genetic makeup all affect susceptibility. Treatment is by oral application of antibiotics. Injection of erythromycin has been used to reduce BKD. Improved management practices help.

Other bacterial diseases also significantly affect the rearing of salmonids. They include columnaris disease due to strains of *Flexibacter columnaris*, bacterial hemorrhagic septicemia due to strains of *Aeromonas hydrophila*, and bacterial gill disease due to miscellaneous strains of myxobacteria.

Protozoa Problems

Protozoa are relatively large single-celled organisms that may proliferate externally or internally and occasionally are responsible for massive losses of intensively reared salmonids. Though many hundreds of different protozoa species may use fish or shellfish as hosts, three of the major protozoal diseases are discussed.

Ichthyophthirius multifiliis is the causative agent of white-spot disease or Ich, in freshwater fish. It affects all freshwater species and occurs worldwide. The disease rarely is a serious problem in coldwater fish, since it requires warmer water temperatures, greater than 65° F (18° C) to proliferate.

Ich appears as 0.5 to 1 millimeter white cottony spots covering the external surface of the fish and the gills. Each spot is one organism, that when mature escapes into the water where it attaches to a substrate and divides to produce up to 2,000 tomites which reinfect fish. Thus the disease is water-transmitted.

Treatment is by immersing infected fish in formalin, malachite green oxalate, or copper sulfate solutions. Elevated temperature also can be used. Treatments must be repeated for 3 to 10 days.

Ceratomyxa shasta is a protozoal parasite affecting juvenile salmonids. The agent of ceratomyxosis, it is widely distributed in juvenile salmonids in the Columbia River basin and commercially reared trout in the western United States. It is not found outside the western United States.

Signs include abdominal distention due to fluid and nodules in the gut, muscle and other organs, protrusion of the eyeballs, and hemorrhaging. Mortality is massive, with no treatment available. Irradiating spore-contaminated water supplies may help control the disease.

Whirling Disease

Whirling disease caused by *Myxosoma cerebralis* is perhaps the most important protozoan parasite of coldwater fish. Virtually all species of salmon, trout and grayling are susceptible, with severity of the disease depending on age and degree of exposure. Whirling disease is worldwide in distribution and has significantly affected rainbow trout

Salmon and Trout Diseases

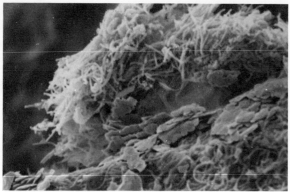

The small rod-like bacteria, Flexibacter columnaris, *as seen by the scanning electron microscope, cover the surface of a gill cell.*

J. Gratzek

culture in Europe and America.

Infected fish swim in a characteristic whirling manner. Since the organism invades the cartilage, it may also cause spine deformities. Mortality can be extensive, with survivors unmarketable. Carriers not showing disease signs may continue to contaminate the fish farm.

There is no treatment for this disease. Diseased animals should be destroyed. Nothing short of drying up the pond, removing the mud, or rearing animals in concrete troughs or raceways will control the disease.

The final group of organisms that significantly affect coldwater fish are the large parasites. These consist mainly of worms of various types (nematodes, cestodes, trematodes, etc.). They are globally distributed and diffi-

cult to control since no effective chemotherapy exists. Some tropical parasites are potentially parasitic to man; therefore, stringent quality control measures are required. The impact of large parasites on wild and cultured animals may be significant.

As is apparent, coldwater fish are susceptible to a host of viral, bacterial, protozoal and parasitic diseases. These significantly affect commercial rearing of coldwater fish. Most do not readily respond to chemotherapeutics. Improved management techniques—including lower densities, disinfecting eggs, rapid removal of moribund or dead animals, eliminating stress due to handling—are all desirable though not necessarily feasible methods of potentially minimizing effects of these diseases.

How to Bring Up Cultured Catfish

By John A. Plumb

Since the beginning of commercial catfish farming in the United States in the late 1950's, the industry has grown to where it was worth about $200 million in 1983. Projections place the potential value of the catfish industry at $1.5 billion by the end of the century.

In 1984 about 85,000 acres of water are in catfish production in the United States, with channel catfish the principal culture species.

The catfish industry is becoming a significant agricultural enterprise in certain parts of the United States, especially the South where water temperatures are warm enough for a 6- to 8-month growing season each year.

In a rapidly expanding

John A. Plumb is Associate Professor, Department of Fisheries and Allied Aquaculture, Auburn University, Auburn, Ala.

agricultural industry such as catfish farming there are many problems. Any time a fish is taken from an extensive environment (such as a farm pond) and placed in an intensive environment (culture pond), health problems occur.

Normal catfish-carrying capacity of a fertilized farm pond is no more than a few hundred pounds per acre. However, the carrying capacity of an efficient catfish culture pond may be 5,000 pounds or more. These high densities result in increased susceptibility to infectious disease. Although there are many potential infectious diseases of cultured channel catfish, only the most serious and frequent will be discussed here.

Fish diseases have some basic characteristics that separate mortalities caused by infections from those caused by low oxygen and other water

Jack R. Smith, USDA-SCS

Tim McCabe, USDA-SCS

In 1984, about 85,000 acres of water are in catfish production in the United States. Channel catfish are the most popular species being commercially produced. These freshly harvested channel catfish in the 3 to 5 pound range are ready for processing. Harvested catfish are skinned and cleaned before they are sold to restaurants and supermarkets.

Tim McCabe, USDA-SCS

Keeping Fish Healthy

quality problems or pesticides. Diseased fish usually have external sores, bloody areas in the skin, swim slowly at the surface, stop feeding before death occurs, and have a gradually increasing mortality pattern over a period of days or weeks. Pesticide- or oxygen-caused fish kills usually occur overnight or in a very short period during which a high number of fish die.

CCV Has High Kill

1) *Virus Diseases.* Channel catfish virus disease (CCV) is the most serious virus disease of these fish. It occurs in fingerling production facilities and may result in 50 to 90 percent mortality in fry and fingerling populations. CCV causes disease during the first summer of the fish's life, while water temperature is above 80° F (27° C). The disease is more severe while fish are less than 6 weeks old. As the fish get older and grow to 4 inches and larger they become more resistant and the mortality is less severe.

Channel catfish infected with CCV have bloody areas at the base of fins and in the skin, swollen bellies, and are popeyed. A clear straw-colored fluid is present in the body cavity. Gills and internal organs are generally pale. Just before death, infected fish swim slowly at the surface with occasional erratic movements.

CCV is easily transmitted from infected fish to noninfected fish by contact through the water. But it is not known how the virus is transmitted from one generation to another. It is presumed, and there is strong circumstantial evidence, that CCV is passed from the carrier broodfish to their offspring via reproduction.

Impact of CCV on the catfish industry as a whole is not as severe as that of some other diseases. However, due to the often high rate of mortality, the effect on fish farms where it occurs can be devastating.

2) *Bacterial Diseases.* There are four major bacterial diseases of farm-raised channel catfish. The most common is "Motile Aeromonas Septicemia" (MAS), usually caused by *Aeromonas hydrophila.* This widespread water-borne bacterium is present in nearly all fresh water.

Stress Is Factor

The disease most often occurs after fish have been stressed due to some environmental problem such as low oxygen, excessively low or high temperatures, improper handling, or some other debilitating infectious or noninfectious disease.

Symptoms of MAS vary. Infected catfish may have frayed fins and/or deeply eroded open sores in the skin and muscle. The body cavity often contains a bloody fluid, and internal organs are mottled in color and very soft. Fish of all ages are susceptible to MAS. It may occur at any time of the year, but most frequently in spring and fall. Mortalities are low to moderate (5 to 30 percent). The disease usually is chronic, with a few fish continuously dying over a long period of time, but mortality may be acute.

Columnaris is a bacterial disease that most frequently causes problems in young fish, but occasionally infects production-size fish. It may occur at any time of the year.

Like MAS, columnaris (caused by *Flexibacter columnaris)* is usually associated with environmentally induced stress or handling. The bacterium produces light areas on the skin and frayed fins, as well as causing white sores on the gills. Although mortality patterns of columnaris infections are generally chronic, with fish dying at a slow rate for a long period of time,

deaths may increase rapidly over a few days.

Fish Gangrene
Edwardsiella tarda causes fish gangrene, a disease that affects cultured channel catfish. This bacterial infection does not result in high losses in production ponds; however, when fish are crowded into tanks, up to 50 percent of them may die.

Infected fish develop light areas on the skin surrounded by small bloody spots. When these areas are cut, there is a pocket of gas in the muscle that has an unpleasant odor.

Fish gangrene usually affects large fish, and most frequently during warm summer months. When fish with fish gangrene are harvested for market, the gas-filled pockets contaminate the processing line during dressing. The contaminated line must then be shut down and facilities disinfected and cleaned, causing loss of time and money.

Edwardsiella ictaluri causes enteric septicemia of catfish (ESC). Although this bacterial disease is the most recently described infectious disease of channel catfish, it has rapidly become one of the most important.

Fish with ESC have severe bleeding in the skin

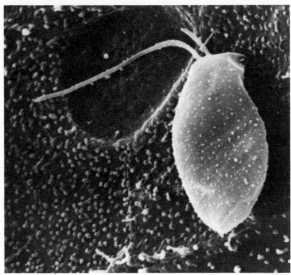

Ichthyobodo (Costia), a single-celled protozoan, on the skin of a fish viewed by a scanning electron microscope. The flagella are visible and may aid in attaching the parasite to the host.

J. Gratzek

around the mouth, under the throat and on the gill covers. There usually is an open ulcer in the skull of diseased fish.

ESC occurs in all size fish, but is most severe when water temperature is between 68° to 80° F (20° to 27° C). This usually is in May and June and again in September and October. Mortalities will range from less than 5 to over 50 percent of infected populations. Some fish disease experts believe ESC is the most serious infectious disease of cultured channel catfish.

3) *Parasitic Diseases.* There are a large number of protozoan and worm parasites of cultured channel catfish, but only a few are of much consequence.

The best known and possibly most serious protozoan parasite of catfish is *Ichthyophthirius* (Ich). The parasite infects skin and gills of the fish where it produces small pinhead size white spots that can be seen with the unaided eye. After the parasite matures on the fish, it drops into the water where it undergoes a series of divisions, and the resulting juvenile parasites then reinfect other fish.

Difficult to Treat
Ich can cause very high mortality but the most severe cases occur when the water temperature is between 65° to 80° F (19° to 27° C). It also is one of the most difficult parasites to treat because part of

How to Bring Up Cultured Catfish

its life cycle is spent imbedded in the skin where it is protected from most chemicals.

Other protozoans that cause problems on the skin of the fish are *Trichodina, Costia (Ichthyobodo), Trichophrya,* and *Ambiphrya.* The signs of these are all similar, and identification requires microscopic examination. They cause excessive mucus on the skin and gills. The skin has a light gray appearance. Infected gills are swollen and pale.

Henneguya is a sporozoan parasite that has several forms which infect the skin or gills of catfish. The most serious is the interlamellar form which occurs in cysts between folds of each gill filament. When cysts are present in high numbers, the gills' respiratory function is destroyed. This form has been thought to cause extensive deaths in young catfish.

Parasitic trematodes, known as gill worms, commonly infest catfish gills. Although the worms are present on gills of most catfish, they are of little consequence unless the parasite becomes overly abundant.

4) *Treatment, Control.* Through experience and experimentation, it has been found that many infectious diseases are stimulated by poor environmental and other stressful conditions which reduce fish resistance to infection. Therefore, the best method of disease control on cultured catfish is by prevention. Optimum environmental conditions in cultured facilities will prevent many infections from progressing to the point where fish are killed.

We also know from experience that despite efforts of the fish farmer to maintain good environmental conditions in culture ponds, infectious diseases do occur in catfish. When this happens, the farmer must apply some type of treatment.

Virus diseases are untreatable, but bacterial diseases may be treated by adding chemicals—such as potassium permanganate—to the water or feeding a prepared feed that contains an antibiotic (Terramycin). Protozoan parasites may be treated by bathing the fish in a chemical such as potassium permanganate, formalin or copper sulfate. When treating fish that are to be used as human food, only chemicals or antibiotics approved by the U.S. Food and Drug Administration may be used.

Disease Control in Food Fish

By Graham L. Bullock

Treatment with drugs and chemicals for control of fish diseases is most feasible with cultured fish; rarely can diseases be prevented or sick fish helped in the wild. Diseases of cultured fish fall into three categories: Infectious, nutritional, and environmental. Infectious diseases of fish are further divided into those caused by viruses, bacteria, parasites (protozoans and worms), and fungi.

Intensively cultured fish are often under stress caused by crowding, which may produce unfavorable environmental conditions such as low oxygen, high ammonia levels. Acting together, or as pathologists say, "synergistically," these factors may give disease

National Fish Health Research Laboratory
A fish pathologist begins an incision into the body cavity of a rainbow trout for diagnosis of disease.

agents an opportunity to cause significant losses.

With few exceptions, viral diseases of fish—like viral diseases of other animals—cannot be controlled by drug treatment. Effective control against these minute disease-causing agents is best

Graham L. Bullock is Scientific Director, National Fish Health Research Laboratory, U.S. Fish and Wildlife Service, Kearneysville, W.Va.

Disease Control in Food Fish

achieved by avoiding infection. This can be done by obtaining fertilized eggs from parents free of viral disease and using a water supply known to be free of fish that harbor viruses.

Bacterial infections are seen most commonly when the fish are under stress. Many of the bacteria persist in the fish environment all the time. There are two general types of bacterial fish diseases: External infections, affecting skin, fins, and gills, and internal infections in which all the internal organs may be invaded.

Treated As A Group
Regardless of the type of infection, cultured fish are treated as a population. Exceptions may occur when individual fish are easy to handle or are extremely valuable—such as brood fish or ornamental fish.

External bacterial infections of fish cultured in concrete raceways or in ponds are treated with different chemicals depending on the particular bacterium causing the disease outbreak.

Chemicals may be applied as a bath treatment, exposing fish to the chemical for a prescribed period, usually an hour. When a flush treatment is called for, the chemical is

flushed through the raceway or pond. Another regimen may prescribe an indefinite bath; the chemical is added and not removed. For a constant flow treatment, the chemical is added at the water inlet for an hour or more.

Commonly used chemicals for bacterial diseases include copper sulfate, potassium permanganate, and quarternary ammonium compounds such as Hyamine 3500. Treatment levels required depend on the particular bacterium causing disease. Consult texts on fish health for recommended treatment procedures.

Medicated Feed
Internal bacterial diseases of fish are treated by incorporating drugs into feed. Treatment must begin in the initial stages of disease when fish are still eating.

In hatcheries, drug treatments range from 3 to 10 grams of drug for each 100 pounds of fish treated. Medicated treatment lasts 10 to 14 days. Commonly used drugs include sulfamerazine and Terramycin.

For treating large numbers of fish, medicated feed is prepared by a feed manufacturer. Medicated feed for treating smaller numbers of fish (1,000 to 2,000 pounds) is prepared by coating feed with the appropriate drug using gelatin or oil as a binder.

Parasites, like bacteria, can be both external and internal infections in fish; external infections generally are regarded as the more important. Severe disease outbreaks in cultured fish are caused by external parasites, and significant mortality will occur if the parasite infection is not rapidly and effectively treated. Such outbreaks may be treated with 166 to 250 parts per million (ppm) formalin (formaldehyde gas dissolved in water) for 1 hour.

Internal parasite infections rarely are treated. So, as with viral diseases, avoidance is the only effective means of control. Some large internal parasitic infections, such as tapeworms, can be effectively treated by incorporating tin oxide in the diet.

Fungus infections occur most often in developing eggs, and as a secondary infection in fish weakened by other diseases. However, they can crop up as a primary infection. The most effective treatment is formalin at 1,000 to 2,000 ppm for fungal infections of eggs and 1 to 3 ppm malachite green for 1 hour on fungal infections of fish.

Cardinal Rules

There are some cardinal rules to follow when treating fish with chemicals or drugs:

1) Begin treatment of cultured fish during early stages of infection or as soon as possible to reduce deaths.

2) If you feel uncertain about treatment levels for different species and ages, use a trial treatment first with a small sample of fish. Mistakes often are made by overdoses, resulting in deaths due to the treatment itself.

3) Drugs and chemicals used for treating fish meant for human consumption must be approved by the U.S. Food and Drug Administration. Currently only sulfamerazine, Terramycin, and formalin are registered.

4) Be careful of effluent containing drugs and chemicals after treatment. Do not contaminate the environment, because this may induce growth of drug-resistant strains in the field.

5) **Keep records of all** treatments and their effectiveness at your station. Individual environmental variations may require modification of prescribed treatments, and you may want to repeat treatments when trouble again occurs.

Immunization Aids Disease Fight

By Guy Tebbit

Large scale intensive culture of fish by State and Federal agencies and the rapidly growing private aquaculture industry have increased our awareness of the prevalence and significance of fish diseases. Economic importance of these diseases has emphasized the need for rapid and accurate disease diagnosis as well as economical and efficacious disease control methods and products.

Intensive rearing of large numbers of fish under conditions of high density and stress has produced ideal situations for the onset and spread of disease. In some cases, fish diseases may be the limiting factor in the success or failure of an aquaculture operation.

Guy Tebbit is Vice President and Laboratory Director, Wildlife Vaccines, Inc., Wheat Ridge, Colo.

Fish cultural management techniques and the strict control of transportation of diseased animals play major roles in preventing the spread of fish diseases. However, in many situations—despite concerted efforts to prevent health problems at the management level—infectious diseases are prevalent and endemic. Effective control measures are then required to reduce impact of the problem.

First step in fish disease control is accurate diagnosis of the problem. With infectious disease, this must consist of a precise identification and a thorough characterization of the microbial pathogen responsible. Fish health specialists then can use this information to decide the most effective and efficient methods of disease control and prevention.

Antibiotics and chemotherapeutics have been the principal products used to con-

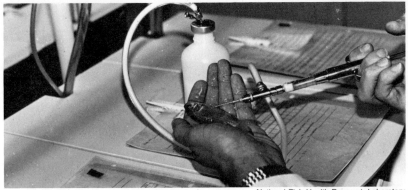

National Fish Health Research Laboratory

Immunization is a common method to control or prevent disease in fish, just as it is for humans and animals. This goldfish is receiving an injection from an automatic repeating syringe, which is designed to immunize a large number of fish in a short period of time.

trol fish diseases. Under certain conditions these products have been very successful in treating diseased fish, and chemotherapeutics are the only products available to control diseases caused by protozoan parasites.

However, antibiotics and chemotherapeutic treatment provide only short term control of disease. After treatment, fish are susceptible again to the same or other diseases. Strict governmental regulation and limitation of these compounds for use in food fish, and the fact that some microbes causing bacterial diseases have become resistant to antibiotic treatments, produced the need for other methods of disease control.

Vaccination

Immunization is a common method used to control and prevent disease in human and veterinary medicine. Scientists have known for many years that fish can be successfully immunized against certain infectious diseases. The major problem in developing fish vaccines was the requirement for a mass method capable of immunizing large numbers of fish in a safe, expedient and economical manner. Obviously, hand injecting the millions of fish that are reared in large aquaculture facilities was not practical.

The problem was solved in 1975 with development of the immersion method of vaccination. It consists of simply

Immunization

placing the fish in diluted vaccine and letting them swim in the vaccine for several seconds. This method is now automated and has been used successfully to immunize hundreds of millions of fish. There is evidence that vaccine uptake occurs through the gills and a large lymphatic vessel associated with the lateral line of the fish.

Fish, like humans and other animals, are able to develop a specific acquired immunity and also possess non-specific defense mechanisms against infectious diseases. Vaccination stimulates specific acquired immunity, and the fish respond to vaccination by developing specific antibodies to components of the vaccine. These components are usually killed preparations of one or more disease micro-organisms.

Lasts About Year

Antibodies produced by the fish after vaccination circulate through their blood and protect them against infection from the specific disease or diseases. Antibodies also are found in the mucus covering the skin of the fish and could be the first line of defense against infection. In general, it is believed that immunity after vaccination lasts about one year. Several factors such as species and size of fish, vaccine doses, water temperatures, stress, and other environmental parameters influence the onset and duration of immunity.

Fish vaccines are considered veterinary biological products and are regulated by the U.S. Department of Agriculture (USDA). In 1976 USDA issued the first two product licenses for fish vaccines. Besides licensing products, USDA also regulates strict quality control measures to insure that each lot of vaccine is tested for safety, potency and purity. Since 1976 three additional product licenses for fish vaccines have been issued.

The five licensed vaccines for fish are administered by immersion, automated immersion, spray and injection methods. A brief description of the administration methods, the five licensed products, and their applications follows.

Methods Used

Immersion. Fish are placed in containers containing aerated and diluted vaccine at a ratio of 1 pound of fish per liter of diluted vaccine for a 5- to 60-second exposure. The same container of diluted bacterin can be reused for 20 consecutive immersions. Usually 20 to 40 pounds of fish weighing from 5 to 15 grams each are vaccinated in each immersion.

Automated Immersion. Here a machine performs the immersion process. Fish are loaded onto a rubber conveyor belt that transports them through a reservoir of vaccine and back to the holding pond via a return slide. Fish are loaded into the unit by net or automated fish pumps. The auto-immersion unit is lightweight, compact, mobile, and designed for large aquaculture facilities that vaccinate thousands of pounds of fish a day. The auto-immersion unit can vaccinate up to 200 pounds of fish a minute.

Spray. Diluted vaccine is sprayed over fish as they are removed from their holding area. Simple contact with the vaccine applied without significant pressure suffices. The process also has been mechanized, and the aquaculturist can devise several ways of using it. Lack of complete and controlled exposure can lead to operator error during large scale vaccination procedures and result in inconsistent exposure.

Injection. This can be used for large valuable fish such as brood fish. The method is made quicker and easier with automatic repeating syringes. A skilled operator can inject 600 to 800 fish an hour. Before injection the fish are usually anesthetized by swimming in a solution of a recommended anesthetic. The injection is given intraperitoneally, just before the pelvic fins. Injection administration allows the vaccine manufacturer to add adjuvants to the products—compounds that stimulate and enhance the fish's immune response to the vaccine.

Products

1) Enteric Redmouth Bacterin, recommended for use in salmonid fishes (salmon and trout) to protect against enteric redmouth disease (ERM) caused by the bacterium *Yersinia ruckeri*. The product is used primarily by agencies or companies raising rainbow trout.

The bacterin is administered by immersion, auto-immersion, or spray. In a study at a commercial trout farm involving 27 million fish, the fish vaccinated by immersion demonstrated 84 percent reduction in ERM mortality, 77 percent reduction in medicated feed (antibiotic) requirements, and 14 percent improvement in food conversion when compared to nonvaccinated control fish.

Immunization

2) Vibrio Anguillarum Bacterin. Vibriosis is caused by the bacterium *Vibrio anguillarum* and is primarily a disease of fish raised in salt water. The bacterin is used to vaccinate trout and salmon raised in pens and anadromous salmon before they migrate to the ocean. This product is administered by immersion, auto-immersion, or spray. Products licensed by USDA contain two serotypes of the Vibrio bacterium.

3) Aeromonas Salmonicida Bacterin. The bacterium *Aeromonas salmonicida* causes a disease of fish known as furunculosis. The bacterin is recommended for use in salmonid fish to prevent furunculosis disease, and in goldfish to protect against ulcerative disease. This product is administered by injection and contains a special adjuvant to enhance the immune response. The bacterin is used mainly to vaccinate large valuable fish such as breeding stocks.

4 & 5) Aeromonas Salmonicida—Enteric Redmouth Bacterin, and Aeromonas Salmonicida—Vibrio Anguillarum Bacterin. These two products are used to vaccinate against furunculosis disease and enteric redmouth disease, or furunculosis disease and vibriosis. The two products are combination vaccines allowing the aquaculturist to vaccinate against two diseases at the same time. Both products contain an adjuvant and are administered by injection.

Vaccination programs have reduced mortality from disease, reduced or eliminated requirements for antibiotic treatment, and improved the food conversion ratio—resulting in faster growth. A healthy fish not only looks better, but utilizes its food better and grows faster.

R&D Underway

In addition to products currently licensed and available, much effort is now directed towards research and development of new vaccines to protect against other diseases. Developmental work is underway to license vaccines for two bacterial diseases of catfish. These are enteric septicemia of catfish and columnaris disease.

A considerable effort is being made to develop an immersion-administered vaccine for furunculosis disease and two products for viral diseases of salmon and trout. These are infectious pancreatic necrosis (IPN) and infectious hematopoietic necrosis (IHN).

Biologicals are common

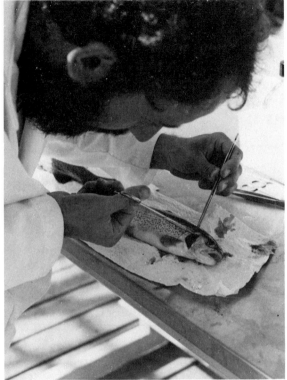

M. Stuckey

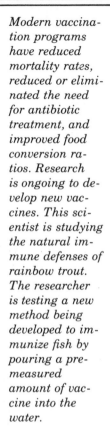

Modern vaccination programs have reduced mortality rates, reduced or eliminated the need for antibiotic treatment, and improved food conversion ratios. Research is ongoing to develop new vaccines. This scientist is studying the natural immune defenses of rainbow trout. The researcher is testing a new method being developed to immunize fish by pouring a premeasured amount of vaccine into the water.

M. Stuckey

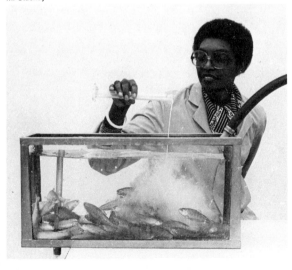

Immunization

components of many diagnostic procedures used to identify the causative agent of infectious diseases. Pure cultures of disease micro-organisms can be used in the diagnostic procedure directly, or used to make specific antibodies for immunological diagnostic tests.

Antibodies are produced by injecting the fish disease bacterium, virus or protozoan into other animals such as rabbits, mice, goats or chickens. Several weeks later serum is collected from blood of the injected animal. The serum contains specific antibodies to the micro-organism that was injected into the animal. These antibodies can be employed in various immunodiagnostic tests to identify the specific pathogen used to make them.

Revolutionary Tests

New types of immuno-diagnostic tests have been developed recently which have revolutionized disease diagnosis in human and veterinary medicine. The tests are accurate and expedient, and are incorporated into kits allowing the physician's office staff or the veterinarian to perform the diagnostic tests without sending samples to an outside laboratory.

Fish health scientists are applying this technology to develop fish disease diagnostic kits which may be used by the aquaculturist or fish health specialist to identify their specific disease problems.

It now takes from several days to several weeks to get a diagnosis. During this time many fish may die awaiting the correct treatment. A fast and accurate diagnosis will allow the aquaculturist to implement the necessary control measures to reduce impact of the disease.

Tropical Fish— Keeping a Giant Industry Healthy

By John B. Gratzek

The tropical fish industry is large and complex. It is estimated that the on-farm value of goldfish alone is $21 million. Tropical varieties raised in Florida are worth at least $15 million. Current data supplied by wholesalers of tropical fish shows that 30 to 40 percent of ornamental fish sold in the United States are produced in the United States.

Of these domestically produced fish, 20 percent are goldfish while 80 percent are warmwater varieties produced mainly in South Florida where production may consist of pond culture and vat culture or combinations of each. A small percentage of domestically raised ornamental fish, such as angelfish and discus-

John B. Gratzek is Professor and Head, Department of Medical Microbiology, College of Veterinary Medicine, University of Georgia, Athens, Ga.

fish, are reared entirely in aquariums or vats in heated buildings. Such facilities may be found scattered throughout the United States.

About 45 percent of the imported fish sold by wholesalers originate in the Far East, 20 percent in South America, and 5 percent in Africa.

Points of origin from the Far East in order of volume of fish include Singapore, Thailand, Hong Kong, Indonesia and Taiwan. Fish from these areas may primarily be caught wild as in Indonesia and Thailand or produced in ponds and vats as in Singapore, Hong Kong, or Taiwan.

Principal exporters of tropical fish from South America—in order of the volume of fish supplied—are Brazil, Peru, Colombia and Venezuela. Fish from these areas are caught wild. Points of export in Africa include Zaire and Tanzania that serve as

M. Knox

More than 200 tropical fish farms such as this one are part of an ornamental fish industry that airfreights more than 4 million live fish from Florida each week.

R. Elliott

*Tropical fish originated from many different parts of the world. The kribensis cichlid (*Pelvicachromis pulcher*) is a species that came originally from tropical west Africa. This popular small freshwater fish is often kept in community aquariums.*

sources of unique species such as Reedfish (*Calamoichthys calabaricus),* mormyrids, and species of Cichlids.

It is estimated that 20 million American homes have aquariums at any given time. However, there is a considerable turnover of individuals or families who keep fish as pets.

Unique Aspects

Innate factors make the tropical fish industry most interesting but also contribute to the problem of keeping fish healthy. These include:

Diverse Species. It is generally accepted that the pet industry distributes about 500 to 600 species of fish. Within a single genera such as the angelfish or swordtails there may be numerous varieties based on color patterns. The end result is that the consumer has a very wide selection of fish available for purchase.

Similar to other animals, there are considerable variances among species in disease resistance. For example, while the channel catfish is very susceptible to nitrite toxicity, the serpa tetra is practically insensitive to high concentrations of nitrite.

Scaleless species such as the clown loach and various species of catfish are ex-

tremely susceptible to the ciliated protozoan, while ornamental catfish such as various species of *Corydoras* are relatively resistant.

Some species are very tolerant of shipping stress. Others such as the lemon tetra are less tolerant.

Some species of ornamental fish tend to have a higher incidence of diseases caused by specific organisms than do other species. For example, species of the intestinal protozoan, *Hexamita,* have been frequently associated with angelfish, goldfish, and various species of anabantids and cichlids. The organism is rarely if ever found in tetras or livebearing fish.

Anabantids such as the Siamese fighting fish or dwarf gouramis, in our experience, have a high incidence of mycobacterial infections. One can only speculate that the higher incidence of infectious agents results from a fortuitous combination of factors. For example, the anabantids take air from the water-air interface where there may be a higher concentration of acid-fast mycobacterial organisms.

Diverse Origins

Since tropical fish are produced using commercial fish farming methods as well as

*The pet industry distributes about 500 to 600 species of fish. Within a single genera such as the angelfish there may be numerous varieties based on color patterns, and so there is a very wide selection of fish available to the consumer. This queen angelfish (*Holancanthus ciliaris*), is a marine fish found from the tropical western Atlantic to the Gulf of Mexico.*

R. Elliott
J. Gratzek

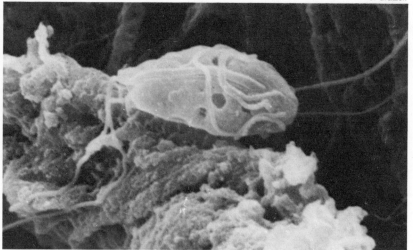

The protozoan, Hexamita, is shown lodged on the surface of the intestine of an angelfish. The scanning electron micrograph magnifies the parasite 4,800 times.

Keeping Fish Healthy

caught in the wild, the types of problems encountered in wild-caught fish vary from those raised under intensive conditions. Our experience with fish captured in areas of South America suggests that protozoan parasites infecting gills are extremely rare, but that infestations with metacercariae of digenetic trematode worms as well as various types of nematode worms are common, especially towards the end of the collecting season.

Another example of the influence of location on incidence of parasitism is our recent finding that various species of livebearing fish originating from some locations in Florida are heavily infested with worm-like linguatulid larvae (*Arthropoda: Pentistomida*). Distribution of this larval form in fish depends on the presence of alligators or possibly turtles which are hosts for the adult worms.

Feed Diversity. Salmonid and channel catfish fry are able to prosper on commercially produced diets. In the commercial production of ornamental fish, brine shrimp are indispensable to raising many types of larval tropical fish.

Some tropical fish producers use various invertebrates such as cyclops, daphnia, and tubificid worms as "natural" foods. These frequently are intermediate hosts of various fish parasites such as nematodes, acanthocephalans, tapeworms, and in some cases small groups of internal protozoans called sporozoans.

For example, some groups of neon tetras imported from Hong Kong will be severely afflicted with the sporozoan *Plistophora hyphessobryconis*. Since all neon tetras in Hong Kong are tank-reared it is reasonable to assume that infections are introduced by the feeding of various live organisms, some of which carry parasites.

In general, fish reared and maintained in aquariums without exposure to parasites carried by live food are devoid of many parasites compared to those captured in the wild or pond-raised.

Transport, Handling

An axiom in producing any kind of fish is to avoid unnecessary handling or transportation. The ornamental fish industry is absolutely dependent on airfreight transportation for its existence. Packing of fish for transport can result in many problems.

Fish are placed in plastic

bags of water which then are filled up with oxygen and shipped in insulated boxes. The number of fish packed per bag depends on the size and, to some extent, the relative tolerance of a particular species to shipping stress.

During transportation, fish may be subjected to oxygen depletion, accumulation of carbon dioxide and ammonia, and temperature variations. To some extent carbon dioxide can be controlled by adjustment of pH while ammonia can be removed by addition of natural zeolites.

Fish shippers naturally tend to pack the highest density possible to minimize air freight costs. The fact that most tropical fish can tolerate the physiologic rigors of shipment testifies to their natural durability. Nevertheless, stress following shipment is a well recognized problem facing wholesalers.

Most often stress is followed by outbreaks of bacterial diseases. Examination of gills of recently unpacked fish often reveals the presence of gill pathology as evidenced by clubbing of the lamellae of the gill filaments, or by aneurisms. Refusal of recently shipped fish to eat is probably associated with oxygen deficiency caused by damaged gills.

Common Diseases

Problems associated with tropical fish can be divided broadly into noninfectious and infectious. Infectious diseases are directly related to the habitat from which fish were collected, feeding practices, shipment and handling stresses, and problems resulting from poor water quality. Lastly, there are potential interchanges of infectious disease agents at wholesale and retail establishments.

Disease problems which occur at each location—producer, collector, exporter, importer-wholesaler, retailer, hobbyist—tend to be different or may not be manifest.

For example, a recently arrived fish shipment from some foreign country may be infected with a bacterium causing columnaris disease. These fish are not salable until the infection has run its course naturally or with recovery assisted by antibiotic therapy. Columnaris disease, therefore, tends to be less of a problem at the retail level than at the wholesale level, and is rare in well maintained home aquariums.

Another example is provided by sporozoan diseases such as neon tetra disease. At the wholesale level, the fish may not be visibly afflicted;

but after some time at the retail level the disease will have progressed to a point where clinical signs are obvious. A third example is provided by mycobacterial infections which may not be apparent at both the wholesale and retail level, only to become clinically apparent after some weeks or months in the display aquarium.

In general, classes of infectious disease agents which can affect ornamental fish are identical to those that affect other species. Because of their diverse geographical origins and requirements for transportation, tropical fish may be exposed to a wider spectrum of parasites and bacteria than fish raised for food.

A very important point is that there appear to be no parasites or bacteria unique to tropical fish. For example, *Hexamita* infections have been reported in trout as causing either no distinct clinical disease or a syndrome referred to as "pinhead". In various tropical cichlids, *Hexamita* are associated with emaciation and death of fish. Possibly the difference is due to the parasite load and rate of infection, which would be greater in a closed aquarium system.

Management Lapses

Another feature of infectious diseases of aquarium fish is that disease problems often are related to lapses in good aquarium management and husbandry techniques, leading to stressful conditions such as ammonia and nitrite accumulation, or a radical pH drop. The resulting stress on the fish is thought to depress its natural capacity for resisting disease, resulting in sick and dying fish.

In home aquariums parasitic and bacterial disease problems often occur during the stressful first 30 to 45 days when ammonia and nitrite levels may be high. Frequently, parasitic diseases follow introduction of a disease-carrying but apparently healthy fish into the aquarium. The husbandry lapse in this instance is the failure to isolate and observe new fish before adding them to a community of healthy fish.

Diet. It is becoming increasingly apparent that a well balanced diet with sufficient vitamins A, C, E, and B complex is essential for fish to maintain their natural disease resistance mechanisms. Storage of food over a long period can result in food essentially depleted of some B vitamins, vitamins A, C, and E.

Other nutritional problems arise when only beef heart or liver are fed fish. Also, feeding some species of raw fish to tropicals can lead to a deficiency of vitamin B (thiamin) due to an enzyme (thiaminase) present in the uncooked fish.

Despite all precautions, tropical fish may be afflicted with infectious disease organisms including various types of protozoans, worms, parasitic copepods, bacteria and viruses. Some of these infections can be treated while others are essentially untreatable at the time when fish appear clinically sick.

Protozoan infections that are very common are *Ichthyopthirius multifiliis* which causes "white spot" disease of fish. Other protozoan parasites which cause serious disease and deaths of fish are *Ichtyobodo necatrix* and species of *Chilodonella*. These organisms are found on gills and skin and cause death by gill damage.

A variety of chemicals such as formaldehyde, malachite green, copper, salt, quinine, potassium permanganate and methylene blue have been used to remove external parasites. These chemicals vary in effectiveness and potential damage to the fish. *Tet-rahymena pyriformis* is an actively invasive carnivorous protozoan which can infect internal organs of various tropical (and wild) fish. Because of its invasive properties, treatment usually is not successful.

Hexamita are flagellated protozoans found in many tropical fish and can be associated with wasting and emaciation. Treatment with 5 parts per million metronidazole in water is effective.

Velvet Disease

The flagellated protozoan *Oodinium* frequently is a problem of tropical fish. There are at least three species associated with this condition, commonly called "velvet disease." Low levels of copper (.11 to .18 parts per million) for a period of 10 days have been used to cure the problem; however, metronidazole may be a good candidate as a treatment.

Other protozoans such as members of the genera *Trichodina*, *Glossatella* and *Ambiphrya* are seen in pond-raised ornamental fish, but rarely at the wholesale or retail level. Stalked ciliated protozoans, of the genus *Epistylis*, occasionally are seen on tropical fish in poorly maintained aquariums. The colonies appear as localized tufts resembling fungal growths.

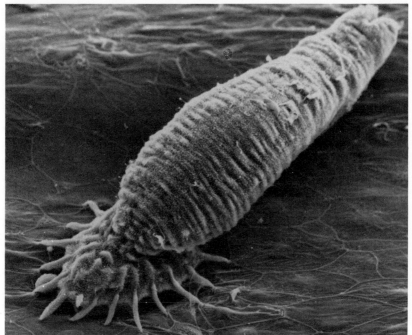

J. Gratzek

Sporozoan parasites are common in tropical fish. Several genera are involved—some are associated with mortalities while others may only form discrete nodules on the skin and other organs of fish. Members of the genera *Plistophora* affect muscle tissue and can cause high mortalities in affected fish.

Other sporozoans such as *Henneguya, Myxobolus* and *Myxidium* frequently cause raised white spots on the surface of fish and may be associated with other organs. *Mitraspora* sp. are frequently found in the kidneys of gold-

This monogenetic trematode worm taken from the tail fin of a goldfish is shown in high magnification (940 ×) by a scanning electron microscope.

fish and are one of the causes of "bloat."

The intestines of goldfish are frequently affected by coccidiosis organisms (*Eimeria* sp.). A therapeutic approach would require that infected fish be treated before target organs are invaded. Anticoccidial drugs would be potential drugs of choice.

Monogenetic trematodes

are frequently found on gills and bodies of various tropical fish. Signs of infection will depend on the numbers of parasites present and can include respiratory distress, frayed fins and small ulcerations. Treatment with formaldehyde or salt baths usually are successful. Organophosphates have been used; however, some species of trematodes have developed resistance.

Problems with Grubs

Digenetic trematodes, commonly called "grubs," can cause severe problems—especially in pond-raised or wild-caught fish. In most cases, aquatic birds harbor the adult worm parasite. Snails frequently are the first intermediate host and fish the secondary intermediate host where the parasite is known as a metacercaria.

Many species exist and many have a particular affinity for a special location such as skin, eye, gills, or internal organs. Control is best accomplished by eradicating snails in production ponds.

Nematodes are common in tropical fish and include members of various genera. They frequently are found in the intestine or migrating within organs of the body cavity or muscles where removal

is not possible. Treatment of intestinal forms can be accomplished with various antiparasiticides mixed with food.

Occasionally, tropical fish are infected with adult tapeworms in their intestines; more commonly found are intermediate forms of tapeworms encysted in the peritoneal cavity. The number of parasites (tapeworms, nematodes) infesting a fish will determine if there is any observable effect on the fish.

Bacteria, Viruses

Bacterial infections following transportation and handling at the wholesale and retail levels are common. Genera of bacteria most frequently involved are *Aeromonas, Flexibacter, Myxobacterium, Flavobacterium,* and *Pseudomonas.* Typical signs of infection can include frayed fins, ulcers, and hemorrhages. Mycobacterial infections are very common in home aquariums.

Treatment of bacterial infections in fish is possible. Problems encountered are bacteria resistant to common antibiotics used, absorbability of the antibiotic, and effect of the antibiotic on the nitrifying bacteria associated with biofiltration of ammonia and nitrites.

The extent of virus infections in tropical fish is not known. However, based on other species of fish, there are probably numerous classes of viruses involved in disease epizootics. About five viruses have been isolated from fish used for ornamental or display purposes.

Our clinical experience suggests that many conditions could be attributable to viruses. The one well recognized virus of tropical fish is lymphocystis virus which stimulates cells associated with external surfaces of the fish's body to enlarge, resulting in unsightly growths.

Diagnostic Efforts

There are factors which dictate how much diagnostic effort should be expended to solve fish problems in home aquariums. The most important factor is the degree of involvement of the client, who may be a breeder and supplier of one exotic species and may have numerous aquariums. Another type of individual is the hobbyist with an aquarium, ancillary equipment, and fish worth hundreds of dollars. One important factor frequently overlooked is the close bond many individuals establish with their fish.

In any of these cases, good diagnostic service is ex-

pected. At this point in time, many home aquarists facing problems with fish expect assistance from the retail outlet where the fish were purchased. Only recently have some Colleges of Veterinary Medicine offered courses stressing basic principles of aquariology and management of closed systems along with the study of diseases of aquarium fish, and control measures. Results of this training will be an increase in the quality of service available to the public.

The diverse geographical origins of fish, along with required transportation, congregation and handling are tailormade conditions for stress as well as spread of disease. It is a tribute to knowledgeable fish importers that relatively so few fish die.

Preventing problems through routine treatment and good husbandry at the wholesale and retail level is important in disease control. Avoiding disease in the display aquarium is best done through quarantine and routine treatment of new fish, water management by regular changes, pH control if required, adequate biological filtration, and by maintaining disease resistance of fish through an adequate diet.

Foreign Fish, Those Pesky Escape Artists

By Paul L. Shafland

Production of aquarium fish makes up one of our most economically important aquaculture crops today. Aquarium fish farming is centered in Florida, from where the industry estimates more than 200 million live ornamental fish are shipped annually, with a retail value of over $75 million.

Most aquarium fish are non-native species that have been imported from other countries and cultured in the United States for many years. These fish are termed foreign or exotic because they do not occur naturally in the United States. Foreign fish represent only a small fraction of the fish being cultured for food in this country today; however,

Paul L. Shafland is Director, Non-Native Fish Research Laboratory, Florida Game and Fresh Water Fish Commission, Boca Raton.

some of these fish such as tilapias have been widely proclaimed as potential food fish.

With human assistance, some foreign food and ornamental fish have found their way to "freedom" in our natural waterways.

Unauthorized release or introduction of live foreign organisms is illegal and appropriately considered a form of biological pollution. This biological littering of live fish in areas where they do not occur naturally is a serious matter since unlike other forms of pollution it is an act that is generally impossible to reverse, should the fish reproduce and become self-perpetuating.

40 Types on Loose

Fortunately, most fish farmers and aquarists are well aware of the problems associated with introducing these fish and have taken steps to prevent future releases. Nonethe-

Keeping Fish Healthy

P. L. Shafland

Shortly after their accidental release from a tropical fish farm, the walking catfish reverted from the albino coloration (right) to the dark gray coloration typical of wild populations. This fish has become an aquacultural pest by crawling into fish ponds and eating expensive aquarium fish.

less, the number of foreign fish that have reproducing populations in the United States continues to increase, with a current tally of 40 species.

Unlike most domesticated livestock, many foreign fish are capable of surviving and even thriving when they escape from culture facilities. The potential of these fish to cause significant environmental changes has been of con-

Foreign Fish

siderable concern to fisheries personnel and ecologists for many years.

These concerns are founded in the knowledge that, besides other considerations, foreign fish 1) may compete directly or indirectly with native fish, 2) are a source of foreign diseases and parasites, and 3) are unpredictable and may behave differently in the United States than in their native range where historic population controls exist.

The unwise use or accidental release of foreign fish could impact detrimentally on important native and commercial fish that support multimillion dollar industries.

Walking Catfish

Foreign fish may even become aquacultural pests. A good example is the walking catfish that were unintentionally released by a fish farmer in Florida in the 1960's. Within a few years, several fish farmers found it necessary to erect low fences around culture ponds to prevent the walking catfish from gaining access to and eating their valuable cultured aquarium fish.

Natural aquatic ecosystems are dynamic and resilient entities capable of adjusting to some external disturbances. But as the number and intensity of chemical, physical and biological (exotic species) pollutants increase, native fish may be stressed beyond their ability to recover. Highly degraded, urban aquatic ecosystems often provide suitable environments for exotic fish, presumably as a result of decreased competition with native fish. Thus, besides representing a specific disturbance, presence of foreign fish may indicate general habitat deterioration.

Foreign fish are playing an increasingly important role in our freshwater fisheries. As a result, State and Federal agencies have developed regulations and research programs that deal specifically with these fish, and persons interested in culturing foreign fish should first become familiar with the regulations in their State. Successful development of new fish management practices incorporating these fish and prevention of future unintentional introductions will ensure the continued availability of foreign fish to the benefit of all concerned.

Aquariums— Getting Into the Swim

By Diane G. Elliott

A well-maintained aquarium makes an attractive addition to a home, office or classroom and can provide hours of fish-watching enjoyment. Numerous species and varieties of ornamental fish are available to suit almost any budget and taste. Modern aquarium products have made ornamental fish-keeping increasingly simple.

A basic knowledge of the principles of aquarium maintenance can help to make an aquarist's fish-keeping experiences enjoyable and rewarding. The following discussion focuses on general procedures for setting up and maintaining a freshwater aquarium, but some of the general principles apply to marine aquariums as well.

A bewildering array of glass and Plexiglas aquari-

Diane G. Elliott is Fishery Biologist, National Fisheries Research Center, Seattle, Wash.

ums—from familiar rectangular tanks to more fanciful shapes such as hexagons and globes—is available to the aquarist. The selection of a particular aquarium shape is partly a matter of esthetics, but not all aquariums of the same water capacity have the same fish-holding capacity.

The area of water exposed to the air is perhaps the most important factor for determining the number of fish an aquarium can safely hold. A shallow 15-gallon tank with a large air surface area can hold more fish than a tall 15-gallon tank with little surface area.

The best size of aquarium to select depends on your budget, personal preference, available space, and—perhaps most important—the types of fish to be kept. In practice, following initial setup, routine maintenance required for a large aquarium is about the same as for a small one. Furthermore, rapid (and unde-

Marie T. Sebrechts

Home and office aquariums are extremely popular in the United States. About 20 million American homes have aquariums of all sizes and shapes.

sirable) fluctuations in environmental conditions (temperature, for example) are less likely to occur in a larger volume of water than in a small.

Setting Up

Clean an aquarium with tepid water and salt only, no detergents or soaps. After rinsing, move it to its final location before filling with gravel and water. Avoid locating the aquarium near strong heat or strong drafts, near sources of toxic fumes, or in direct sunlight. The latter will bring excessive algal growth.

Aquarium gravel is now available in a rainbow of colors, thanks to a process that coats gravel particles with non-toxic colored materials. Natural gravel is also available. All aquarium gravel, even that labeled as prewashed, should be rinsed thoroughly with water to remove silt. Unrinsed gravel may cause cloudiness of the water, and the suspended particles may irritate the gills of fish.

For an attractive display, about two pounds of gravel are recommended for each gallon capacity of the aquarium. The gravel bed is generally

Keeping Fish Healthy

sloped (for example, from about 3 inches deep at the rear of the tank to about half an inch deep at the front) so solid wastes will collect at the front of the tank for easy removal by siphoning. Perhaps the best way to fill an aquarium with water without disturbing the gravel is to pour the water slowly into a bowl placed on the gravel.

Water used directly from the tap often is not satisfactory for aquarium fish. Most municipalities chlorinate their water supplies, and chlorine is toxic to fish. Chlorine can be neutralized easily and made safe for fish by adding sodium thiosulfate, which is available in pet supply shops under various trade names.

Adjusting pH

Water pH may need adjustment. The pH is a measure of the hydrogen ion (H^+) concentration in the water. The greater the hydrogen ion concentration, the lower the pH value. A pH value of less than 7 is acid, a pH value of 7 is neutral, and a pH value higher than 7 is basic or alkaline.

The optimum pH for a particular aquarium will depend on the types of fish and plants kept. The preference of most freshwater aquarium fish falls in the range between pH 6 and 8.6. Many plants prefer a neutral or slightly alkaline pH. Simple pH test kits accurate enough for aquarium use can be obtained at pet supply stores, and buffer chemicals for adjusting pH also can be purchased there.

Water hardness also can be measured with an inexpensive test kit. Hardness is a measure of the total dissolved salts, principally calcium and magnesium, in the water, and is frequently expressed as the total amount of calcium carbonate present. Soft water, water with low concentrations of dissolved salts, is usually acidic; and hard water is alkaline.

Some fish species prefer soft water while others prefer hard, but none thrive in distilled water. Some salts must be present for proper physiological functioning. Salt mixtures for increasing the hardness of very soft water are available at aquarium supply shops.

Decorations selected for an aquarium are largely a matter of personal choice. Many non-toxic ornaments such as plastic plants are sold by aquarium supply shops.

Plastic plants generally are realistic in appearance and are particularly useful for

Aquariums

R. Elliott

Be careful in selecting rocks and driftwood for decorations, as they can contain soluble substances harmful to fish. (Fish in center are clown loaches, Botia macracantha, *popular and peaceful fish from Asia.)*

aquariums housing plant-eating fish. However, many aquarists prefer to grow live plants. Some aquarium plant growers now supply plants in small pots or cushions impregnated with a supply of slow-release fertilizer, so that plants will obtain an adequate nutrient supply even in a new aquarium.

Rocks, Driftwood

In addition to plants, materials such as rocks or freshwater driftwood, if waterlogged or weighted, make attractive aquarium decorations. Exercise caution in selecting such decorations, how-

ever, as some rocks and wood contain salts or other soluble substances, such as copper, which may be harmful to fish.

Seashells and shell grit, sometimes used in place of sand, are occasionally observed in freshwater aquariums. These materials dissolve in the water, making it too hard or alkaline for many fish species.

Books on aquarium management frequently contain suggestions and diagrams for arranging plants or other decorations. An often-stated rule of design is that taller plants and other tall decorations should be placed toward the back and sides of the aquarium, with smaller plants and short decorations towards the front. Leave some open swimming room for the fish. Some decorations such as rocks are easier to arrange when a tank is empty. Others such as plants are easier to manipulate when the tank is at least partly filled with water.

Light is needed for aquarium plants. An aquarium reflector or hood fitted with a light serves several purposes even if live plants are not grown in the aquarium. A full reflector prevents excessive evaporation and heat loss from the tank, prevents fish from jumping out (and cats from jumping in), and provides lighting for an attractive display.

Either incandescent or fluorescent lights may be used. The initial cost of fluorescent lights is generally greater, but they are less expensive to operate. Each watt of fluorescent lighting provides about three times the light given by one watt of tungsten filament lighting. Fluorescent lights designed specifically to enhance plant growth are available.

Heaters, Filters

Temperature changes of more than a few degrees may cause shock, which frequently may be followed by disease. Most tropical fish prefer temperatures generally within the range of 70° to 80° F (21° to 27° C). Aquarium temperatures can be maintained easily through use of thermostatically controlled submersible heaters. Aquarium thermometers are widely available.

An aquarium filter is one of the most useful accessories. Many filter types are available. Some are placed under the aquarium gravel and use the gravel as the filtering medium. Others are contained in small boxes which fit in a corner inside the aquarium. Some pump water to a filter box or canister outside the aquarium. All filters use a filtering medium such as the above-mentioned gravel, activated carbon, clay beads, glass wool, or synthetic fiber pads. Often a combination is used.

Aquarium filters serve a variety of functions. Besides drawing off suspended irritating particles from the water, they can remove ammonia that is excreted by fish as a waste product and certain other dissolved chemical impurities from the water. Some of this water purification is achieved by chemical means: activated carbon removes chlorine and clay beads remove ammonia, for example.

Aquariums

Helpful Bacteria

A mechanism known as biological filtration is more important than chemical filtration in many types of filters. During the first two to three weeks after a new aquarium is set up, populations of beneficial bacteria become established in the filter medium. The first bacteria established (members of the genus *Nitrosomonas*) convert toxic ammonia excreted by the fish to another compound, nitrite. Nitrite is also very toxic to fish but is subsequently converted by a second population of filter bacteria (members of the genus *Nitrobacter*) to nitrate, which is relatively nontoxic.

The maximum concentration of ammonia considered safe for continuous exposure of fish is 0.02 parts per million (ppm); more ammonia is present in a toxic form as pH increases. The maximum concentration of nitrite for continuous exposure is 0.1 ppm in soft water and 0.2 ppm in hard water.

To help speed establishment of the filter bacteria and prevent buildup of toxic levels of ammonia and nitrite in new tanks, many aquarists "seed" the filters in these tanks with some filter medium from healthy, established tanks. It is also wise to merely rinse and retain some of the old filter medium when cleaning a filter in an established tank, as a total change of filter medium will result in loss of the beneficial bacterial populations in the filter.

Besides their water purification functions, many filters serve to aerate the aquarium water—largely by increasing water movement and gas exchange at the air-water interface. To further increase aeration, aquarists often place one or more airstones driven by a small electric pump in the aquarium.

After an aquarium has been set up complete with a filter, heater, lights and decorations, wait a few days before introducing fish. This allows time for the aquarist to check for leaks and make sure all systems function properly.

Selecting Fish

With the large number of fish species available to the aquarist, it is often difficult to narrow choices. A good book on aquarium fish and a knowledgeable aquarium shop proprietor can assist greatly in this task.

Several important factors must be considered in selecting fish. One is the maximum size the fish will attain. For

Keeping Fish Healthy

example, although an arowana may be attractive in a 15-gallon tank as a 3-inch juvenile, this attractiveness may quickly diminish if its owner has not planned for its eventual growth to 18 inches or more.

Temperament is another consideration. Fish species that tend to be bullies or fin-nippers generally will make life miserable for timid species.

A third important factor is water condition requirements. Fish which require hard alkaline water may have difficulty adapting to a tank set up with soft acid water conditions, and fish with a preferred temperature range

Temperament of the fish. The Labeotropheus fuelleborni, *a popular cichlid species, is relatively easy to spawn, but has an aggressive temperament, while the dwarf gourami* (Colisa lalia) *is a peaceful, somewhat timid fish popular for community aquariums.*

Aquariums

R. Elliott

Water condition requirements.
There are many bizarre goldfish
varieties bearing names such as
bubble eye, celestial telescope,
lionhead, pearlscale and, pictured
here, the red cap oranda goldfish.
Peaceful and hardy, goldfish have
a wide temperature tolerance, but
preferred range is 50°–70° F
(10°–21° C).

R. Elliott

Food requirements. The cichlid
prefers live food and is probably
not a suitable companion for one-
inch tetras. Sea anemones are
carnivorous and will kill many
fish, but the clown or anemone
fish (Amphiprion sp.) are not
harmed by the stinging tentacles.

of 65° to 70° F (18° to 21° C)
probably will have difficulty
adapting to a tank at 80° F
(27° C).

A fourth consideration is
habitat requirements. A cichlid which loves to dig in the
gravel and move it about the
tank is probably not the best
candidate for an aquarium
with a carefully manicured
aquascape.

A fifth factor is food requirements. An eight-inch
cichlid that prefers live food is
probably not a suitable companion for one-inch tetras,
and a plant-eating silver dollar characin is probably not
the best addition to an aquarium beautifully decorated
with live plants.

Look Fish Over

After selecting fish species for
an aquarium, observe them
carefully in the tanks at the
store. Watch for disease signs
such as listlessness, clamped
fins, poor coloration, emaciation or visible lesions, abnormal spots, skin ulcers, and
frayed fins. A conscientious
and knowledgeable dealer will
not knowingly sell diseased
animals, but time may not always be available to scruti-
nize each tank carefully.

Move fish to their new
aquarium as quickly as possible. Avoid overheating and

chilling. A car trunk is not a good place for tropical fish on a freezing winter day.

Before putting fish in the aquarium, check the temperature in both the aquarium and the container holding the fish. If there is a difference of more than a few degrees, float the fish container on the aquarium surface for 15 to 30 minutes (or until temperatures are about the same) before releasing the fish. When new fish are to be put into an established tank of fish, it is best to first place the new fish in a quarantine tank for about two weeks and observe them for disease signs.

Feeding Guidelines

Nutritional requirements of most aquarium fish are not thoroughly known. With so many species and diverse feeding habits, no single diet will satisfy all the fish. Fortunately, many pet shops and most aquarium fish specialty shops supply a good selection of live, frozen and dried fish foods. Separate formulations of dried foods now are available for herbivorous, carnivorous and omnivorous fish.

Many beginning aquarists have a tendency to overfeed their fish. Uneaten food will quickly foul a tank, overload the filter system, and have fa-

tal consequences. It is better to feed fish small amounts several times a day then to give them one huge meal per day. A general rule is that fish should be fed only enough prepared food at one time so that practically all of it is consumed within five minutes. If fish are overfed accidentally, siphon uneaten food from the tank.

Crowding is another common tendency among aquarists. Adding "just one more fish" to an already crowded aquarium is dangerous, as it may overtax capacity of the filtration and aeration systems—resulting in an outbreak of disease.

A commonly-used guideline for aquarium capacity is that one inch (length) of fish can be maintained in each gallon of water without aeration or filtration, or that two inches of fish can be maintained in each gallon of aerated and filtered water.

The guideline is only a rough approximation of fish-carrying capacity, however, as many factors may affect fish-carrying capacity. These include water surface area, water temperature (less oxygen dissolves as temperature increases), or fish species (active species consume more oxygen than sedentary ones).

Aquariums

Avoiding Stress

Many disease problems develop because fish are stressed by unfavorable environmental conditions. It is therefore important to regularly monitor temperature, pH, and ammonia and nitrite concentrations. Check aeration and filtration systems periodically to make certain they are functioning properly. Water should be smelled for foul odors, observed for general clarity and cleanliness, and gravel looked over to be sure it is loose and free of excessive or matted debris.

Finally, the fish themselves are good indicators of environmental quality. Fish should be alert, with good appetites and fin spread. They should not exhibit peculiar swimming motions such as "head-wagging" or "flashing" (rubbing against the sides or bottom of the tank).

Regular water changes, including siphoning accumulated debris from the aquarium bottom, can help to prevent dangerous deterioration of environmental conditions. At least once a month replace about 25 to 50 percent of the aquarium water with clean dechlorinated water. Take care to avoid sudden drastic changes of temperature and pH at this time.

With a minimal amount of regular monitoring and maintenance, an aquarium of ornamental fish can be both enjoyable and educational. If maintained under proper environmental conditions, many ornamental species will even reward their owners by breeding in the aquarium.

FURTHER READING

Aquaculture: The Farming and Husbandry of Freshwater and Marine Organisms. J.E. Bardach. John Wiley and Co., Inc., 1 Wiley Drive, Somerset, NJ 08873. $34.95.

Diseases of Pacific Salmon: Their Prevention and Treatment. J. Wood. Washington State Fisheries, 115 General Administration Building, Olympia, WA 98504. $5.00.

Exotic Tropical Fishes. H.R. Axelrod. Tropical Fish Hobbies Publishing Company, 211 Sylvia Avenue, Neptune City, NJ 07753. $39.95.

Fish Biologics: Serodiagnostics and Vaccines. D.P. Anderson and W. Hennessen. Karger Publishing Inc., 150 5th Avenue, Suite 1105, New York, NY 10011. $56.60.

Fish Disease Leaflets. Technical Information Service, U.S. Fish and Wildlife Service, Leetown—National Fisheries Center, Box 700, Kearneysville, WV 25430. Free.

Fish Farming Handbook. E.E. Brown and J.B. Gratzek. Avi Publishing Company, 250 Post Road East, Westport, CT 06881. $27.50.

Fish Hatchery Management. R.G. Piper. American Fisheries Society, 5410 Grosvenor Lane, Suite 110, Bethesda, MD 20814. $26.50.

Parasites of North American Freshwater Fishes. G.L. Hoffman. University of California Press, 2120 Berkeley Way, Berkeley, CA 94720. $39.50.

Keeping Fish Healthy

VII. DOGS AND CATS

Marie T. Sebrechts

Marie T. Sebrechts

How Diseases Invade and Are Fought

By Johnny D. Hoskins and
John D. Rhoades

Disease may be defined as an alteration of the state of the body, or of some of its organs, which interrupts or disturbs the proper performance of bodily functions. Functional disturbance soon is manifested by physical signs which the animal detects by its sensations and which usually can be detected by humans.

Disease may be of external or internal origin. Little is known about the fundamental causes of the intrinsic diseases. These include metabolic and endocrine disturbances, degeneration of organs from age, tumors, and possibly autoimmunity.

Johnny D. Hoskins is Professor of Veterinary Clinical Medicine, School of Veterinary Medicine, Louisiana State University, Baton Rouge. John D. Rhoades is Professor of Veterinary Medicine and Coordinator of Public Programs at the school.

It is probable that many of these disorders are initiated by extrinsic causes as yet unrecognized. The external causes of disease may be living agents such as bacteria, protozoa, or viruses, or they may be nonliving agents such as injury, heat, cold, chemical poisons, or food deficiencies.

When living agents enter an animal body and set up a disturbance of function in any part, infection is said to have occurred. An infectious disease is one caused by the presence in or on an animal of a foreign living organism, which creates a disturbance leading to the development of signs of illness.

Spread of Infections

Most infections are caused by living organisms that have escaped from the same or another species. This occurs when a human develops rabies from a dog bite, or when a lapdog contracts tu-

USDA

George Robinson, USDA

USDA

Robin West, USDA-APHIS

The choice of a pet means multiple choices . . . a dog or a cat? . . . will it live indoors or out, fenced in or running free? . . . will it help you at work, go hunting with you or be a companion for you and your children? . . . what is the personality, lifestyle and age of the person who will be the pet's master? . . . the choice is yours. You should consider that dogs and cats have personalities as varied as those of man . . . passive, aggressive, lazy, active, loving, independent, you name it.

How Diseases Invade   373

berculosis from its consumptive master.

An infection may be obtained indirectly, as when typhoid fever is contracted by people from contaminated drinking water. Some infections originate from organisms that normally live a free existence in nature—for example, the bacillus of tetanus.

Fates of Invaders. Several possible fates await organisms that cause infections. Some organisms are destroyed by the infected animal's tissue. Infections are not accomplished without resistance on the part of the host, because the host-parasite relationship is not a natural one.

Capacity of the host to destroy invading agents is so great that a large majority of the foreign agents that manage to reach living tissues and fluids of the body are rapidly and completely destroyed. In other cases the resistance is not sufficient to prevent growth and multiplication in the tissues, but the infection does not become extensive, and after a brief time the invading organisms are destroyed.

Sometimes the agent persists and makes slow headway against the resistance of the host, in which case the infection is called chronic.

In a few infections, resistance of the host is overwhelmed so quickly that the organism multiplies in all parts and early death of the host ensues. These cases are known as acute.

Eliminating the Agent
Some organisms usually are eliminated in the secretions or excretions of the host. The diseased animal usually eliminates, in a manner that varies with the disease, the organism that causes it. In chronic infections the host usually eliminates large numbers of the infecting agent.

Sometimes this agent is removed through pus, as when an abscess bursts or is lanced; sometimes through droplets that are discharged when the individual is suffering from one of the respiratory infections, as canine distemper, tuberculosis, or human diphtheria; sometimes in the intestinal discharges (feces) as in the various forms of intestinal parvovirus infections of animals and in human intestinal infections; and sometimes in the urine, as in leptospirosis and in typhoid fever of humans.

In some diseases that become extensive and even fatal, the causative organism may be eliminated in small numbers or not at all, as in some cases of tuberculosis.

The more chronic the disease becomes, the less likelihood there is that the animal will continue to retain all the infecting organisms.

In some diseases the mechanism by which the infection escapes from one animal to another is peculiar, as in rabies, where the seat of the infection is the nervous system and the means of escape is through the salivary glands.

Dead Animal Risks

If the disease proves fatal to the animal, many of the infecting organisms are destroyed with the carcass. However, death of an animal from infection always traps in the carcass a large number of the involved organisms.

If the carcass is disposed of properly by incineration or deep burial, these organisms perish. Improper disposal of the dead bodies of animals may result in serious outbreaks of disease.

Impasses. In some instances the organism and host reach an impasse. The organism is unable to cause serious damage to the host, and yet the host is unable to eliminate the organism.

This situation may continue throughout the lifetime of the animal, or it may be terminated either by the final elimination of the infection or by a change in which the infection becomes more active and signs of disease are manifested by the host.

In tuberculosis of both humans and animals, the tubercle bacilli may become walled off by dense tissue in some of the organs and the case is said to be arrested. Such cases are not entirely cured because living tubercle organisms may continue to exist in the tissues and sometimes they break forth and cause a flareup of the disease.

In people, recovery from typhoid fever usually leaves the individual with many typhoid bacilli in the urine and stools that may persist for weeks, months, and years.

Individuals who discharge virulent organisms with their excretions, although apparently normal otherwise, are said to be *carriers*. The carrier is one of the great problems in the control of many infectious diseases. Animals that are obviously diseased may be recognized, but there is no simple way of recognizing the carrier.

Sources of Infection

The courses by which infections reach dogs or cats may

How Diseases Invade

be indirect and complicated. Direct or immediate contact with a diseased individual is the most common way an infection is acquired.

Indirect methods may include contact with objects such as food bowls, water containers, bedding and toys that serve to carry infections from one animal to another; contact with bacterial or fungal laden soil, ingestion of contaminated food and water; inhalation of contagious airborne organisms; infections from blood-sucking insects; infections from organisms residing in part of the body and spread through an action such as bite wounds or from breeding.

Ability to invade and multiply in living tissues varies among disease-producing organisms. Some organisms that are malignant-disease producers have little invasive ability and do most of their damage while growing in restricted parts of the body. They generate powerful poisons, or toxins, that are absorbed and circulated throughout the body.

The tetanus organism usually remains localized in a wound which may be very insignificant in size, but generates tetanus toxin which is carried to the nervous system where the damage is done.

The organism of human diphtheria is rarely found in the internal organs but is usually restricted to membranes of the throat, where the diphtheria toxin is generated. These bacteria produce systemic diseases only because of the absorption of their toxins.

Host Defense System

When organisms penetrate the body they usually are quickly recognized as foreign to the host. A sequence of host responses are elicited that may be local or distributed over the body.

Elevation of body temperature is frequently the initial host response to infection. Thereafter, any one or more of the constitutional signs of depression, not eating, vomiting, diarrhea, inactivity, coughing, sneezing, and difficulty in breathing follows.

The body defense mechanisms are sequentially activated which results in immunoglobulins with specific antibody activity by the host animal. In addition to antibodies being formed, specific cells in the body are recruited such as lymphocytes and macrophages to further combat the infection.

Preventing infection. One of the most significant advances in medicine in the last

376

50 years has been the prevention of many infectious diseases that once killed large numbers of dogs and cats. Prevention is possible because it has become technologically feasible to develop safe and efficacious vaccines that are easily administered and offer long-term protection.

The purpose of a vaccination program is to prevent the development of clinical disease, either by preventing or limiting infection.

Vaccine introduced into an animal will heighten the host defense system primarily by stimulating production of antibodies and secondarily by stimulating activity of both lymphocytes and macrophages.

Numerous factors can influence the host defense system and thus affect the immune response to the vaccine. These factors include the effects of colostral antibody, nature of the vaccine, route of administration of the vaccine, age of the animal, its general nutritional condition, concurrent infections, and drug treatments.

Soon after birth, puppies and kittens born to immune mothers absorb large quantities of immunoglobulin from the first milk or colostrum. Following absorption, the colostral antibodies have the ability to prevent most vaccines from generating an active immunity.

It is necessary, therefore, for this acquired antibody to reach low levels before active immunization is possible. For puppies and kittens with high levels of colostral antibodies, this period of uncertain response to vaccination may be as long as 12 to 16 weeks after birth.

Colostral antibodies also are extremely important for protection of the newborn against a multitude of potentially harmful organisms during the first few weeks of life. Therefore, it is essential that puppies and kittens have access to colostrum at birth.

Handling Vaccines

Manufactures make killed, modified live, or live vaccine according to the type of organism one is protecting the animal against. The vaccine should always be handled according to directions supplied by the manufacturer so that it will do what it is supposed to do.

To achieve maximum success the entire dose of vaccine should be given as recommended. Vaccine should be given by the method recommended by the manufacturer

How Diseases Invade

because the animal's response depends on the route of administration of the vaccine.

Age also is important because of a relative decrease in body temperature during the first week or two of life that causes a state of body unresponsiveness. Vaccination during this early period generally is not recommended.

There also is evidence to suggest that certain older animals (seven years of age or more) may have a decreased ability to respond to infections and vaccines. Annual vaccination during these later years is particularly important to maintain an active state of immunity.

Severely debilitated animals may not respond adequately to a vaccine. The general state of nutrition should meet minimal standards to ensure that nutritional factors do not interfere with immune responsiveness. Animals with the disease or incubating the disease will not respond to vaccine against a particular disease agent.

A detailed history about the possibility of exposure to infected animals should be known and a thorough physical examination should be done for every animal receiving a vaccination in order to minimize this risk. Some diseases also suppress the animal's response and may potentially interfere with successful vaccination. Vaccines should not be given concurrently with drugs that suppress the animal's response.

A vaccination program for dogs and cats is an extremely important part of the health care of the animal when it is done properly.

Keeping 'Em Healthy

To sum up and add a few things, preventive medicine is the dominant theme in owning and caring for dogs and cats.

Disease incidence can be reduced by altering animal susceptibility and decreasing exposure of susceptible animals. Isolation and treatment of animals with disease is necessary.

For most infectious agents, the spectrum of host response is wide. Some animals may not develop disease following infection but may become important as a source of infection for other dogs and cats by becoming carriers.

In many infectious diseases, the period of maximal shedding and communicability precedes the signs of disease.

Recognition and interruption of the spread of disease organisms is an important

USDA-APHIS

Robin West, USDA-APHIS

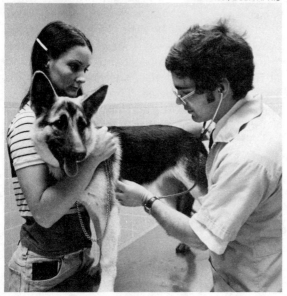

Preventive medicine is the key to dog and cat health. A thorough physical examination should be done for every animal receiving a vaccination. There's no need to be concerned when your pet needs some treatment. If you can relax, you'll help your pet relax.

How Diseases Invade

379

role in disease control. The vector-borne or fecal-oral transmitted diseases can be controlled by good sanitation and hygiene.

Disinfectants, antiseptics, and sanitizers are used to reduce or eliminate pathogenic micro-organisms. These commercial solutions usually will be effective in doing what they claim if diluted and applied as recommended by the manufacturer.

Of the infectious diseases of dogs and cats, the viruses that cause canine parvovirus infection and feline panleukopenia are most resistant to disinfectants. A 0.175 percent sodium hypochlorite solution (household bleach) is the only presently known effective disinfectant for these two diseases.

Many excellent vaccines are available for immunizing cats and dogs against infectious diseases. If the vaccines are used correctly and at the proper ages, animals should be protected against very severe infections. It behooves cat and dog owners to immunize their animals regularly and let the animals benefit from modern medical technology.

Getting a New Pet. When you get a new dog or cat, avoid getting an animal that is sick. The animal should have clear eyes that are free of irritation, tears or other discharges; have clean ears free of ear mites and any other foreign material; have pink gums free of sores; have a full normal haircoat and a firm and muscular body that is free from rashes.

The animal also should come from clean premises to clean premises.

If an animal has died of an infectious disease on your property, new animals should not be brought in for at least three to four weeks following removal of the dead animal and after the premises are disinfected. Thoroughly disinfect water and food bowls and remove those items that are disposable.

Distemper, Other Infectious Dog Diseases

By Johnny D. Hoskins and
John D. Rhoades

The most important infectious diseases affecting dogs are canine distemper, infectious canine hepatitis, leptospirosis, parvovirus infection, kennel cough, and rabies. Other infectious diseases that affect dogs do not occur as frequently.

Canine Distemper

Canine distemper is a severe, highly contagious, worldwide viral disease of dogs and other carnivores. It is caused by a virus closely related to but not the same as measles virus. All forms of the disease are caused by the same virus but the duration and type of diseases produced by different

---

Johnny D. Hoskins is Professor of Veterinary Clinical Medicine, School of Veterinary Medicine, Louisiana State University, Baton Rouge. John D. Rhoades is Professor of Veterinary Medicine and Coordinator of Public Programs at the school.

canine distemper strains vary greatly.

In the early stages it is characterized by discharges from eyes and nose and signs referable to digestive and respiratory involvement. In later stages there are signs referable to nervous system involvement.

The disease's incidence is highest in young dogs, but susceptible dogs of all ages may become infected. Young dogs become susceptible to canine distemper when they lose colostral antibody, usually between 6 and 12 weeks of age. Young dogs between 3 and 6 months of age are affected most often by the disease.

Infection of susceptible animals usually occurs by inhalation of airborne organisms, and the virus spreads throughout the body. These animals develop fever, depression, eye and nose discharges, and coughing. Diarrhea and

Infectious Dog Diseases

occasional vomiting frequently occur simultaneously.

The animal's condition deteriorates with accompanying weight loss and dehydration. Animals eventually become moribund with or without nervous system signs.

Some dogs may show improvement after the first signs are seen, but weeks or months later develop nervous system disturbances that terminate in death or lifelong impairment of the nervous system.

Chewing Gum Fit. Convulsions, chomping the jaws (chewing gum fit), incoordination, pacing, circling, and psychic changes are common in early disease states. Rhythmic movements of the jaws, ears, or legs, caused by twitching muscles and usually called chorea, may occur after other signs subside. Blindness, hardpad disease, and reproductive failures are other problems that can occur because of canine distemper.

With the use of vaccines and antibiotics, canine distemper disease has changed. Use of vaccines has controlled viral strains that induce early disease better than strains causing delayed disease. Use of antibiotics has reduced the incidence of digestive and respiratory involvement due to bacterial infections that ac-

company the viral infection.

Diagnosis can be difficult to make in dogs that have a delayed form. Laboratory tests, such as fluorescent antibody tests, virus isolation and neutralization test, frequently are required to diagnose canine distemper.

Immunization is the preferred method of preventing canine distemper. Potent and safe modified live-virus vaccines are available and induce good immunity in dogs.

Because colostral antibody interferes with vaccination, dogs should be vaccinated repeatedly. In most cases, 3 vaccinations are given, at 8 weeks, 12 weeks, and 16 weeks of age.

Because of antibody loss, vaccinated dogs can develop canine distemper several years later after receiving vaccinations as puppies. Annual revaccinations throughout the dog's life are recommended because of loss of their antibody protection.

Infectious Canine Hepatitis also is a severe, highly contagious, viral disease of dogs. It is caused by an adenovirus and is related to the large group of adenoviruses that cause a variety of diseases in humans and lower animals.

The virus that causes infectious canine hepatitis is not infectious for people. The virus is spread from dog to dog through the urine, and a dog may shed the virus from the kidneys in the urine for long periods of time after apparent recovery. Infection usually is acquired by contact of infective material such as urine or saliva in the mouth.

This disease is seen most frequently in young dogs, but can be seen in all ages of dogs. The affected animal becomes apathetic and loses its appetite and may frequently have an intense thirst. At this time the body temperature increases and swelling of the head, neck, and lower portion of the abdomen may occur.

Vomiting and diarrhea are common. Many animals manifest pain by moaning, especially when pressure is brought to bear on the abdominal wall.

Only rarely does jaundice occur. The gums usually are pale and sometimes hemorrhages appear on them. The tonsils frequently are enlarged and painful.

Progression of this disease is much more rapid than distemper. Most dogs have either recovered or are dead within 2 weeks. Many die within a few days.

Tests, Vaccines. Infec-
tious canine hepatitis must be differentiated from canine distemper, leptospirosis, parvovirus infection, and the effects of certain poisons. Diagnosis is especially difficult in young puppies. Results of laboratory tests reflecting damage to liver and kidneys strengthen a presumptive diagnosis which has been based on history and physical examination.

Specific diagnosis depends on demonstration of the virus in blood or liver tissue. This is accomplished by using fluorescent antibody test or virus isolation in liver cell cultures.

Recovery from infectious canine hepatitis produces a long-lasting immunity.

Modified live-virus vaccine is mostly used for immunization. Vaccination will be ineffective until the puppy has lost essentially all of its colostral antibody.

Products currently available for immunization against infectious canine hepatitis are usually combined with canine distemper virus.

Blue Eye. The first modified live-virus vaccine for infectious canine hepatitis contained the virus called adenovirus-1 which occasionally caused an immune-mediated "blue eye" condition. The eye problem would disappear spontaneously and did not cause damage if managed conservatively.

Recently a modified live-virus called adenovirus-2 was approved to replace canine adenovirus-1 in vaccines and the "blue eye" condition is no longer a problem. This modification has been very helpful in improving the protection against infectious canine hepatitis.

Vaccination of puppies is given at the same time as canine distemper, 8 weeks, 12 weeks, and 16 weeks. Annual revaccination is also recommended for dogs of all ages.

Leptospirosis

This disease of dogs is caused by *Leptospira canicola* and *Leptospira icterohemorrhagiae*. Leptospirosis is significant from a public health aspect because dogs and other animals can act as reservoirs for human infections.

Leptospira organisms are easily killed by heat and disinfectants. They will survive for long periods outside the body in water or sewage. Alkalinity of urine or water favors their survival, and acidity will cause their death within a few hours.

Infected animals, such as wild rodents and livestock, can contaminate food and water. The most common method of spread is thought to be direct contact or ingestion of contaminated food and water.

Outbreaks have occurred in humans and dogs after floods, or after swimming in or drinking water contaminated by urine of rodents or other animals. Leptospira organisms enter the body through abrasions in the skin or mucous membranes.

Animals may carry the organisms and shed them in the urine for months or years after apparent recovery from the disease.

Signs of leptospirosis in dogs are quite varied in severity depending on an individual animal's response to the infection. The onset of signs generally is sudden with high fever, not eating, vomiting, and diarrhea. Dehydration and depression result if the preceding signs are severe.

Reddening of the membranes of the eyes and mouth is common. Jaundice usually occurs with infection caused by *Leptospira icterohemorrhagiae*.

Pain in the abdomen is evident when liver, kidney or gastrointestinal tract is severely affected. Ulcers in the mouth are seen in animals that develop kidney failure.

A positive diagnosis of leptospirosis is based on finding organisms in the urine or blood with a history of liver and kidney disease. Demonstration of a rising leptospira titer in paired blood serum samples when taken at least one week apart is evidence of active infection.

Antibiotics are very effective for treating leptospirosis in dogs.

Owners of infected dogs should be aware of the potential health hazard and efforts should be made to determine the source of the infection.

Death occurs frequently from severe damage to the liver and kidneys.

Leptospiral vaccine is available and effective in preventing the disease in dogs. Animals should be vaccinated for leptospirosis when they receive their distemper-hepatitis vaccine. Annual revaccination is recommended for effective immunity.

Canine Parvovirus Infection is a relatively new disease of dogs, which was first described in 1977. The disease is caused by a small DNA-containing virus that requires rapidly dividing cells for its growth to occur in the body. Therefore young, rapidly growing dogs are most susceptible to severe disease.

Susceptible dogs are rapidly infected and canine parvovirus is very contagious. The main source of infection is ingestion of materials contaminated with feces from infected dogs.

Two Forms of Disease. There are two distinct forms of the disease. One involves the intestines and the other the heart.

Severity of the disease depends primarily on the age and immune status of the dog. The most severe and often fatal disease occurs in puppies less than 12 weeks old.

In the *intestinal* form the parvovirus grows in epithelial cells of the small intestine and rapidly destroys them.

Young dogs are affected initially by vomiting followed by diarrhea, refusal to eat, and severe dehydration. The feces appear yellow-gray and often are streaked or darkened by blood. Elevated body temperature and a decrease in white blood cell numbers are usually present in severe cases.

Recovery from the infection may be complicated by additional problems such as bacteria, parasites, or other viruses.

Young puppies less than 8 weeks old may suffer severe heart problems due to virus

Infectious Dog Diseases

damage. The heart enlarges, leading to severe circulatory malfunction and heart failure.

The Heart Form of the disease may be preceded by the intestinal form or may occur suddenly without apparent previous disease. Although the infection of the heart may occur at 6 to 8 weeks of age the dog may not experience heart failure until 6 to 9 months of age in some cases.

Fresh feces taken from affected animals early in the course of intestinal disease may contain large numbers of virus particles. These can be identified by electron microscopic examination of the feces or by performing other laboratory tests on them. Virus identification or isolation accompanying the history and physical examination usually is diagnostic for the disease.

Diagnosis of the heart form of this disease generally is based entirely on the history of heart disease confirmed by physical examination.

An effective immunization program is the key to controlling canine parvovirus infection. Safe and effective killed-virus and modified live-virus vaccines are commercially available for use in dogs. Dogs should be vaccinated for canine parvovirus infection when they receive their distemper-hepatitis-leptospirosis vaccine. Annual revaccination is recommended for effective immunity.

Kennel Cough

Any contagious respiratory disease of dogs that is manifested by coughing and not caused by canine distemper is often referred to as kennel cough.

The disease is more accurately called infectious tracheo-bronchitis and is defined as an infectious respiratory disease of dogs marked by coughing and in some cases by fever, not eating, and pneumonia. It is caused by various viruses and/or bacteria alone or in combination.

The viruses most frequently incriminated as causes of kennel cough are canine distemper virus, canine adenovirus-2, and canine parainfluenza virus. Many different bacteria have been incriminated as causing signs of kennel cough but *Bordetella bronchiseptica* can produce signs that are indistinguishable from those of virus-caused kennel cough.

Kennel cough occurs primarily when dogs of varying ages and susceptibility are congregated under less than

USDA-APHIS

When you have to kennel your dog, make sure the kennel you choose is clean and well-managed.

ideal hygienic conditions.

Animals taken immediately from pet shops, animal shelters, animal control facilities, and boarding and training kennels are more likely to experience kennel cough. The kennel cough agents are quickly spread when an infected dog coughs.

The most prominent sign of disease is a cough. Except for the cough, a dog usually appears to be healthy. The cough is mostly dry and hacking and followed by gagging or expectoration of mucus. Excitement, exercise, drastic changes in weather, or even gentle pressure on the trachea will induce episodes of coughing.

Shedding of the kennel cough organisms in respiratory secretions of dogs that are asymptomatic accounts for the persistence of these infections in dog kennels, animal control facilities and boarding facilities. Most dogs with kennel cough infections are older than 6 months of age.

Puppies Hard Hit. The most severe form of kennel cough is seen in dogs that are 6 weeks to 6 months of age. Animals seen in this age range generally are not vaccinated and have a fever and lack of appetite.

In this form the cough is less apparent and if present is moist. Coughing may be so painful that the animal attempts to suppress it. This form of kennel cough progresses rapidly into pneumonia.

It is extremely difficult to distinguish the signs of this

Infectious Dog Diseases

form of kennel cough from those of canine distemper. Many cases originally diagnosed as severe kennel cough prove to be canine distemper and vice versa.

Diagnosis of kennel cough is difficult and usually based on the history and physical examination. It is established by eliminating other possible causes of coughing.

Viral and bacterial vaccines now are available to control the principal agents involved in kennel cough. Combination vaccines are available to use against canine distemper, canine adenovirus-2, canine parainfluenza, and *Bordetella bronchiseptica* infections in dogs.

Dogs should be vaccinated for kennel cough when they receive their early puppy immunizations. Annual revaccination is recommended for effective protection against kennel cough.

Coronavirus
Canine Enteric Coronavirus
Infections. In 1971 a canine coronavirus was isolated from feces of military dogs that were suffering from severe vomiting and diarrhea. This is known to cause a highly contagious viral disease that spreads rapidly from infected dogs to susceptible dogs by

way of contaminated feces.

Animals usually experience a sudden onset of diarrhea preceded at times by vomiting. The feces generally is orange in color, very malodorous, and infrequently contains blood.

Inactivity and loss of appetite are common signs accompanying the diarrhea. Elevation in body temperature is infrequent.

When complicating factors such as parasites, bacteria, or other viruses are present, the disease can be significantly prolonged.

Diagnosis usually is based on the history and physical examination and the identification of coronavirus by electron microscopic examination of feces or by performing other laboratory tests on the feces. At the present time an acceptable vaccine is not available for immunization.

Canine Brucellosis
This may be caused by bacterial species of the genus *Brucella;* however, the most common in the dog is *Brucella canis.* Brucellosis occurs worldwide and *Brucella canis* has been reported in nearly all States in the United States.

Infection can occur readily across all mucous membranes. The oral and venereal routes are the most common. Transmission occurs readily when an uninfected bitch in heat is mated to an infected male. Similarly, males may acquire the infection from infected females in heat.

The organism can be isolated from urine of infected dogs, but urine does not appear to be an important factor in natural spread of the disease.

Semen from infected males contains the organism for long periods of time presumably due to persistent infection in the prostate and epididymal tissues. Materials aborted by an infected female will contain large numbers of organisms which contaminates the environment around the animal.

Human Infections have occurred in owners of infected dogs. Owners of infected animals should be aware that the disease can occur in people and they are at risk being around the animal.

Diagnosis of canine brucellosis cannot be established by physical examination alone. In general, dogs with canine brucellosis are not seriously ill, and deaths of adult dogs due to *Brucella canis* infection have not occurred.

What to Look for. One is alerted to brucellosis by sudden abortion by an otherwise healthy bitch, failure to conceive after breeding, and alteration in size of the male genitalia. In rare cases the organism can cause damage to the spine and causes extreme pain and neurological problems in the rear legs.

Diagnosis may be suspected on historical information but should be confirmed on demonstration of specific antibodies in the dog's blood. Attempts to isolate *Brucella canis* from the blood, semen, or vaginal discharge from suspected animals should be done.

The potential of canine brucellosis being transmitted to people should be considered when contemplating treatment. Currently dogs are treated with antibiotics for canine brucellosis with some success.

Treatment must be evaluated by attempts to isolate *Brucella canis* from blood and specific antibody tests performed 6 to 8 weeks after cessation of therapy. Additionally, infected animals should be castrated or spayed in order to reduce spread of the disease through breeding.

No vaccine currently is available against canine brucellosis.

Infectious Dog Diseases

Because of the devastating effect of brucellosis on the reproductive usefulness of infected dogs, breeders should be strongly encouraged to mate their dogs only to animals which have been proven brucellosis free. Prebreeding examination for any bitch or stud should be required.

Rickettsial Diseases

These diseases in dogs vary in occurrence according to the availability of the reservoir and vector of the organism. Canine ehrlichiosis, Salmon disease, Elokomin fluke fever, and Rocky Mountain spotted fever are all diseases caused by rickettsial organisms. Canine ehrlichiosis is caused by infection with *Ehrlichia canis*. *Ehrlichia canis* is transmitted to dogs by bites of the brown dog tick, *Rhipicephalus sanguineus*.

Salmon disease refers to the disease of dogs resulting from ingestion of raw salmon, trout, lampreys, sculpins, and redside shiners that carry rickettsial-infected flukes. Elokomin fluke fever is another fluke-transmitted rickettsial disease which occurs when dogs ingest raw salmon infected with rickettsial-infected flukes.

The term "fluke" applies to a large group of internal parasites of animals and man. They infest various parts of the body, and like insects can transmit certain diseases.

Canine Rocky Mountain spotted fever is caused by infection with *Rickettsia rickettsii*. The *Rickettsia rickettsii* is transmitted to dogs by bites of an infected American dog tick, American wood tick, or brown dog tick. Reservoirs and vectors of the rickettsial disease have to be present in a region for the disease to occur.

Signs of rickettsial disease may vary among dogs but usually include high fever, decreased appetite, and depression. Enlarged lymph nodes frequently are detected.

Dehydration, weight loss, and swelling of the legs and lower portion of the abdomen may occur. Hemorrhages also may be seen on membranes of the mouth and nonpigmented skin.

When death occurs, it usually is due to uncontrolled bleeding or secondary infection resulting from low white blood cell numbers.

Recovery from rickettsial disease in dogs is invariably accompanied by persistent relapses with the organisms unless appropriate antibiotic therapy is given.

The rickettsial diseases in general are very responsive to

antibiotic therapy. Diagnosis is usually suspected through a medical history and confirmed by identification of the organism in blood or tissue cells or specific antibody tests.

Canine Babesiosis

This is caused by the infection with *Babesia canis*, which is prevalent in dogs in the southern United States but has been reported in other parts of the country.

The organism is a one cell animal parasite that usually occurs inside the red blood cells. Common dog ticks transmit the organism from infected dog to a susceptible dog.

Signs of an infection are characterized by fever along with increased pulse and respiration rates. A progressive decrease in red blood cells and jaundice are frequently seen.

Diagnosis of babesiosis is usually based on the history and physical examination along with identification of the red blood cell-laden organisms and specific antibody tests.

Tetanus in dogs is caused by the bacterium, *Clostridium tetani*, whose spores are present in the soil and the feces of various animals.

Most cases of tetanus result from contamination of small puncture wounds and lacerations with the organism from soil or feces. The organism produces toxins that cause the nervous system of the dog to be overstimulated.

The dog experiences spasms of facial muscles that lead to abnormal expressions, erect carriage of the ears, and wrinkling of the skin of the forehead. Spasticity, lockjaw, inability to stand, prolapse of third eyelids, and overextended head, neck, and legs may be seen as the disease progresses. Hypersensitivity to external stimuli occurs in severe cases.

Death usually occurs as a result of failure of the muscles of respiration or other complications that develop during the illness' course.

Regular immunization for protection of dogs against tetanus usually is not recommended.

Botulism in dogs results from ingestion of a toxin produced by the bacterium *Clostridium botulinum*. Animals usually acquire the toxin by ingesting contaminated material such as rotting carcasses or garbage.

Signs of botulism result from the paralyzing effects of the toxin at junctions of the muscles and nerves. The onset is sudden and the animal usually loses normal muscle function with total flaccid paralysis.

Diagnosis of botulism usually is based on history of exposure to contaminated material, and physical examination.

Canine Herpesvirus

This infection causes severe illness and death only in puppies less than 6 weeks old. The agent is a DNA virus and only dogs are known to be susceptible.

Spread of the disease is by direct contact between infected and susceptible dogs. Infected adult dogs may shed virus in oral, nasal, and vaginal secretions for as long as 2 weeks following infection.

Because of the suckling behavior of puppies, a single infected puppy in a litter may readily transfer the infection by way of saliva, feces, and urine to susceptible littermates.

Unborn puppies may be infected in the mother's womb by primary infection of the mother or during passage through the birth canal of the recently exposed bitch.

Illness in young puppies usually occurs between the 5th and 18th day after birth. Signs of illness in puppies are change in the color of feces,

difficulty in breathing, abdominal pain, ceasing to nurse and constant crying. Affected puppies usually die shortly after the onset of signs of disease.

Adult dogs show no real signs of illness during primary infection.

Diagnosis of canine herpesvirus infection usually is based on microscopic examination of tissues taken from dead puppies and by isolating the virus. No vaccines are available for this disease.

Pseudorabies is caused by infection with DNA virus. The disease is seen in areas where dogs are in daily contact with infected swine.

Dogs experience sudden onset of nervous system derangement manifested by intense itching. Self-mutilation is a prominent feature of the disease by the dog's attempt to relieve itching.

The disease progresses to convulsions and paralysis and the dogs die in a coma within 24 to 72 hours.

Diagnosis of canine pseudorabies is based on the history and physical examination. At the present time the low incidence of the disease in dogs in this country has not warranted routine vaccination.

Immunization of Dogs

Disease	Vaccine	Type of Vaccine	Age for Vaccination
Distemper	Canine distemper virus and/or	Modified live virus	First vaccination at 8 weeks; second vaccination at 12 weeks; third vaccination at 16 weeks; revaccinate annually
	Measles virus		Vaccinate at 6 weeks of age, then vaccinate with distemper vaccine at 12 and 16 weeks.Do not use in bitches of breeding age
Hepatitis	Infectious canine hepatitis	Modifed live virus	Vaccination schedule is same as for distemper
Leptospirosis	Leptospirosis	Killed bacterin	Vaccination schedule is same as for distemper
Rabies	Rabies virus	Killed virus or Modified live virus	First vaccination at 3 months of age; revaccinate at 1 year and at least every 3 years thereafter
Respiratory Disease Complex	Canine parainfluenza virus	Modified live virus	Vaccination schedule is same as for distemper
	Canine adenovirus 2	Modified live virus	Vaccination schedule is same as for distemper

Infectious Dog Diseases

Disease	Vaccine	Type of Vaccine	Age for Vaccination
	Bordetella bronchiseptica	Killed bacterin or Live attenuated	First vaccination at 2 to 6 weeks; second vaccination at 12 weeks; 3rd vaccination at 16 weeks; revaccinate every 6 months or annually
Enteric Disease Complex	Canine parvovirus	Killed virus or Modified live virus	Vaccination schedule is same as for distemper
	Canine coronavirus	None licensed	
Herpes	Canine herpesvirus	None available	
Brucellosis	Canine brucellosis	None available	

Infectious Diseases Affecting Cats

By Johnny D. Hoskins and
John D. Rhoades

The most important infectious diseases affecting cats are feline panleukopenia, feline viral respiratory diseases, feline infectious peritonitis, and the feline leukemia virus disease complex. Other infectious diseases affect cats, but do not occur as frequently.

Feline Panleukopenia also is variously termed feline infectious enteritis, or cat distemper. It is caused by a parvovirus (DNA virus).

The virus infects cats of any age but is a disease principally of young cats, with worldwide distribution.

Transmission of the virus

Johnny D. Hoskins is Professor of Veterinary Clinical Medicine, School of Veterinary Medicine, Louisiana State University, Baton Rouge. John D. Rhoades is Professor of Veterinary Medicine and Coordinator of Public Programs at the school.

usually is by direct contact among susceptible and infected cats. Transmission also can occur by way of contaminated food and water dishes, bedding, litter containers, and the hands and clothing of owners.

Recovered cats may shed the virus in their feces for long periods and act as carriers of the disease. The main route of infection to a susceptible cat is the ingestion of contaminated feces.

Infected cats usually will experience fever first, followed by decreased interest in eating, vomiting, and diarrhea. The diarrheal stools are large quantities of liquid feces that are dark with partially digested blood. Frank blood with a lot of mucus in the feces may be seen occasionally.

Severely affected cats will show marked dehydration and depression with their mucous membranes appearing pale.

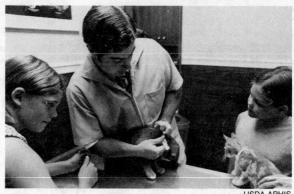

Kittens should be vaccinated at 9 weeks and 12 weeks of age. Because of antibody loss, annual revaccinations are recommended throughout the cat's life.

USDA-APHIS

The virus is capable of passing the placental barrier in pregnant cats. Infection of the fetus results in abortion, stillbirth, early fetal death, or permanent structural brain damage.

Diagnosis of feline panleukopenia depends on recognition of the signs of illness and demonstration of the decrease in the white blood cell numbers.

The virus will affect production of white blood cells formed in the bone marrow and a severe decrease in circulating white blood cells will be seen. If the cat recovers, the white blood cells will quickly return to normal numbers and the diarrhea stops.

Cats that die of panleukopenia generally die of bacterial infection which has complicated the viral infection.

Immunization is the preferred method of preventing feline panleukopenia. Both killed-virus and live-virus vaccines are available and either will induce good protective immunity in cats.

Because colostral antibody interferes with vaccination, cats should be vaccinated repeatedly. In most cases, a minimum of 2 vaccinations are required.

Kittens should be vaccinated at 9 weeks and 12 weeks of age. Because of antibody loss, annual revaccinations are recommended throughout the cat's life.

Vaccinated cats can develop panleukopenia several years after receiving vaccinations as kittens if annual booster injections are not given.

Respiratory Infections

Two viruses, feline herpesvirus and feline calicivirus, have been implicated in respiratory infections in cats. These viruses have been isolated with approximately equal incidence and account for the majority of feline respiratory diseases.

It has been acknowledged for many years that it is not possible to distinguish these viral diseases on grounds other than virus isolations.

Feline herpesvirus is a DNA virus and feline calicivirus is a RNA virus. Shedding of both viruses occurs in all discharges from the nose, eye, and throat, but transmission is largely by direct nose-to-nose contact or by droplets from sneezing cats.

The viruses may persist in cats for a long period after infection, hence infected cats become carriers of the viruses. Infected carriers excrete virus intermittently from the nose and throat.

Infection generally remains in the upper portion of the respiratory tract, although the viruses may cause infection of fetuses and abortion in pregnant cats.

Early in the course of the disease infected cats usually will experience depression, sneezing and coughing. Progression to serous ocular and nasal discharges with elevated body temperature is rapid. Both viruses may cause ulcers in the mouth but corneal ulceration appears only in feline herpesvirus infections.

When the herpesvirus infection is confined to the upper respiratory tract, it generally is referred to as *feline viral rhinotracheitis.*

Pneumonia is more likely to occur with calicivirus infections.

Diagnosis of feline viral respiratory disease is made on the basis of signs of the illness, especially the pronounced sneezing and the ocular and nasal discharges. Definitive diagnosis of the viral cause of the infection depends solely on virus isolation and identification.

Immunization for both viruses produces significant protection following vaccination. Vaccines against the viruses are included in combination with the panleukopenia virus.

Two vaccinations are required for all ages. Kittens should be vaccinated at 9 weeks and 12 weeks. There should be a 3-week interval between vaccinations for adult cats. Annual revaccination is recommended.

Some vaccinated cats may sneeze, and an occasional one may have watery eyes for one to two days. Severe disease does not occur in properly immunized cats.

Infectious Cat Diseases

Infectious Peritonitis

This disease was first seen in the early 1950's in various parts of the United States and named in 1966. The disease has been reported throughout North America.

Cause of feline infectious peritonitis is a coronavirus. Coronavirus infections are relatively common in domestic cats but the majority of these infections do not produce signs of disease.

Feline infectious peritonitis affects cats of all ages, although the prevalence is highest in animals one to two years old. There appears to be no apparent breed predisposition. Initial exposure to the virus may result in mild respiratory disease as indicated by runny eyes and nose.

The majority of cats with this mild respiratory disease recover, with some of them serving as carriers of the virus. An even smaller number of cats will not recover but experience the primary disease. The viral infection spreads from an infected cat to a susceptible cat by direct contact.

Two Forms. The disease occurs in two forms. In one form the abdomen and chest accumulates fluid as part of the infection. As a result the cat experiences fever, reluctance to eat, depression and weight loss.

As body cavities continue to fill with the fluid, organ systems will become compromised and cause signs of specific organ failure such as jaundice from severe liver involvement or breathing problems from fluid pressing on the lungs. Eventually the disease process becomes so extensive the cats die of organ failure.

The other form of feline infectious peritonitis is more insidious and frequently is associated with involvement of specific organs. Signs of kidney and/or liver failure, pancreatic disease, and nervous system disease may be observed in cats with severe organ impairment.

Lesions affecting the infected cat's eyes are very common and may be the first sign of a problem seen with the disease.

In both forms the disease process becomes so extensive that affected cats die of organ failure.

The mechanisms of disease with feline infectious peritonitis have been studied for many years but the explanation as to how an infected cat recovers or develops one or the other form of disease is not well understood.

The coronavirus may serve as a stimulator of the body immune system which leads to immune complexes being formed. These complexes then collect in blood vessels in the various body organs and cause severe vascular damage to occur.

Organ failures occur as a result of the complexes damaging the blood vessels and interfering with vital organ function. Also, the coronavirus has the capability of altering various parts of the immune system—causing either the fluid accumulation or forms of the disease in which specific organs are attacked.

Diagnosis of feline infectious peritonitis is made by evaluation of history and signs of disease and the results of supportive laboratory tests. Considering the grave prognosis associated with diagnosis of this disease and the lack of curative therapy, it is essential to differentiate the disease from other conditions with similar symptoms.

Laboratory tests used include analysis of chest and abdominal fluids, measurements of total serum protein, clinical chemistry profiles, and serum coronaviral antibody titer and biopsies of affected organs.

Routine immunization against feline infectious peritonitis is not possible currently. Newly acquired cats can be tested for coronaviral antibodies. Tested cats that are negative for coronaviral antibodies 3 to 4 weeks apart are considered free of infection. Only those cats that test coronaviral antibody negative should be used for breeding.

Cats that test positive for coronaviral antibody should be evaluated periodically for development of disease and should not be used for breeding. Breeding these cats may result in fetal resorptions occurring at 4 to 6 weeks of gestation, birth of weak kittens, abortions at mid to late gestation, and stillbirth. Once disease is established in the cat no curative therapy is presently known.

Leukemia Virus

Feline leukemia virus disease complex is caused by infection of cats with feline leukemia virus, an RNA virus present worldwide. The overall infection rate and the proportion of cats that become infected with the virus is related to density of the cat population.

About 25 to 60 percent of free-roaming cats in urban and suburban areas ultimately are infected, but only 2 to 6 percent remain infected for life. The infection rate in

Infectious Cat Diseases

rural cat populations, and in closely confined single cat households, usually does not exceed 5 to 6 percent, with about 0.2 percent of those cats remaining infected for life.

The infection rate is most severe in multiple cat households and catteries.

The virus is excreted primarily in the infected cat's salivary secretions. The virus also is present in respiratory secretions, feces, and urine.

Leukemia virus-infected cats spread the virus through daily intimate contact of social grooming habits, licking, biting, sneezing, and by sharing litter boxes and feeding bowls.

Infection occurs primarily by ingestion of the virus. In addition the virus can be transferred in the womb of a pregnant cat and also excreted into the colostrum. Prolonged close contact among cats is necessary for the most efficient transmission of the virus.

The time period between initial exposure to the feline leukemia virus and the development of either infection or immunity is quite variable and depends on route of virus transmission, age of susceptible cat, and the amount of virus received.

Signs of feline leukemia virus infection may not be present or may be very subtle in the infection's initial phase.

Kittens may show more disease signs in the initial phase than do older cats. Cats that are ill during this phase will show varying degrees of fever, malaise, loss of appetite, lymph node enlargement, and decrease in the number of white blood cells, red blood cells, and blood platelets.

The cat's defense mechanisms are weakened and kittens die of pneumonia, pyothorax (accumulated pus in the chest), intestinal infections or blood infections.

Cats that survive the infection's initial phase make an apparent recovery but some cats may enter into the second phase of infection in which most will die. About 95 percent of infected cats will recover during the initial phase and about 5 percent will become carriers of the virus or die in the second phase.

Related Illnesses

Feline leukemia virus-related illnesses that occur during the persistent phase of infection account for most of the deaths.

Before becoming ill these persistently infected cats can live for months to years in a totally normal state. When they relapse they are afflicted with lymphoid and myeloid cancers, bone marrow suppression (lack of production of white blood cells, red blood cells, and blood platelets), reproductive failures in queens (abortion, fetal resorption, stillbirths, weak kittens), eye lesions, and a number of neurologic disorders.

Besides illnesses caused directly by the virus, a large number of disorders result from persistent viral infections. These conditions are caused by the lowered resistance of infected cats to other infections.

The disorders include haemobartonellosis, feline infectious peritonitis, upper respiratory infections, urinary bladder infections, slow healing abscesses, abscesses of teeth, ear infections, intestinal infections, pyothorax, fungal infections, toxoplasmosis, and severe arthritis.

Because of the wide range of disorders associated with feline leukemia virus infections, it is not surprising that about 30 percent of all severe illnesses in cats are due directly or indirectly to this virus.

Diagnosis of feline leukemia virus diseases is made by evaluation of history and signs of disease and laboratory tests.

Currently three basic laboratory tests are available commercially to assist in identifying the feline leukemia virus and virus-immune status of an animal: 1) detection of viral antigens; 2) detection of virus-neutralizing antibodies; and 3) detection of membrane-associated antigen.

Most of the time a cat is tested for detection of viral antigens. A positive test indicates the cat has virus circulating in its bloodstream. It implies that a cat is shedding virus and is a potential health hazard to uninfected susceptible cats and possibly humans.

There has been some concern over the possible public health hazard to people. However, studies to date indicate that feline leukemia virus is not associated with any human illnesses or a cause of leukemia in people.

There is controversy over whether feline leukemia virus-infected cats should be treated medically or put to sleep. Owners must be aware that if they keep a feline leukemia virus-infected cat alive, it should be kept confined and isolated from susceptible cats.

Owners of healthy feline leukemia virus-infected cats ask continuously if there is anything that can be done to prevent overt disease and virus-related illnesses. There is

Infectious Cat Diseases

nothing that can be done except to limit stress, and provide a wholesome diet and plenty of love and attention.

When and if an illness occurs, it must be rapidly diagnosed and the proper treatment instituted. If a problem arises that is untreatable, the owner must ultimately decide whether to give palliative care until death or to have the animal put to sleep at some earlier point.

Vaccines to protect against feline leukemia virus infections are not available currently. A vaccine probably will be available in the very near future.

Two Other Infections

Feline enteric coronavirus is the cause of an inapparent or mild intestinal infection in kittens between 4 and 12 weeks old.

The virus is related to *feline infectious peritonitis* but not the cause of the disease. It is spread from a coronavirus-infected cat to a susceptible kitten by the ingestion of contaminated feces.

Infected kittens demonstrate signs of low-grade fever, intermittent vomiting, and soft or watery stools. Fresh blood occasionally is seen in the feces. Dehydration is seen only in the most severe cases. The virus affects epithelial cells of the small intestine, causing an alteration in the feces.

There is no way presently to prevent the infection in cats.

Feline pneumonitis is caused by an infection with *Chlamydia psittaci*. Transmission of this agent is by direct contact with ocular or nasal discharges from infected cats. The infection produces mild signs of illness.

Affected cats seem to recover rapidly but may show signs of illness shortly after apparent recovery. The infection does not confer good protection against relapses or reinfections.

Runny eyes and nose are the most characteristic signs of the infection. Diagnosis of feline pneumonitis is made based on the history and signs of the illness and laboratory identification of chlamydial organisms in cells of the conjunctiva.

A vaccine is available to protect cats against the chlamydial infection. The age at which to vaccinate is not critical since there appears to be little interference by colostral antibody. A single injection appears to afford adequate protection. Annual revaccination is recommended.

Immunization of Cats

Disease	Vaccine	Type of Vaccine	Age for Vaccination
Panleukopenia	Feline Panleukopenia	Killed virus or Modified live virus	First vaccination at 9 weeks; second vaccination at 12 weeks; revaccinate annually.
Respiratory Disease Complex	Viral rhinotraecheitis	Modified live virus	Vaccination schedule is same as for panleukopenia
	Calicivirus	Modified live virus	Vaccination schedule is same as for panleukopenia
	Chlamydial pneumonitis	Live attenuated	Vaccination at 9 weeks of age; revaccinate annually
Rabies*	Rabies virus	Killed virus or Modified live virus	First vaccination at 3 months of age; revaccinate at 1 year and at least every 3 years thereafter
Feline Leukemia Disease Complex	Feline leukemia virus	None available	
Enteric Disease	Feline coronavirus	None available	
Feline Infectious Peritonitis	Feline coronavirus	None available	

*Rabies of cats is covered in the next chapter

Rabies and Other Infectious Diseases of Dogs and Cats

By Johnny D. Hoskins and
John D. Rhoades

The most important infectious diseases affecting both dogs and cats are rabies and toxoplasmosis. They are discussed in this chapter along with several other infections.

Rabies is one of the oldest recorded diseases in history and dates back to the Promosaic Eshunna Code which was written in about 2300 B.C. It is caused by an RNA virus which causes infection in all warmblooded animals.

The virus can be found in nerve tissue, saliva and salivary glands, the pancreas, less often in urine and lymph, rarely in milk, and in other body fluids of infected animals. Rabies is more prevalent in temperate zones and when large numbers of unvaccinated dogs and cats are present.

Rabid dogs and cats are the main source of human infections. Wild animals such as rabid skunks, foxes, raccoons, coyotes, bats, and bobcats are other infection sources.

Spread of rabies most commonly is by the bite of an infected animal, through presence of the virus in the saliva. Broken skin of the bite wound allows the rabies virus to get into the body where it can flourish.

Once inside the body the virus is drawn to the nerves and follows nerve fibers to the brain and salivary glands. After the virus infects the brain it reproduces rapidly, causing severe brain damage. The brain lesions lead to altered behavior, aggressiveness, progressive paralysis,

Johnny D. Hoskins is Professor of Veterinary Clinical Medicine, School of Veterinary Medicine, Louisiana State University, Baton Rouge. John D. Rhoades is Professor of Veterinary Medicine and Coordinator of Public Programs at the school.

Dogs and Cats

and in most species death.

After the virus gets into the salivary glands, the infected animal can spread the virus by way of its contaminated saliva to susceptible animals.

Signs of the Disease

Not all rabid animals show the same signs of the disease. Some animals will ultimately show the classic "mad dog" behavior while others may withdraw fearfully to a dark, sheltered place.

A usually quiet, friendly cat may suddenly become aggressive and attack every moving object or person. A skunk, which normally moves at night, may appear in broad daylight and act as if it wants to be petted. A bat may be lying on a playground or sidewalk and bites when picked up.

Other than the altered behavior states, there are no specific signs which say that these animals are infected with rabies virus.

Diagnosis of rabies usually is based on the history and physical examination. A history of abnormal behavior, the suspected animal's involvement in a fighting or biting espisode, presence of rabies in the area, and the dog's or cat's vaccination record can be used as supportive information for diagnosing rabies.

Confining Dogs, Cats

Any unprovoked attack by an animal should suggest the possibility of rabies. Dogs and cats that are rabies suspects should be confined to a cage where they can be observed and fed without risk.

No acceptable diagnostic tests can be used to evaluate a live dog or cat for rabies. All laboratory tests for rabies are presently done on the dead animal.

The preferred technique to diagnose rabies is by using fluorescent antibody tests and by injecting brain tissue of the suspect animal into the brains of mice. Rabies virus will cause the death of the injected mice.

The inoculation test of mice is very sensitive for detecting the presence of rabies virus and has potentially saved many people from dying of rabies.

Act Fast. Although exposure to rabies is a cause for concern, when prompt action is taken there is no cause for panic or hysteria. If you or someone with you is bitten by a rabid animal you should:

1) Wash the wound vigorously with soap or detergent and flush it repeatedly with

Rabies & Other Infectious Diseases

courtesy of John D. Rhoades, Louisiana State University

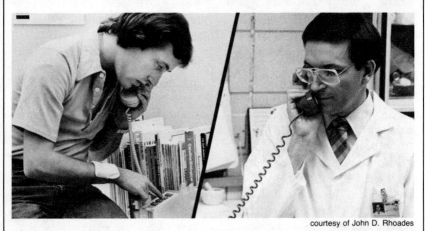

courtesy of John D. Rhoades
courtesy of John D. Rhoades

If you or someone with you is bitten by an animal you should: Wash the wound thoroughly; contact your physician, veterinarian and local animal control officer and identify the suspected animal so that it can be confined.

RABIES SUSPECT

Dogs and Cats

large amounts of water

2) Contact your physician as soon as possible about the bite wound and the type of animal that bit you, and

3) Contact your veterinarian or local animal control officer and report the attack.

Keep track of the animal involved in the attack episode and where it can be found. Responsible authorities will either quarantine the animal for observation or kill the animal and check for the rabies virus.

Vaccination. To reduce your exposure to rabies, vaccinate all your dogs and cats and encourage your neighbors to do the same.

Rabies vaccines produced today for use in dogs and cats are both safe and effective. Their costs are relatively inexpensive when compared to the cost of confining an animal for observation or the loss of life of a human being.

Regular rabies vaccination every one to three years should be a part of any responsible pet health program. A dog or cat is never too old for a rabies vaccination.

No vaccines have been tested or approved for use in any wildlife species. Vaccination of wildlife species may cause rabies or death of the animal.

Toxoplasmosis

This disease is caused by infection with *Toxoplasma gondii* and occurs throughout the world. Infection has been observed in a wide range of birds and mammals.

Toxoplasma organisms living in body cells of the host cause illness when they escape these body cells. Cats are the primary host but other mammals and birds may also be infected.

Animals acquire the toxoplasma organism by eating infected raw meat or by ingestion of contaminated feces. Some species can also acquire the toxoplasma infection during pregnancy which may infect the developing fetus.

Human infections with *Toxoplasma gondii* can occur both prenatally and postnatally. The two postnatal modes of transmission are by the ingestion of infected raw or undercooked meat or feces.

Inadvertent ingestion of organisms in feces is usually related to contact with cat litter boxes or contaminated soil.

Prenatal transmission occurs when a woman acquires the infection during pregnancy. Fetuses appear to be at great risk to toxoplasmosis during late pregnancy.

The great majority of toxoplasmosis infections cause no

apparent illness. The most frequent signs of illness in cats and dogs are associated with infections of the nervous system, eyes, respiratory tract, and gastrointestinal system.

Cats may experience fever, jaundice, enlarged lymph nodes, difficulty in breathing, anemia, eye inflammation, abortion, encephalitis and intestinal disease. Cats may also develop stiff, painful muscles from the infections so that they are unable to move.

Pneumonia, liver disease, and ocular, nervous system, and muscle damage may result as signs of illness in the dog.

Diagnosis of toxoplasmosis based on history and signs of illness alone is usually not possible because of the wide variety of signs of illness that can occur. Identification of toxoplasma organisms in the feces of infected cats is possible in early infections but only are excreted for one to two weeks.

Laboratory tests currently used in the detection of *Toxoplasma gondii* antibodies are generally preferred to the identification of organisms in feces. Presence of toxoplasma antibodies suggests that the animal may be immune to infection.

Lack of antibodies usually indicates the animal is susceptible and could shed or be shedding organisms in the feces. If a rise in antibody titer occurs over a 2 to 4 week period of time the test indicates the animal may be infected.

Vaccination of animals against toxoplasmosis is not possible at the present time.

Avoiding Infection

Some recommendations can be made to prevent ingestion of infected meat and to minimize exposure to contaminated feces.

To prevent infections of cats and other animals, confine the animals to their home environment, avoiding exposure sources. Feed animals only commercial or well-cooked meat and never feed raw meat to cats and dogs.

Change cat litter boxes frequently and dispose of the feces so that no animals or man will come in contact with the feces.

For human consumption, cook meat throughout to 66° C (150° F) to destroy any organisms present. Always wash your hands thoroughly after handling meat.

Wear gloves while gardening, especially in areas favored by cats for defecation, and when changing cat litter

Marie T. Sebrechts

Marie T. Sebrechts

Marie T. Sebrechts

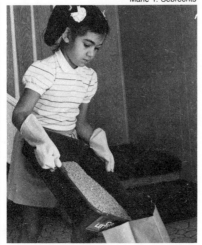

Two keys to preventing infections in your dogs and cats are: A) Never feed raw meat to them; choose a commercial feed or well-cooked meat as part of a well-planned balanced diet. B) Change cat litter boxes frequently and dispose of the feces so that no animals or people will come in contact with them.

Rabies & Other Infectious Diseases

boxes. Cover children's sandboxes when not in use so cats cannot defecate in them. Encourage children to always wash their hands thoroughly before eating.

To reduce the risk of infection, pregnant women should not eat undercooked meat and should avoid all contact with cat feces.

Salmonellosis

Salmonella species are ubiquitous bacterial organisms that are found in both wild and domestic animals. *Salmonella typhimurium* is the serotype usually isolated from cats and dogs with salmonellosis. It is usually spread by ingestion of the organism in food contaminated by infected feces.

An outbreak of infections in dogs or cats may be initiated by an animal with an active infection, a carrier animal shedding the organism without showing signs of illness, or a relapse in a carrier animal that has been subjected to stress of illness or surgery.

People who care for and handle animals may be susceptible to the infection from the animals or may transmit the infection to the animals because they are active carriers of the organisms.

Because of the highly contagious nature of the infection, strict attention must be focused on disinfection of the premises and on the personal hygiene of individuals around the animals.

Primary route of infection is by ingestion of the organism. After ingestion the organism invades the bloodstream and establishes infection in the intestinal tract.

The infected animal experiences fever, diarrhea, and vomiting. Dehydration and severe inactivity usually accompany these signs of infection. Early in the infection, the white blood cell numbers may be severely decreased which allows other types of infections to occur.

Salmonellosis can be confused easily with other gastrointestinal diseases such as canine distemper and parvovirus infections. Confirmation of a diagnosis of salmonellosis is made on the history and signs of the infection and the isolation of the organism.

Vaccination of dogs and cats against salmonellosis is not done at the present time. Identification of those animals that serve as carriers of the organisms should be done, and the animals should be treated with antibiotics to decrease exposure of other animals to the organism.

Haemobartonellosis

This illness is caused by the infection of dogs and cats with *Haemobartonella canis* or *Haemobartonella felis*. Haemobartonella organisms attach tightly to the surface of red blood cells, which causes destruction of red blood cells in an infected animal.

Haemobartonellosis can occur in cats and dogs of all ages. The most common signs associated with the illness are fever, pale mucous membranes, weight loss, and depression. Enlargement of the spleen and jaundice are frequently noted. Infected cats may be predisposed to other infections such as feline leukemia.

The illness has been seen in dogs that have been severely stressed or infected concurrently with *Ehrlichia canis* or have had their spleens surgically removed.

A diagnosis of haemobartonellosis is based on the history and signs of the infection and the demonstration of the haemobartonella organisms on the red blood cells.

The illness is very responsive to antibiotic therapy and most animals survive without permanent damage.

Mycobacterial Ills

Mycobacterial organisms cause several infections in dogs and cats.

Mycobacterium tuberculosis and *Mycobacterium bovis* are the primary organisms that cause tuberculosis in dogs and cats. Animals are infected by inhaling the organisms from respiratory excretions or by drinking infected milk from infected animals.

Infections in dogs and cats are manifested as lung disease and/or draining, non-healing abscesses. Diagnosis of tuberculosis is based on history, signs of the infection, radiographs of the chest, and isolation of the mycobacterial organisms.

Mycobacterium fortuitum, Mycobacterium smegmatis, and *Mycobacterium chelonei* can cause draining, nonhealing abscesses or tracts in dogs and cats that have been present for months to years. Except for the obvious lesions the affected animals are normal.

Sometimes local pain is noted and diagnosis is made by isolating the organisms from the lesions. Surgical removal of the lesions is the preferred treatment.

Response to antibiotic therapy is poor in infections involving these organisms.

Campylobacteriosis

This disease is caused by infection with *Campylobacter jejuni*. The organisms are spread to susceptible animals by direct contact with infected animals or consumption of contaminated water and food of animal origin.

The organism has been isolated from human feces and has caused diarrhea in people. Origin of the human campylobacter organisms has been blamed on infected dogs and cats.

Symptoms in animals with campylobacteriosis are loss of appetite, inactivity and mild diarrhea. Diagnosis of the disease is based on the history, signs of the disease and isolation of the organisms from diarrheic feces.

The disease is responsive to antibiotic therapy. Vaccination for the protection against the disease is not possible at the present time. Simple hygienic measures such as handwashing and isolation of diarrheic animals are helpful in preventing the spread of the disease.

Respiratory Ills, Heart Disease

By James C. Keith, Jr.

Respiratory diseases are very important in dogs and cats. They account for a large percentage of illnesses and include diseases which affect the nose and throat, those which affect the trachea, and those which affect the lungs. Viral, bacterial, and parasitic infections all occur in both species. Congenital defects also occur which can interfere with normal respiratory function.

Clinical signs are similar in dog or cat respiratory diseases. One of the most reliable signs is a cough. When severity of the disease process increases, labored breathing develops. As a general rule it is more difficult to detect these signs in cats, due in part to their stoic personalities.

James C. Keith, Jr. is Assistant Professor, Virginia-Maryland Regional College of Veterinary Medicine, Virginia Tech, Blacksburg.

Cleft palate is the most common congenital defect of the nasal cavity. It is caused by failure of the hard palate (the roof of the mouth) to form completely. This condition is diagnosed in kittens and puppies when milk is seen running out of the nose while they are nursing. In addition to difficulty with eating, the animals often inhale the milk—and this causes pneumonia to develop.

In breeds such as the bulldog, pekingese and pomeranian, narrowing of the nostrils and excessive length of the soft palate are often combined to cause difficulty in breathing. Another disease which occurs in these and other miniature breeds is the collapsing trachea syndrome. This disease may be manifested early in life, or may not become a problem until much later. The condition is caused by a congenital weakness in the tracheal rings, which are composed of cartilage.

Infectious diseases of the nose, throat and trachea also occur, but they will be mentioned only briefly. Several are covered in greater detail elsewhere in this section of the Yearbook.

Upper respiratory disease complex is a viral disease which causes devastating problems in young kittens. The nares (openings of the nose) become blocked by inflammatory secretions, and the kitten will not eat if it can't smell. Viral infections of the nose and throat also occur in the dog, but they are mild in comparison to the feline syndrome.

Often during a viral upper respiratory infection, bacterial infections develop and cause an even more severe disease. Dogs can contract kennel cough which is usually caused by combined viral and bacterial infections. It often develops after the animal has been boarded at a commercial kennel facility, hence the name of the disease.

Trauma (injury) to the nose, throat or trachea can cause profound problems in dogs and cats. Trauma to the nose usually results in nosebleeds. Airway obstruction can occur if the injury results

in fracture of the nasal bones.

Excessive pulling on a leash can produce a fracture of the larynx in the throat, and this can cause life threatening airway obstruction.

Dogs can get several chest diseases, and probably the most well known is canine distemper. It causes a mild viral pneumonia, but secondary bacterial pneumonias often develop.

Primary bacterial pneumonias also occur in dogs and are diagnosed by bacteriologic techniques and x rays. Fungal infections of the lungs and chest occur and can be difficult to treat. Cancerous tumors rarely develop in the chest cavity or the lungs as the primary site. However, it is common for cancer to spread to the lungs from other organs.

Cats also can acquire many lung and chest diseases. Following an upper respiratory infection, cats can develop a bacterial infection of the chest called pyothorax. Large amounts of inflammatory fluid accumulate in the chest and cause severe breathing problems. Often this disease can be caused by wounds suffered in cat fights, so the disease is more common in non-neutered male cats.

Dogs and Cats

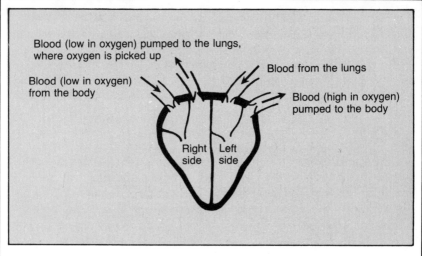

Blood (low in oxygen) pumped to the lungs, where oxygen is picked up

Blood (low in oxygen) from the body

Blood from the lungs

Blood (high in oxygen) pumped to the body

Right side   Left side

Normal, healthy heart.

Cancer within the chest cavity is much more common in cats. The most common type is a form of feline leukemia.

Lungworms can infect cats, and cause severe respiratory problems. The immature forms can be found in a stool sample from the affected animals.

Feline asthma can cause breathing problems in cats. The most current information indicates that this condition is probably an allergic disease, as with people.

Heart Disease

This occurs in dogs and cats with moderate regularity. Two general types have been documented. They are congenital defects which are present at birth, and acquired heart diseases which occur with variable incidence and appear to depend on the particular breed of animal.

Fortunately for both species, the classic "heart attack" almost never occurs. They hardly ever develop the high levels of blood cholesterol responsible for causing the blood vessel blockages which result in heart attacks in humans.

Dogs and cats will exhibit similar signs when affected with heart diseases, although the signs may be more difficult to detect in cats due to their more sedentary lifestyle.

The most common signs include coughing at night during sleep, coughing during exercise, inability to exercise, fainting spells during exercise, development of blue gums during exercise, open mouth breathing at rest (not panting, which is the dog's normal way of perspiring), reluctance or inability to breathe when lying down, and development of a large pendulous abdomen due to the accumulation of fluid in the abdomen.

Rarely, sudden death may occur with no previous signs of problems. Swelling of the extremities seldom is seen.

Congenital heart defects are more common in purebred dogs and cats, although the overall incidence in cats is much lower than in dogs. If the defects are severe or multiple, the puppies or kittens may die at birth or shortly after. However, if the defects are less severe they may survive for extended periods of time.

Depending on the severity and the type of defect, medical or surgical treatment may be feasible. If the defect lends itself to medical management or surgical correction, the owners should be advised against breeding the animal and possibly spreading the undesirable trait.

Patent ductus arteriosus (PDA) is the most common defect. It results from failure of a small duct to close. When open the duct allows blood to bypass the lungs in the developing fetus since the lungs are nonfunctional in the uterus. In the normal animal the duct closes immediately after birth when the lungs begin to function.

This defect causes a severe strain on the left side of the heart, and heart failure will result if the defect is not corrected. Fortunately, correction is easily done by simply closing the duct during open chest surgery.

Other congenital defects such as narrowing of the aorta, narrowing of the vessels leading to the lungs, or defects of the interior of the heart are more difficult to correct.

Acquired heart disease has several causes. Once again the incidence can vary depending on the breed of dog or cat.

Degenerative diseases of the heart valves occur very commonly in dogs. Generally, these abnormalities begin slowly and increase in severity as the animal ages. The defects rarely cause heart failure before the animal is 10 to 15 years old.

As the valves degenerate their deteriorating function places increasing stress on the heart, until it begins to fail.

This results in clinical signs of heart failure.

Bacterial infections of the heart valves, or the heart muscle itself, can also cause heart failure in the dog and cat. Although these are difficult to diagnose, they sometimes can be treated with long-term antibiotic therapy.

Cancerous tumors occasionally can spread to the heart and replace the normal muscle, causing heart failure. In these cases, little can be done.

A degenerative disease of the heart muscle called cardiomyopathy can affect both dogs and cats. This disease occurs with a higher frequency in cats, but a significant number of dog cases also are reported.

One form of the disease causes the heart to develop massive amounts of muscle wall at the expense of the heart's interior chambers. This results in poor cardiac function. The other form of cardiomyopathy causes loss of cardiac muscle, and the heart becomes a dilated, inefficient pump. The dilated form can be treated for only a short period of time before terminal heart failure occurs.

One parasite problem that affects the dog's heart is heartworm disease. Until a few years ago, it was limited to those areas along the coast where mosquitoes were present, since the infective stage is spread by mosquitoes. Today the disease is found throughout the country. Presence of adult heartworms causes vessels leading to the lungs to thicken, and this thickening eventually causes the heart to fail.

Several techniques are used to diagnose heart conditions in dogs and cats. Just as in human medicine, x rays of the chest, electrocardiograms and dye studies of the heart are used to determine the type and severity of heart disease present.

Neutering, Other Surgery; Tumors and Injuries

By Mark J. Dallman and
Kent C. Roberts

Surgery can be an effective treatment for many conditions affecting dogs and cats. A careful physical examination and diagnosis of the animal's problem should precede surgery. Diagnosis will often involve x rays and/or laboratory tests to evaluate the animal's condition.

Surgery usually is performed under general anesthesia which may be an injectable drug or the inhalation of a mixture of an anesthetic gas and oxygen, or combination of both.

Most surgery is elective (owner's choice) and can be scheduled ahead at a convenient time. Emergency surgery must be performed as soon as

possible to achieve the desired result.

Neutering. Ovariohysterectomy and castration are two of the most frequently performed surgical procedures. These operations prevent the animal from reproducing.

Ovariohysterectomy (spay) is performed on the female, commonly not before 6 months of age, and consists of abdominal surgery to remove both ovaries, oviducts, uterine horns and the uterine body. Removal of the ovaries will prevent the animal from coming into heat (estrus) and removal of the uterus prevents infection of that organ.

Castration is performed on the male cat or dog, preferably after six months of age, and will sterilize the animal and prevent objectionable behavior such as roaming, fighting and spraying urine. Both testes, the epididymis and part of the spermatic cord are removed in this procedure.

Mark J. Dallman is Assistant Professor, Virginia-Maryland Regional College of Veterinary Medicine, Virginia Tech, Blacksburg. Kent C. Roberts is Associate Professor at the college.

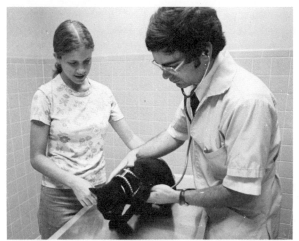

Careful examinations always precede surgery. Many pet owners who do not plan to breed their cats and dogs opt for neutering their animals. As a result, this is the surgical procedure veterinarians most frequently perform on dogs and cats.

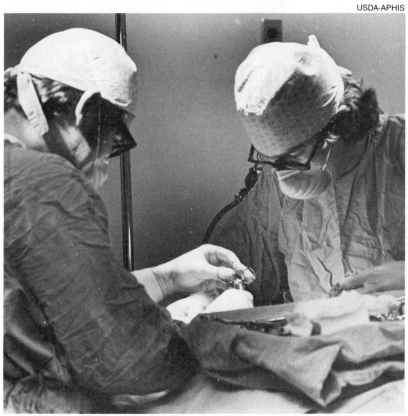

Neutering, Tumors & Injuries

Declawing. This surgery is performed in cats and kittens to prevent damage to household belongings. Claws on both front feet are removed under general anesthesia. The procedure is best performed at 6 to 12 weeks of age as it causes less discomfort at a young age.

Tumors. Surgical removal of tumors in dogs and cats is a frequently performed procedure. These tumors vary in size and location. Some require only minor surgery using local anesthesia while others are complex operations involving vital organs.

Bone and Joint Surgery. Trauma (injury) to the animal is most often the reason for surgery of the bones and joints. Fractures, dislocations and partial dislocations may require surgery to correct. This orthopedic surgery often involves use of stainless steel pins, bone plates, bone screws and wire in repairing broken bones and damaged joints.

The key to good bone healing is immobilization of the affected bones and may involve a variety of internal (within the bone) or external immobilization techniques such as pins, plates, splints and casts.

Ligament and tendon damage may accompany bone damage and require surgery to repair also.

Neurosurgery in dogs and cats most often involves damage to the spinal cord from trauma or prolapsed intervertebral discs. Spinal surgery usually is done to relieve pressure (decompression) on the spinal cord and must be done in time to prevent permanent cord damage.

Eye surgery is being done with increasing frequency to correct such problems as cataracts, glaucoma and corneal opacities.

Emergency surgery is performed frequently on dogs and cats, often as a lifesaving procedure.

Some of the more common emergency operations are to relieve blockage of the urethra from urinary bladder stones (calculi); to relieve bloated stomach in dogs due to a twisting of the bowel; to remove damaged sections of intestine; or to repair a tear in the diaphragm which allows abdominal organs to enter the chest cavity.

Also, to replace a prolapsed eyeball; to remove foreign bodies from the digestive system; and to remove kittens or puppies via Cesarian section from the dam unable to deliver them normally.

Types of Tumors

Tumors can occur in every organ and area of the body of cats and dogs. They may be either malignant or benign and often spread (metastasize) to other organs or areas.

The tumors of greatest importance and incidence in dogs include those found in the skin, mammary gland, bone, lymph nodes, liver, spleen, lung and oral cavity. Cats experience a high incidence of leukemia, which affects the blood-forming cells of the bone marrow and the lymph nodes.

Canine lymphosarcoma is a common form of cancer found in dogs. The cause is unknown but the disease attacks lymph tissue in the body and may involve any organ. Most commonly the lymph nodes are enlarged with secondary involvement of the lung, liver, spleen or bowel. Diagnosis can be confirmed by biopsy of affected tissue and blood studies.

Mammary tumors occur frequently in female dogs and less frequently in cats. Half of these tumors are malignant in dogs and over 90 percent are malignant in cats. Spread to the lungs and lymph nodes is a common occurrence and should be evaluated before treatment. Mammary tumors rarely occur in bitches and queens spayed at an early age.

Bone tumors are not found often in cats and dogs. Most of those that do occur are malignant. The larger breeds of dogs have the highest incidence. Use of x rays and surgical biopsy are the best methods of diagnosis. Bone tumors have a high degree of malignancy.

Tumors of the abdominal organs occur with moderate frequency in dogs and cats. All the abdominal organs can be affected, individually or in combinations. The liver and spleen have the highest incidence of involvement followed by the lymph nodes, pancreas, bowel and kidney.

Tumors of the chest cavity are relatively common in both dogs and cats. The dog's lungs are both a primary and secondary target for various types of tumors, more often malignant than not. Tumors around the heart are more common in the cat.

Skin tumors are very common and cover a wide range of type, appearance and location in both dogs and cats. They range from small benign nodules and wart-like growths to highly malignant, rapidly growing squamous cell carcinomas.

Neutering, Tumors & Injuries

Treatment of tumors in dogs and cats can involve three general methods of therapy: Surgical removal, use of drugs (chemotherapy), and use of x rays. Treatment can be successful if started in time, planned well and pursued aggressively.

Feline leukemia is a complex, widespread disease that is caused by a virus capable of spreading from cat to cat. The virus infection may be very apparent or not cause the infected animal to show any obvious signs of the disease. It may be acute or chronic and result in death, apparent recovery or development of a wide range of seemingly unrelated diseases at a later time.

Diagnosis is by blood test and the long range prognosis is poor. Treatment is directed at the symptoms but cures are rare and complications are common. Work on an effective vaccine holds hope for the future in preventing the virus disease.

Dogs and cats have an incidence of cancer comparable to that in humans, and higher when their shorter life expectancy is taken into account.

Pet Injuries

Traumatic injuries most commonly are the result of being struck by a vehicle. Other causes include falls, blows, penetrating wounds from weapons, sharp objects or fights with other animals. Proper control or confinement of pets will reduce the frequency of such injuries.

Injuries can be divided into major and minor trauma. Minor trauma is a nonserious insult to the body. This includes skin cuts (lacerations) from broken glass, barbed wire, bite wounds and penetrating wounds from fish hooks or gunshot. Bruises may result from a fall or blow.

Major trauma is the result of damage to one or more body systems. Care must be taken because the animal may appear outwardly normal. The results of damage to internal body organs may not show up for hours or even days later. An uncharacteristic quietness, physical weakness, decreased sensation, and decreased body temperature may indicate post traumatic shock.

Shock is a condition characterized by physical and mental depression and circulatory failure. Trauma may cause conditions that bring about circulatory failure. The most obvious of these conditions is hemorrhage.

Severe hemorrhage (blood loss) reduces the volume of blood the heart can pump, so

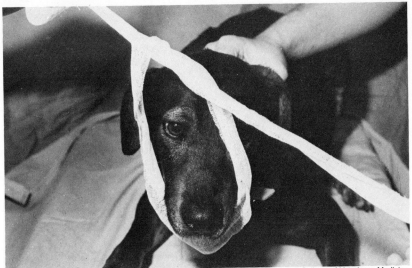

Donald Massie, Virginia-Maryland Regional College of Veterinary Medicine

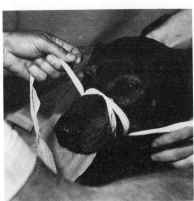

Donald Massie

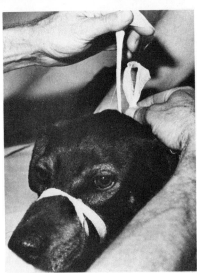

Donald Massie

A seriously injured dog in pain may attempt to bite even its owner. Before you attempt to help it, approach cautiously, speaking in a comforting voice, and muzzle the dog with a long strip of gauze as shown.

Neutering, Tumors & Injuries

Examination and treatment by a veterinarian as soon as possible following traumatic injury in animals is important in treating shock and in reducing possible damage to vital organs.

USDA-APHIS

blood pressure decreases. The body attempts to compensate for this blood loss by causing constriction (narrowing) of the blood vessels. This is a means of maintaining adequate circulation of blood to the heart and brain.

The process results in a coolness and loss of pulse to the limbs. Burns cause fluid loss which can lead to the same circulatory failure. Death may occur when blood loss excedes 35 percent of the initial blood volume.

A decrease in blood volume may result in reduced blood flow to internal organs such as the kidneys and liver. Decreased circulation to these organs can allow toxic waste products to build up in the bloodstream. Animals are seriously affected as body organs have reduced function and the backup of toxic wastes occurs.

Obvious damage following trauma may be accompanied by unseen damage. Internal pressure caused by severe trauma may cause organ contusions and even rupture. Lung damage can result in difficult breathing and the passage of bloody froth from the nose and mouth. Rupture of the liver or spleen can be the source of severe internal hemorrhage. Rupture of the urinary bladder may accompany pelvic fractures or abdominal trauma.

Examination and treatment by a veterinarian as soon as posible following traumatic injury in animals is important in treating shock and in reducing damage to body organs.

USDA

Neutering, Surgery, Tumors & Injuries

Birth, Pediatrics, Genetics, Aging

By D. Phillip Sponenberg and
Kent C. Roberts

Problems involving birth in dogs and cats are relatively uncommon. One problem that does occur in both species is uterine inertia, or failure of the uterine muscles to contract at the proper stage of labor.

These contractions are essential during delivery because they move the newborn through the dam's birth canal. Lack of, or weak, contractions delay expulsion of the young and without prompt and effective treatment they may be stillborn. This problem is more common in overweight and poorly conditioned animals.

Difficult birth (dystocia)

D. Phillip Sponenberg is Assistant Professor, Virginia-Maryland Regional College of Veterinary Medicine, Virginia Tech, Blacksburg. Kent C. Roberts is Associate Professor at the college.

may result from the presence of malformed puppies or kittens in the birth canal. This problem also can result from an abnormally large puppy or kitten, or in certain breeds that have pups with large heads and shoulders.

Prompt assistance is needed in such cases to save the newborn and even to save the dam. Caesarian section to deliver the fetuses is standard procedure when manual assistance does not produce the desired results within a reasonable time.

Bitches and queens with unusually small birth canals or those with injuries to the pelvis that have narrowed the pelvic canal should not be bred, as the best means of preventing birth problems.

Infections of the female reproductive tract occur with some frequency. Acute metritis is a bacterial infection of the uterus following delivery of the young. It is more likely to occur following dystocia and may involve retained placenta.

Persistence of a dark green or reddish-brown discharge from the vulva more than 24 hours after birth of the young is an indication of trouble in the uterus which requires veterinary treatment.

Pyometra is a filling of the uterus with pus following a heat (estrus) in the bitch. Discharge from the vulva may or may not be evident but there is absorption of toxic products into the bloodstream causing depression, increased thirst, anemia and toxemia. This can be a life threatening problem and needs effective veterinary attention.

Vaginal and uterine prolapse are infrequent occurrences, particularly in the cat. They are characterized by a large mass protruding from the vulva and should be treated promptly by a veterinarian.

Pediatrics

Canine and feline pediatrics is the study of the growth, development and diseases of the young of these species. Pediatrics starts with care of the expectant bitch or queen, preparation for birth of the young and providing a clean, dry and warm environment during the first weeks of the puppies' or kittens' lives.

Nutrition plays a critical role in condition of the dam as well as the size and weight of the unborn or newborn fetuses. Proper levels of nutrition during pregnancy and nursing the young are very important to the health of both the dam and her newborn.

Loss of puppies and kittens during the first few days of life is quite high. Reasons for this mortality vary from still birth to starvation due to failure of lactation in the dam. Still birth is often the result of prolonged labor.

Exposure is a leading cause of death during the first week of life. Chilling of the newborn can occur rapidly and if not reversed in time death results. Warm, clean, dry whelping and kittening facilities are important.

The dam (bitch or queen) plays an extremely important role in the birth and care of her young. Inexperienced dams may damage the newborn accidentally to the point of death. Weak, injured or chilled puppies or kittens cannot nurse and become stronger. Swollen, infected mammary glands also make it difficult for the newborn to obtain milk.

Infectious disease can cause the loss of individual young or entire litters. Umbilical (navel) infection is common as are eye, respiratory and skin infections. Prompt diagnosis and effective treatment are important to save the very young or prevent permanent damage to the affected organs. Good sanitation is necessary to reduce the chances for these opportunistic infections to cause disease.

Fading Pup Syndrome is a disease entity of young puppies apparently normal and healthy at birth which quickly become listless, uncomfortable with distended abdomen, weak and comatose when a few days old. A number of infectious agents including canine herpesvirus are thought to cause this syndrome.

Toxic Milk Syndrome in puppies is an apparent incompatibility between the pup and the bitch's milk. Affected pups will bloat, cry and develop a greenish diarrhea. This may be due to toxins in the milk or infections in the bitch's reproductive tract. Treatment requires removing the pups from the dam, feeding them an orphan puppy formula and keeping them warm and dry.

Virus diseases that may infect the young puppy are distemper, herpesvirus, adenoviruses, coronavirus and parvovirus.

Fading Kitten Syndrome and *Kitten Mortality Complex* are not well understood disease problems that cause significant death loss of kittens each year. The role of virus diseases such as feline infectious peritonitis (FIP), feline leukemia, rhinotracheitis and calicivirus is not yet understood but the incidence of these diseases is widespread in the overall cat population.

Proper management, nutrition and observation of the dam and her young cannot be overstressed in successful pediatric husbandry. Prevention or the early detection of problems is particularly critical when dealing with the newborn.

Most problems are not due to infectious disease but include small size, ineffective nursing, chilling, and genetic or congenital abnormalities. Prompt attention to problems, including puppies or kittens that cry continuously, offers the best approach to solving these problems.

Genetics

The study of how characteristics are passed from one generation to the next is called genetics. Differences in hair type, body type, hair color are all under genetic control, which allow them to be accurately passed from one generation to the next. These differences are frequently used as hallmarks of certain breeds, and the fact that they are consistently passed from parent to offspring results in the various breeds being "bred true" to type.

Traits that pop up periodically in some pure breeds are most likely due to recessive genes. This allows them to be masked by the more usual form of the gene for several generations, until two of the same form combine and cannot be masked. When these concern color or hair characteristics it is usually not possible to have the offspring registered, although they are normal representatives of the breed in every other regard.

Other simple changes can result in altered metabolic pathways or severe structural changes that cause death of the affected animal. Some of these are more severe than others and usually are called "genetic diseases." Such structural abnormalities include cleft palate in pups, or kittens with brains herniated through defects in the skull. These are severe and generally cause the animal's death. Others are

less severe, such as blue-eyed white cats which frequently are deaf. These can lead a fairly normal life if protected from an adverse environment.

Altered metabolism can also occur and result in disease. Included here are such things as hypertrophic neuropathy in some dogs, which causes paralysis at a young age. These and other abnormalities are sometimes studied in animals in the search for a cure for similar diseases that cause severe suffering in affected humans.

Other diseases that are genetic are not so well understood as they involve the interaction of several (up to hundreds) gene pairs. Hip dysplasia, which sometimes results in crippling arthritis in dogs, is one such disease.

The diseases are usually subject to both genetic and environmental influences, which makes their elimination from some breeds a very difficult and slow task. This is due to the environment occasionally masking the severity of the disease in some animals.

When such animals are bred they pass on the tendency for the defect, and offspring contain a high percentage of affected animals. Progress in eliminating diseases such as these can only occur slowly over a period of many generations.

Care of Older Pets

As cats and dogs live longer lives, the care and treatment of older animals becomes increasingly important. Maintaining good health in our older pets is a special area of veterinary medicine known as geriatric medicine.

All tissues, organs and systems in the body are affected by the aging process. There is a loss of organ reserve and a decrease in metabolic rate, volume of cell water, bone mineral and neurons in the brain.

There is a tendency for increased dental disease, a loss of muscle mass and tone, blood vessel fibrosis, and constipation due to loss of bowel tone. The senses are dulled (eyes, ears and nose) and output of the heart is decreased. Response to disease by the body's immune system is lowered.

Pet owners can help their aging animals by remembering and doing a few simple things:

1) Keep weight down by exercising the pet regularly and not overfeeding. Overweight cats and dogs have too high an intake of calories

2) Feed three or four times daily instead of one large meal. The older pet's digestive system can't assimilate food as well as younger animals

3) Groom pets daily. Skin and haircoat changes result in less elastic skin and duller, drier, more brittle hair coats

4) Supplement the pet's diet with additives that help to reduce aging deficiencies. Examples are brewers yeast, unsaturated fatty acids (vegetable oil), vitamins B_1, B_{12}, C and E

5) Provide dental care (once or twice each year by a veterinarian and weekly at home)

6) Arrange for an annual physical examination by a veterinarian

7) Provide companionship

Diet is especially important in caring for the older pet. A number of commercial pet food companies market complete diets for older dogs and cats. These are of definite value in meeting nutritional needs of the aging animal.

Geriatric vitamin/mineral supplements are also available commercially as an aid in maintaining good health when pets get older.

USDA-APHIS

Young pets require special care and pediatrics is the study of the growth, development and diseases of the young. As cats and dogs live longer lives, the care and treatment of older animals has become increasingly important. Maintaining good health in older pets is a special area of veterinary medicine known as geriatric medicine.

Birth, Pediatrics, Genetics, Aging   431

Teeth, Ears, Eyes, Kidneys, Bladder

By Kent C. Roberts and
Irving Cashell

Dogs and cats depend on their teeth for survival. The teeth play a vital role in eating and protection from other animals.

Both dogs and cats have two sets of teeth over their life-time. The first or "baby teeth" are present at, or soon after, birth. These "baby teeth" are replaced at four to eight months of age by the adult or "permanent" set of teeth. Replacement is gradual and many owners don't realize that their pets are exchanging a small, sharp set of teeth for a larger, stronger set.

Occasionally one or more

Kent C. Roberts is Associate Professor, Virginia-Maryland Regional College of Veterinary Medicine, Virginia Tech, Blacksburg. Irving Cashell is a former veterinary practitioner who resides in Fairfax County, Va. He is chief editor/writer for this section of the Yearbook.

of the "baby" or deciduous teeth—most often the long, sharp canine (corner) teeth—will be retained and interfere with the incoming adult teeth. These retained deciduous teeth need to be carefully removed to prevent defects in the location of the permanent teeth.

Bite Problems. Tooth and oral abnormalities are common in dogs and to a much lesser extent in cats. Some of the more common defects that cause bite problems are overcrowding of teeth, malocclusions (mismatched upper and lower teeth), shortened lower jaw (overshot), shortened upper jaw (undershot).

The most common oral infection in animals is periodontitis, which can result in damage to the gums and subsequent loss of teeth. It is a serious problem in dogs and cats and requires awareness and preventive measures by the pet owner.

Marie T. Sebrechts

Donald Massie

Cats and dogs depend on their teeth for survival. Their teeth play a vital role both in eating and in protection from other animals.

Symptoms of periodontal disease, often called pyorrhea, are bad breath; tartar accumulation; inflamed, receding gums; pus discharge around the teeth; and loose teeth.

Treatment of periodontal disease by a veterinarian in the early stages before the loss of teeth is very important.

A preventive oral hygiene program can be started and managed by the pet owner at home. This program should include diet (firm, dry foods are best for the prevention of plaque and tartar formation), chewing exercise (rawhide chews), and cleaning the teeth.

Where dogs and cats have severe periodontal problems the teeth may be brushed daily with a soft infant toothbrush or a soft rag wrapped around the index finger. Baking soda is a suitable dentifrice. Detergent commercial tooth pastes are not recommended.

Root Canals. Treatment of disease of the tooth's internal (pulp) tissues is called endodontics. Discoloration of the tooth indicates damage to the pulp and devitalization. Root canal therapy and the use of drainage and antibiotics can save affected teeth.

The use of wire and appliances can reposition teeth and prevent serious dental problems if done in time.

Although relatively rare

in dogs and cats, cavities do occur, usually at the exposed surface of the tooth's root rather than on the enamel covered crown. Early treatment of dental cavities can prevent the loss of important teeth.

When teeth are damaged or decayed or loosened beyond repair, removal or extraction of the affected tooth or teeth is necessary. This is best done by a veterinarian using anethesia to control pain.

Ear Problems

The ear performs an important function in animals, and any condition that interferes with that function should be treated effectively.

Microscopic parasites called mites can live in the dog or cat's ear, causing an irritation and inflammation of the sensitive membrane lining the ear. This irritation may cause the animal to shake its head and scratch at the ear vigorously.

Treatment for these mites involves thorough cleaning of the ear using an ear syringe and warm water, followed by application of soothing ear drops or ointment containing a drug to kill mites. Gentle massage of the ear following cleaning and treatment is often helpful. Treatment

should be repeated daily.

Infection. The ear may become infected with both bacterial and fungal agents, causing odor and discharge from the affected ear. Infection often goes hand in hand with ears damaged by mites, excessive wetness, foreign bodies and other chronic irritation of the ear lining.

Before effective treatment can be started, a culture of the ear may be needed to determine the cause of the ear inflammation. Bacterial and fungal infections would require different types of drugs to overcome infection. Cleaning prior to treatment helps the treatment to be more effective.

Hematoma. A soft swelling may appear on the inner surface of the ear flap, particularly in dogs with pendulous ears. This swelling is filled with blood and results when a small blood vessel ruptures between the skin and the ear cartilage. The rupture may occur when the animal shakes its head too vigorously.

This condition requires treatment by a veterinarian before the blood forms an organized clot, shrinks, and leaves a permanently disfigured ear.

Wounds of the ear flap or ear canal are common as a re-

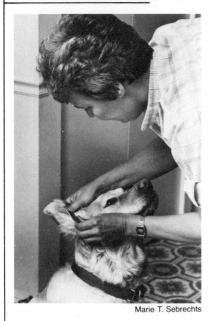
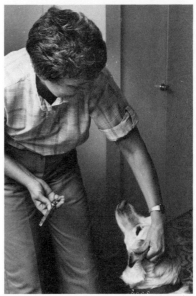

Marie T. Sebrechts   Marie T. Sebrechts

It's important to treat ear problems following the instructions of your veterinarian. Many problems involve cleaning the ear using a syringe and warm water, followed by application of ear drops or ointment. Gentle massage of the ear following cleaning and treatment often helps.

sult of barbed wire, sharp objects or bite wounds. These wounds need careful cleaning and treatment, and surgical repair by a veterinarian when necessary. Antibiotics locally and by injection may be indicated to prevent infection.

The first step in most ear problems is inflammation of the ear membranes, called otitis. Inflammation can affect the external ear, middle ear or inner ear. Treating this inflammation usually is not simple and should involve the services of a veterinarian

trained in treating animal problems.

Use of an otoscope for examining the ear canal, cultures to identify causative organisms, and the proper drugs to give effective results are all of great importance in diagnosing and successfully treating problems of the ear.

Eye Diseases

The eye is an extremely important organ to dogs and cats. Loss of vision is a serious handicap which limits their usefulness and abilities. Inju-

Teeth, Ears, Eyes, Kidneys, Bladder   435

Donald Massie

Donald Massie

Your veterinarian will also check your cat's and dog's eyes during routine exams. The eye—"the window of the body"—tells your veterinarian a lot about your pet's health. Eye injuries, unusual discharge or clouding of your pet's eyes warrants a trip to the veterinarian.

ries and diseases of the eye are common, particularly in dogs.

Eye injuries involve primarily the cornea and require prompt treatment to minimize eye damage. Prolapse (falling out) of the entire eyeball may occur in short-nosed breeds with protruding eyes. This is an emergency situation requiring veterinary care. Successful replacement can be accomplished if done in time and if the optic nerve isn't damaged. Keeping the injured eye moist and protected until treatment can be provided is important.

Foreign bodies such as weed seeds may enter the eye and work beneath the lids. Removal may require local anesthesia followed by eye medication.

Diagnosis of eye disease requires a thorough examina-

tion of the eye and may involve dilation of the pupil, ophthalmascopic examination of the internal structures, measurement of intraocular pressure, corneal staining, a tear test and bacterial culture. Response of the pupil to light is a valuable diagnostic method of determining problems involving the neuroanatomy of the eye.

Conjunctivitis, inflammation of the membrane lining the inner surface of the eyelids, and keratitis, inflammation of the cornea, are common eye problems caused by a variety of irritants, infections and injury.

Dogs and cats have a third eyelid originating in the inner corner of the eye. This protective structure may become inflamed and may protrude over part of the cornea, particularly in cats. Inflam-

Dogs and Cats

mation and enlargement of the gland of the third eyelid results in a condition in dogs called "cherry eye."

Dog Cataracts

The lens performs the same function as the lens in a camera; it focuses images on the retina of the eye. Dogs have cataracts which are a cloudy white opacity of the lens. Cataracts may be hereditary or non-hereditary and will cause blindness when fully developed (mature). Removal of the lens surgically is the only effective treatment.

Glaucoma is a serious eye disease involving an increase in pressure within the eyeball caused by a variety of problems with the production, transport and absorption of aqueous humor, the fluid within the eye.

Pressure may build up rapidly and cause irreversible damage to the retina and optic nerve within a matter of hours, so the onset of glaucoma is considered an emergency. Treatment must be prompt and specific to prevent eventual loss of vision in the affected eye.

Progressive retinal atrophy is a hereditary loss of retinal function in dogs which first manifests itself as night blindness. There is no effec-

tive treatment known for this insidious disease. Genetically it is a recessive trait with a great many carrier animals capable of transmitting the disease. Affected animals should not be used for breeding.

Abscesses occur behind the eyeball (post orbital) causing the eye to protrude from its socket. This painful condition is often associated with dental problems. Antibiotics and proper drainage are indicated.

Entropion, turning in of the eyelid margin, is a common problem in puppies and usually affects both eyes to varying degrees. Left untreated it may cause chronic keratitis and damage the cornea. Treatment consists of corrective surgery on the affected lids.

The eye is the window of the body and often presents indications of systemic disease upon careful examination. Examination of the eye and the diagnosis of eye disease is an important area of veterinary medicine.

Kidney Disease

The kidneys have a large function in eliminating waste produced by the living body and its organs. These are largely nitrogen containing byproducts from the body's use of protein. Another equally essential kidney function is the "intelligent" maintenance of normal levels of the chemicals of blood.

Blood, feeding constantly through kidney tissue, has a normal level of sugar. If the level rises above normal the kidney will "spill" it out into the urine and bring the level to normal. Other chemicals containing such elements as sodium and potassium, and of course water, have normal levels. Any excess is spilled into the urine and eliminated. The kidneys "know" just how much to keep and how much to eliminate.

Kidney disease of any kind becomes apparent when these functions are damaged. The pileup of waste compounds and the derangement of other blood chemicals cause *physical symptoms*. Nausea, lassitude, loss of appetite should lead to an examination by a veterinarian.

The kidneys may be damaged by viral or bacterial infections, chemical poisons or physical injuries. The latter includes pressure damage resulting from stoppages in the exit passages from the kidneys such as the bladder and urethra.

Treatment is based on re-moving the cause and by reestablishing full flow of urine with fluids by mouth or by injection. Survival after severe damage is possible, but when only one fourth to one third of the kidney tissue remains life becomes precarious.

Urinary Bladder

Problems involving the urinary bladder are common in dogs and cats. They include inflammation, infection, tumors and stones (calculi) affecting the bladder. These problems can cause all degrees of illness and discomfort from mild to life threatening.

Inflammation of the urinary bladder is called cystitis and is a very common problem in both dogs and cats. It may or may not be associated with infection of the bladder. Cystitis is an almost invariable component of infections, tumors and calculi of the bladder. The main signs of cystitis are more frequent urination than normal, and blood in the urine.

Cystitis tends to be a chronic condition and has a tendency to recur in affected animals. It predisposes the bladder to infection, and treatment often involves the use of urinary antibacterial drugs. Medication to make the urine more acid is of value to con-

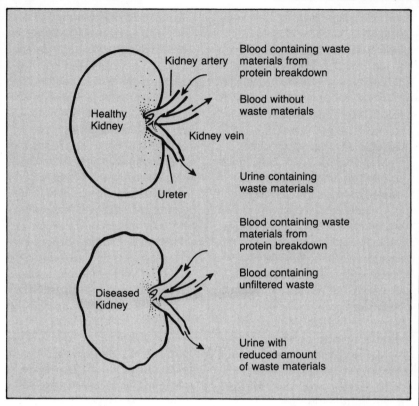

Healthy Kidney

Kidney artery

Blood containing waste materials from protein breakdown

Blood without waste materials

Kidney vein

Ureter

Urine containing waste materials

Diseased Kidney

Blood containing waste materials from protein breakdown

Blood containing unfiltered waste

Urine with reduced amount of waste materials

The hard-working kidney functions 24 hours per day and is responsible for the "intelligent" maintenance of normal levels of chemicals of the blood and elimination of waste materials.

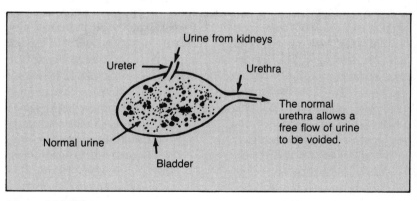

Urine from kidneys

Ureter

Urethra

The normal urethra allows a free flow of urine to be voided.

Normal urine

Bladder

Normal bladder.

Teeth, Ears, Eyes, Kidneys, Bladder

trol cystitis due to infection by creating less favorable conditions for most bacteria.

In dogs, bladder "stones" (calculi, uroliths) frequently occur as the result of urinary tract infections, alkaline urine and genetic factors. The makeup of these stones includes a variety of inorganic compounds such as struvite, urate, cystine, silica and calcium oxalate. These compounds precipitate out of the urine which is supersaturated with them. Alkaline urine seems to increase the rate of precipitation.

Diagnosis of bladder stones in dogs is by clinical signs of cystitis, palpation of the urinary bladder and x rays of the posterior abdomen. Treatment is surgical removal of the stones using general anesthesia and an abdominal operation. Some stones can be removed nonsurgically with the use of a special diet available commercially.

In cats, the most common urinary problem is feline urologic syndrome (FUS). It includes a range of conditions from mild cystitis to blockage of the urethra, uremic poisoning and death. The exact cause of FUS is not known but would seem to be a combination of factors including diet, reduced water consumption, and possibly a virus.

Cats with cystitis as a result of crystals ("sand") in the bladder are in no danger but may urinate frequently and pass blood-tinged urine.

Cats with enough material in the bladder to block the urethra (invariably males) need prompt, emergency treatment to prevent uremic poisoning as a result of the backup of toxic waste products into the bloodstream. Male cats with a blocked urethra are restless and uncomfortable as indicated by frequent howls of pain. A greatly enlarged urinary bladder can be felt in the posterior abdomen.

Surgical relief is available for male cats suffering repeated attacks of FUS blockage. Long term medical treatment for any cat with FUS offers the best hope for control or cure of this disease.

In both dogs and cats, tumors of the lining of the urinary bladder are not rare and can be both malignant and benign. At least five general types are recognized. Tumors of the bladder wall also may occur. Blood in the urine (hematuria) is the most common sign of bladder tumors.

Diagnosis of tumors is by x rays and surgical biopsy. Treatment is by surgical removal when possible.

Bone, Joint Ills; Nervous System, Fits, Disks

By Mark J. Dallman and
Irving Cashell

Musculoskeletal problems in dogs and cats are most often evident as lameness or an abnormal gait. This usually is due to pain or discomfort that interferes with normal use or normal movement of the affected bones, joints or muscles. Common causes of musculoskeletal disease are inflammation, fractures, tearing, sprains, strains, congenital malformations, and breakdown of normal bone, joint or muscle tissue due to age or trauma (injury).

Bone Diseases. Panosteitis is a painful inflammation of the long bones of the legs in medium and large breeds of dogs 5 to 18 months of age. The lameness that results shifts from one leg to another and gradually disappears as the dog matures.

Secondary nutritional hyperparathyroidism is seen in both dogs and cats as the result of a calcium and phosphorus imbalance in the diet. The bones will weaken and may fracture spontaneously due to a lack of calcium in the bones withdrawn by the parathyroid gland to balance an excess of phosphorus in the diet. High phosphorus diets are often made up entirely of red meat.

Bone tumors are not uncommon in dogs. Osteosarcomas, fibrosarcomas and chondrosarcomas are seen in older dogs. These tumors cause pain and may interfere with normal musculoskeletal function. They are malignant and often spread (metastasize) to the lungs or other organs from the affected bone.

Hypertrophic osteodystro-

Mark J. Dallman is Assistant Professor, Virginia-Maryland Regional College of Veterinary Medicine, Virginia Tech, Blacksburg. Irving Cashell is a former veterinary practitioner who resides in Fairfax County, Va.

phy is a disease of young, rapidly growing dogs of the larger breeds that affects the distal ends of the radius and ulna bones in the front legs. There is inflammation of the bones, pain, swelling and fever which gradually disappears as the dog matures.

Joint Diseases. Hip dysplasia is a very common disease of the larger breeds of dogs, affecting the hip joint. It is transmitted genetically and the severity may vary widely from dog to dog and litter to litter.

This widespread disease causes a hind leg lameness as the result of pain originating in the malformed ball and socket type joint. Flattening of the socket (acetabulum) and a rubbing movement of the ball (femoral head) produces inflammation and eventually arthritis of the hip joint. The diagnosis is confirmed by x rays of the hips (pelvis).

Affected dogs exhibit pain on attempting to arise and when moving, particularly in damp, cold weather. Treatment is aimed at relief of the joint pain.

Osteochondroses are a group of joint diseases involving a disturbance in bone formation of the growth centers at the ends of certain leg bones.

The shoulder joint is most commonly affected and the result is a painful joint condition called *osteochondritis dissecans*. Lameness involving one or both front legs is caused by a loose flap of joint cartilage in the shoulder joint. It is seen most often in young, rapidly growing male dogs, usually weighing 50 pounds or more. Diagnosis is confirmed by x rays, and treatment involves surgery of the joint.

Similar problems may affect the elbow and hock joints in dogs.

Legg-Calve-Perthes disease involves the hip joint of young dogs of the miniature breeds. Damage to the head of the femur occurs as the result of either congenital or traumatic damage to the blood supply of that area. Lameness and pain result.

Luxation of the patella is a congenital problem in miniature and toy breeds of dogs affecting the knee (stifle) joint of the hind legs. The patella (knee cap) moves out of its normal position as the joint is flexed and extended. Joint looseness, abnormal gait, and pain usually result. This condition can be successfully treated using surgery.

Degenerative joint disease and arthritis are characterized by joint pain and lameness.

Degenerative joint disease involves breakdown of the articular (joint surface) cartilage and thickening of the joint capsule accompanied by excess bone formation (calcification) around and in the joint.

Nervous System

Paralysis—loss of control of muscle activity—usually is due to an interruption to the conduction of signals from the brain or spinal cord to the affected muscles.

Interruption can occur anywhere from the involved brain center to the muscle itself. A brain damaged by the presence of a tumor, infection, or injury cannot begin the signal that orders muscle activity. A nerve damaged temporarily by a blow, or permanently by being crushed or cut, cannot transport the signal to the muscle.

Infections capable of causing central nervous system damage in dogs and cats include rabies, distemper, toxoplasmosis and systemic fungus diseases.

Tumors of the brain and spinal cord are not common. Symptoms are varied and depend on location and size of the tumor.

Changes from accustomed patterns of behavior, persistent spasm or weakness of muscles, loss of vision or hearing can be signs of central nervous system damage. Diagnostic procedures must be guided by the veterinarian.

Epilepsy (Fits)

Epilepsy is a disturbance of brain function. It occurs more often in certain breeds and certain families of dogs and cats, which suggests a hereditary basis.

The characteristic fit or seizure begins with a dazed appearance or other odd behavior, quickly followed by toppling over and more or less violent muscular contractions over most of the body. Profuse salivation and passage of urine and feces may occur.

Seizures may last for several seconds up to several hours. Some are so slight as to pass unnoticed. Others are of great severity. Seizures rarely result in death but they are very alarming. After the seizure the dog or cat may hide quietly for a time.

Frequency of the seizures varies from several times a day to perhaps once a year. At the time, protecting the convulsing animal from injury is the only home treatment. In hot weather soaking the dog or cat with cold water will prevent heat buildup and heat stroke due to the violently exercising muscles.

Diagnosis is based on the character of the seizures and the repetition of the episodes. Electroencephalograms are useful for diagnosis but not often available for animals.

Treatment with anticonvulsant drugs can be very effective in suppressing epileptic seizures. Since no cure is expected, treatment is often needed for a lifetime.

Cooperation between the owner and the veterinarian is needed in working out the most effective medication and the proper dose. Drugs commonly used are phenobarbital, diphenylhydantoin, and primidone.

Infrequent mild seizures may not justify treatment once the benign nature of the particular case is understood.

Disk Syndrome

Interruption of nerve conduction in the spinal cord may be brought about by a bulging or displaced disk. Disks are the tough, flexible cushions that occupy the flat round spaces between the vertebrae.

Degeneration of disk material leaves them a soft pasty consistency which may become hardened with calcium. The cushioning effect is lost and the disk material bulges or bursts out of its position, usually in the direction of the spinal cord. Severe pain is followed by loss of muscle control from the site of the disk downward, away from the brain.

Disks most often affected are in the neck and again in the back just to the rear of the last ribs. Displaced neck disks are by far the most painful, but may correct themselves in time. Symptoms may be transient as the disk shifts by itself. Surgery to relieve the pressure is less drastic than in the lower back.

Paralysis resulting from cord damage in the neck may be fatal because of the possible loss of nerve supply to the muscles of breathing. This would be unpredictable and possibly instantaneous.

The course of disk problems in the lower back can also be erratic but is less likely to be. Often there is a period of varying length of back pain stiffness and reluctance to go up steps. This could disappear with no further consequence. More often it will proceed to a stumbling, scuffling gait in the hind legs, then to paralysis of hind quarters, but with an end to the pain.

Treatment of disk pain is difficult because of the deep-seated nature of the cause. Continuous use of narcotics has side effects which are hard to deal with.

Surgery is aimed at removing displaced disk material and relieving pressure on the spinal cord. Good results have been obtained when it is done early. There is, however, a temptation to wait because in more than half the cases the problem will go away in two to six weeks. Complete or at least adequate recovery can occur without treatment even in animals unable to walk. If no recovery occurs, surgery may be too late.

The decision to operate can be evaluated by the veterinarian at the time based on the individual case.

Nutritional Needs; Commercial Food Usually Best Idea

By Allan Paul

A lot of research has been done to determine the nutrient needs of dogs and cats. In fact, probably more is known about pet nutrition than human nutrition.

Proper feeding of pets has been made much easier with the development of commercial pet foods. A good, brand name, complete and balanced commercial pet food contains all the nutrients the pet needs and in the proper proportions.

Most pets today are fed commercial foods and since most of these are well-formulated, nutritional deficiencies now are uncommon. When deficiencies are seen, they usually are in animals fed solely on a homemade diet. It is difficult to prepare a homemade diet that contains all the nu-

trients the animal requires so in most cases it is easier and safer to feed a commercial food.

If you are determined to feed a homemade diet, make every effort to balance the nutrients in the ration.

Feeding an unbalanced diet for a length of time can lead to some serious diseases. For instance, dogs fed an all meat diet may develop severe skeletal problems characterized by lameness, joint pain and swelling, and even bending and fractures of the long bones. This is due to the fact that meat is very low in calcium and phosphorus and the calcium:phosphorus ratio is about 1 to 15, whereas 1.2 to 1 is the optimal ratio.

Skeletal problems also are seen in cats fed diets composed primarily of liver. That is due to excessive intake of vitamin A.

These are just a couple of examples of problems that can

Allan Paul is Small Animal Extension Veterinarian, College of Veterinary Medicine, University of Illinois at Urbana-Champaign.

Dogs and Cats

develop in pets fed unbalanced diets. So if you decide to feed a homemade diet, discuss it first with a nutritionist or veterinarian. They can provide you with the information needed on how to balance the diet properly.

Many good books on pet nutrition can be found in the library. One of these, *The Collins Guide to Dog Nutrition* by D. R. Collins, Howell Book House, Inc., New York, 1973, contains an excellent section on how to formulate your own home diet.

Read Label Carefully

When selecting a commercial pet food it is important to read the label very carefully. Certain foods, especially some of the generic products, are not designed to be the sole source of the animal's diet, but only intended for supplemental or intermittent feeding.

The label on the food you select should contain the words "complete and balanced" or "100 percent nutritionally complete." If this claim is made on the label, the product must either meet or exceed all the National Research Council (NRC) requirements or pass strict testing protocols.

There are three basic

Recommended Nutrient Allowances for Dogs and Cats
(Percentages or Amount per Kilogram of Diet, Dry Basis)
—National Research Council

Nutrient	Dog	Cat
Protein	22%	28%
Fat	5.0%	9%
Linoleic acid	1.0%	1%
Arachidonic acid	–	0.1%
Minerals		
Calcium	1.1%	1%
Phosphorus	0.9%	0.8%
Potassium	0.6%	0.3%
Sodium chloride	1.1%	0.5%
Magnesium	0.04%	0.05%
Iron	60 mg	100 mg
Copper	7.3 mg	5 mg
Manganese	5.0 mg	10 mg
Zinc	50 mg	30 mg
Iodine	1.54 mg	1 mg
Selenium	0.11 mg	0.1 mg
Vitamins		
Vitamin A	5,000 IU	10,000 IU
Vitamin D	500 IU	1,000 IU
Vitamin E	50 IU	80 IU
Thiamin	1.0 mg	5 mg
Riboflavin	2.2 mg	5 mg
Pantothenic acid	10 mg	10 mg
Niacin	11.4 mg	45 mg
Pyridoxine	1.0 mg	4 mg
Folic acid	0.18 mg	1.0 mg
Biotin	0.10 mg	0.05 mg
Vitamin B_{12}	0.022 mg	0.02 mg
Choline	1,200 mg	2,000 mg
Other		
Taurine	–	0.05%

types of commercial pet foods available today—dry, semi-moist, and canned. If they are

Nutritional Needs

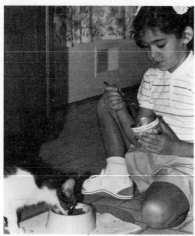

Marie T. Sebrechts

Kevin Shields

complete and balanced products, all three are equally nutritious and each has its own advantages and disadvantages.

One important factor in selecting the type of food is cost. Canned foods contain over 75 percent water, semi-moist around 25 percent and dry food about 10 percent. As a result, canned foods can cost up to 8 to 10 times as much as dry food when compared on a nutritional basis. An added advantage of dry food is its abrasive action which helps keep the pet's teeth clean.

The amount of food a pet needs depends on its size and age but also on its activity, environment, and disposition. For example, high-strung or very active animals expend more energy and need to eat

There are three basic types of commercial pet food available today—dry, semi-moist and canned. If they are complete and balanced products, all three are equally nutritious. Read the label very carefully when selecting a commercial pet food, since some products are not intended to be the sole source of an animal's diet. Look for the claim "complete and balanced" or "100 percent nutritionally complete" before you use just one food for your pet.

more. Also, the food required by animals kept outdoors in the winter will increase 50 to 75 percent over that needed in the summer.

The most practical method for maintaining a dog or cat is to establish an ideal or desired body weight and then feed a sufficient quantity of food to maintain that weight.

Growing Pet Needs
Feeding levels also vary according to the various stages

in the animal's life. Growing pups or kittens require a greater quantity of nutrients than adults. These are required to build bone, muscles, and organs.

That is an important stage in the life cycle and a good quality commercial puppy or kitten food should be used. These contain the added nutrients the young animal needs; hence supplementation is not required during the growing period.

Breeding animals should be maintained in a good muscular condition without obesity. Overweight females may encounter more problems at conception and whelping. Overweight males may be physiologically and anatomically inefficient for mating.

During the first month of pregnancy the bitch or queen doesn't need any extra food, but during the last month their food intake should be gradually increased so that at the time of birth they are receiving about $\frac{1}{4}$ to $\frac{1}{3}$ over their normal intake.

Lactation places heavy energy demands on an animal. Between the first and fourth weeks of lactation a sharp increase may need to be made in the dog's or cat's food intake. By the fourth week of lactation they may need to consume $2\frac{1}{2}$ to 3 times the normal maintenance level of food.

During this time, they should have access to all the food they want to meet the increased nutritional demands of heavy milk production. If the litter is large the ration could be supplemented with 10 to 15 percent meat or liver.

The process of weaning can leave a female in a stressed condition. To help reduce milk production do not feed her on the day of weaning. On the second day feed $\frac{1}{4}$ the normal maintenance amount; on the third day $\frac{1}{2}$; on the fourth day $\frac{3}{4}$; on the fifth day the food should be offered at the normal maintenance level.

Obesity Problems

While nutritional deficiencies are uncommon today, problems commonly occur in animals that are overfed or oversupplemented. The most common nutritional disease today is obesity. It is estimated that between 25 to 40 percent of animals seen by veterinarians are overweight.

There are various causes of obesity in pets. Feeding table scraps and treats, feeding highly palatable diets in unlimited quantities, and feeding diets that are high in fat

Kevin Shields

Nutritional deficiencies are uncommon today. Obesity, on the other hand, is the most common nutritional problem today. Feeding table scraps and treats to pets is not a good idea, since it can contribute heavily to weight problems.

It is simple to check to see if your pet is getting fat. If your dog or cat is overweight, plan a good weight-reducing program in order to keep your pet healthy for a long time.

Marie T. Sebrechts

may all contribute to obesity. As in people, lack of exercise also plays a role.

Obesity may pose some serious health problems to the animal. If an animal is 20 percent overweight, its mortality rate increases by 50 percent.

Being overweight reduces heart and lung efficiency, promotes skeletal problems, increases surgical risks, and can cause digestive, skin, reproductive, liver, and pancreas disorders. It also increases susceptibility to infection, makes the animal less tolerant of heat, and interferes with diagnostic procedures.

Because of all these potential problems, it is important to prevent pets from becoming overweight.

Testing for Fat

You can determine if your pet is overweight by performing the following test:

Stand behind the animal, place both thumbs side-by-side on the midline above the chest with fingers spread over the ribs. With thumbs pressing on vertebrae and fingers on ribs, slide the hands gently backwards and forwards.

Ideally, a moderately thin layer of fat should be felt. Visibly protruding bones generally suggest the animal is too

thin. A cushion of fat that cloaks edges of the ribs, allowing only a smooth wavy feel to the chest, suggests the animal is too fat.

If your pet is overweight, start a good weight reducing program such as the following. With the help of a veterinarian, establish an optimal weight for the pet. Reduce caloric intake to 60 percent of the recommended allowance to maintain that optimal weight.

Change the diet to a commercial reducing diet and eliminate all table scraps and treats. To decrease begging, feeding should be split into five to six times a day. Start a slow and gradual exercise regimen.

Following this program, most pets will reach their optimal weight in about 8 to 10 weeks. It is important that all family members cooperate.

Supplements

Another problem seen today occurs when a pet's diet is oversupplemented with vitamins and minerals.

In most cases, healthy dogs and cats on good commercial diets do not need any additional vitamins and minerals. However, some owners believe their pets need more and oversupplement the diet, particularly with calcium, phosphorus, and vitamin D. Too high a level of these can cause a reduced growth rate, bone problems, and interference with other minerals.

If you feel you must supplement your pet's diet, do so wisely and under the direction of your veterinarian.

Many pet owners own both dogs and cats and ask "Is it OK to feed dog foods to cats?" The answer to this question is a definite No.

Nutritional studies have shown that cats have certain special dietary requirements which may not be met if dog food is fed. For instance, cats need more protein than any other known species of mammals during all stages of life.

In addition, it has been recently discovered that cats require an amino acid called taurine in their diets. A deficiency in taurine can cause eye problems which can lead to blindness.

Cats have their own vitamin and mineral requirements as well. So it is best to feed cat food to cats and dog food to dogs.

Cat Addiction

Another common mistake in feeding cats is feeding primarily or exclusively a single food item such as fish, meat, liver

or kidney. The cat then becomes addicted to the food and refuses to eat anything else.

Although many of these foods are excellent sources of protein in a balanced diet, they are very unbalanced nutritionally when fed as a majority of the diet and can cause a number of nutritional diseases. For example, meat, liver, and kidney are all very low in calcium and if fed in excess, extensive bone malformation can occur.

Viscera of certain fish contain a substance which destroys vitamin B, the lack of which can result in severe brain damage. Also, the exclusive feeding of certain fish such as red tuna can cause a deficiency in vitamin E. This deficiency causes inflammation of the body fat which can lead to death.

Thus, if these items are fed they should not account for more than ¼ of the cat's diet. Again, it is much easier and safer to feed a good complete and balanced commercial food.

Further Reading
The Collins Guide to Dog Nutrition. D. R. Collins. Howell Book House, Inc. 230 Park Avenue, New York, NY 10169. $15.95.

Worm Parasites Cause Variety of Problems

By Edward L. Roberson

Ascarids of dogs, commonly called "roundworms" and scientifically named *Toxocara canis,* are large worms which reach 4 to 8 inches in length when mature. As egg-laying adults, they live in the small intestine of young dogs less than 6 months old.

Probably 75 percent of pups and young dogs in the United States are infected with this parasite which passes eggs in the dog's feces (excrement). The adult worm is seen only rarely in older dogs because these dogs develop resistance to the adult worm. Older dogs, however, can harbor the small larval stage of this parasite.

Edward L. Roberson is a professor in the Department of Parasitology, College of Veterinary Medicine, University of Georgia, Athens.

The major means of infection of dogs with *T. canis* is by ingestion (eating) of infective ascarid eggs or transmission of infective larvae from a mother dog to her unborn or nursing pups. Ascarid eggs which are passed in the feces of a dog harboring adult worms are not immediately infective to another dog; they require a couple of weeks of warm temperature to develop a larval stage in the egg which is infective to any age dog.

If a young dog ingests the infective egg, the small larva which hatches in the dog's stomach will grow to a large adult worm which begins to produce eggs about 4 weeks after the infective stage was originally ingested.

When an older dog, however, ingests an infective egg, the hatched larval stage does not grow to an adult worm in the intestine. Instead, the larva migrates to the adult

Worm Parasites

courtesy of Dr. M. Goldschmidt, U. of Pennsylvania

Roundworms in the intestine of a dog.

dog's musculature and there remains inactive. A dog throughout its life can acquire hundreds or even thousands of such quiescent larvae in its musculature.

Migrate to Fetus

In male dogs these ascarid larvae have no escape. In female dogs which become pregnant, however, the larvae become active and migrate via the umbilical cord to the liver of the fetuses during the final third of pregnancy (after the 42nd day). Thus newborn pups can be infected with *T. canis* ascarids from the start.

From the pup's liver the larvae make their way to the lungs, are coughed up, swal-lowed, and in the intestine will grow to large egg-laying adults in 4 weeks. While this intrauterine route of trans-mission is by far the most prevalent means of bitch-to-pup transmission of *T. canis* larvae, the parasites also can pass to pups through the mother dog's milk. Less than 5 percent of larvae, however, are transmitted by the latter route.

If the mother dog's initial supply of quiescent larvae is large, she can infect three suc-cessive litters of pups even in the absence of acquiring addi-tional larvae in her muscula-ture.

Clinical signs of *Toxocara* infection in pups depend on

Dogs and Cats

the number of larvae the pups have acquired from their mother or on the number of infective eggs ingested from contaminated environment where the pups live.

With but a few worms (10 or so), there may be no clinical evidence of infection. However, if the pup has several hundred worms which are growing to mature adults, the worm mass will distend the abdomen and give the pup a potbellied appearance. These worms deprive the pup of nutrients so that heavily infected pups are malnourished and slow growers. The pup's feces often are loose and frothy.

Diagnosis of ascarid infection is made by the above clinical signs and by microscopic examination of the feces for ascarid eggs. A veterinarian uses a salt or sugar flotation procedure to isolate the eggs from the feces.

Treat Pups Early. It is important to treat pups so that ascarids are expelled before they become egg-laying adults, that is, before pups are 4 weeks of age. Preferably pups should be treated at 2, 4, 6, and 8 weeks of age. The initial treatment will expel intrauterine acquired ascarids. Subsequent treatments will expel ascarids acquired

through the mother's milk.

Two drugs are available to veterinarians for treating young pups. They are pyrantel pamoate (Nemex) and fenbendazole (Panacur). Both are in suspension form and thus easy to administer to pups not yet eating solid food. The drugs also are effective in treating hookworms which are discussed below.

Treatment of the mother dog to destroy the larval ascarids in her musculature before the pups are born is difficult but possible. Only one drug, fenbendazole (Panacur), has been extensively tested for this purpose. It reduced ascarid burdens by 90 percent in pups born to treated bitches while pups born to unmedicated control bitches harbored an average of 400 worms each.

The regimen of treatment for the pregnant bitch must begin, however, about the 40th day of pregnancy and continue daily until 2 weeks after whelping—that is, about 37 consecutive days.

Hookworms of Dogs

Hookworms are bloodsucking parasites. The most common species is *Ancylostoma caninum*. While the adult worm is only about an inch in length, it has a large mouth by which it attaches to the wall of the small intestine and digests a plug of tissue. This causes a small bleeding site. When 50 to several hundred worms are present, the total loss of blood can be dangerous even to an older dog but especially to small pups.

Dogs with heavy hookworm infections become anemic. The loss of blood into the intestine results in dark tar-colored feces. Gums of the animal will be blanched white instead of pink and the animal is weak. These clinical signs plus a fecal examination for eggs give a positive diagnosis of hookworm infection.

Both young and adult dogs can have infections with adult hookworms which shed eggs in the dog's feces. Once passed in the feces, hookworm eggs develop an infective larval form which hatches from the egg shell and can infect dogs either by penetrating the skin when dogs lie down in damp contaminated places or by being ingested with the dog's contaminated food or water.

Thus, dog food should never be placed directly on the ground. Use of food and water bowls which are cleaned daily will help minimize a yard-confined dog's exposure to infective hookworm larvae.

Older dogs, besides harboring adult hookworms in their intestines, also accumulate the immature larval stage of *A. caninum* in their body tissues (muscles, mammary glands). These larvae do not infect the fetuses of a pregnant dog as did *Toxocara* larvae, but they do pass in the milk of the mother to her nursing pups. About 60 percent of the larvae which do so will pass during the first week of nursing, but some larvae are transmitted every week as long as the mother dog is lactating.

These larvae will grow to egg-laying adult hookworms about 2 weeks after infecting the pup. So a pup as young as 2 weeks old can be contaminating the environment with hookworm eggs. The milk-borne route is the principal means by which young pups become infected with *A. caninum* hookworms.

If the number of hookworms is great, pups will begin showing clinical signs of anemia about 2 weeks of age and may die before 3 weeks of age.

Treatment. The regimen of treating pups for ascarids at 2, 4, 6, and 8 weeks of age is also ideal for eliminating hookworms as they are constantly acquired through the mother's milk. The two drugs, pyrantel pamoate and fenbendazole, mentioned earlier for use against ascarids, are effective also for hookworms of nursing pups.

Several additional drugs are available for treatment of hookworms in older dogs. Older dogs generally are given a single 1-day deworming once or twice per year as the owner seeks routine veterinary care. These treatments eliminate only the parasites which occur in the digestive tract.

Treatment of the pregnant bitch to kill larval hookworms and to prevent heavy mammary transmission of hookworms to her pups can be done as described earlier for ascarid larvae—that is, treatment with fenbendazole daily from the 40th day of pregnancy until 2 weeks after whelping.

Worms in Cats

Cats also can be infected with ascarids and hookworms but the common species in cats are not the same species of parasites which occur in dogs. The common ascarid *(Toxocara cati)* and hookworm *(Ancylostoma tubaeforme)* of cats do not infect dogs and vice versa.

Ascarids and hookworms do not occur as frequently in cats as they do in dogs. This is probably related to the cat's burying its feces (excrement) while feces from dogs remain on the ground surface where ascarid eggs and hookworm larvae can be scattered more readily by rainwater, thus contaminating a wider area.

Cats acquire ascarid infections from ingesting infective eggs which have been passed in the feces of a cat harboring adult worms. Both young and older cats may harbor such infections. Nursing kittens may also acquire ascarid larvae through the milk of the mother cat, but intrauterine infection of the fetus during pregnancy is not known to occur.

Feline hookworm infections evidently are acquired by the larvae penetrating the skin or by larvae being ingested orally (contaminated food or water). The milk-borne route which is important in bitch-to-pup transmission apparently does not occur in cats.

Clinical signs of ascarid or hookworm infections in cats are like those described for the dog but seldom occur because cats usually have only light inapparent infections. In general, the same drugs used for deworming dogs can be used to deworm cats.

Worm Parasites

Disposal of cat feces helps tremendously to reduce potential exposure of other cats to parasites. Litter can be discarded daily and the box should be rinsed with scalding water before adding new litter.

Marie T. Sebrechts

Disposal of cat feces helps tremendously to reduce potential exposure of other cats to these parasites. With outdoor cats this is not practical but with indoor cats, litter can be discarded daily. The box should be rinsed with scalding water before adding new litter.

Human Infections

Both ascarids and hookworms of dogs and cats can infect human beings. These worms do not grow to the adult intestine-dwelling stage in people. They remain in the infective larval form but occasionally are able to cause serious consequences.

Larvae from accidentally ingested ascarid eggs migrate in the human body and can cause enlarged liver, elevation in numbers of eosinophils (a specific type of white blood cell), and damage to the retina of the eye with consequent impaired vision.

Larvae of canine and feline hookworms sometimes penetrate the outer layer of the human skin. They cannot completely penetrate the human skin, however. The result is that the larvae migrate aimlessly within the skin for a month or more creating an itching, tortuous tract if not treated.

The best way to insure against human exposure to parasites of pets is to have pets dewormed when they first enter the household and to submit a fecal sample to a

Dogs and Cats

veterinarian at least twice each year for parasite examination.

Whipworms of Dogs

Whipworms *(Trichuris vulpis)* live in the lower digestive tract of dogs, specifically in the cecum which is comparable to the human appendix. The adult worm is indeed shaped like a whip, broad at one end, long and narrow at the other end. It is about 2.5 inches long.

These worms thread their narrow end into the lining of the cecum to hold on. They produce football-shaped eggs which are passed in the feces of infected dogs. After passing, the eggs develop an infective larval stage which, protected by the thick egg shell, can live in the soil for several years.

Heavy infections most often occur in dogs which are confined to a small yard pen where the ground is continuously being contaminated with eggs and the dog is continuously reinfecting itself.

Signs. Presence or absence of clinical signs depends on the number of worms. With a light infection (less than 50 whipworms), a dog may show no apparent signs. With heavy infection (several hundred worms), the irritation to the gut lining causes a loss of tissue fluids which results in a watery feces that is usually red-tinged with blood.

After several days of fluid loss, a dog may become dangerously dehydrated. In such cases, intravenous replacement of body fluids is essential as well as immediate deworming of the dog.

Several drugs are available to veterinarians for removal of whipworms. These include dichlorvos (Task), butamisole HCl (Styquin), mebendazole (Telmintic), and fenbendazole (Panacur).

If a dog has to be returned to the same infected yard pen, it is important that it be retreated at 3-month intervals thereafter. Treatment at this frequency will eliminate newly acquired worms before they begin to lay eggs and, therefore, will prevent further contamination of the ground. Of course, selecting a new site for the pen would be of greater advantage to the dog and should prevent the necessity of 3-month treatments.

Eggs of the canine whipworm are not infective to human beings. The human race has its own species of whipworm, however, which is transmitted from one person to another.

Dog, Cat Tapeworms

Tapeworms are flat segmented worms, usually a foot or more in length, which live in the small intestine of animals. One species of tapeworms, *Dipylidium caninum,* infects about 30 percent of dogs and 15 percent of cats in the southern part of the United States. Less frequently, dogs are infected with *Taenia pisiformis* and cats with *Taenia taeniaeformis.*

All three of the above tapeworms shed their egg-filled terminal segment in feces of the infected animal. Such segments are about the size of a grain of rice and may be seen crawling on the surface of the feces.

An initial host is required for development of the young tapeworm to a stage that will be infective for dogs or cats. In the case of *Dipylidium,* fleas serve as the initial host in which the ingested tapeworm egg develops to a small larval stage that is infective for either dogs or cats which may accidentally (or intentionally) swallow the flea.

For *Taenia* tapeworms of dogs, wild rabbits serve as the initial host; for *Taenia* of cats, rats or mice serve as the initial host. Dogs or cats become infected with *Taenia* tapeworms by eating the respec-

tive initial host. The larval tapeworm then develops to a large adult worm in the small intestine of the dog or cat.

None of these tapeworms are known to be harmful to the dog or cat. Nevertheless, pet owners want their pets rid of tapeworms. Fortunately, a fairly new drug, praziquantel (Droncit), available now to veterinarians, is 100 percent effective in treating tapeworm infections.

One must also control fleas, however, to prevent reinfection with *Dipylidium.* Preventing rural dogs from eating wild rabbits or cats from eating rats and mice may not be practical as a preventive measure for *Taenia* infections.

Only a few cases of human infection with *Dipylidium* are documented. These occurred because of accidental swallowing of an infected flea. These infections were not harmful to the children involved and were easily treated by a physician. The species of *Taenia* which infect the dog or cat are not able to infect humans.

Heartworms of Dogs

Heartworms, scientifically known as *Dirofilaria immitis,* indeed live in the heart of dogs or in the major artery

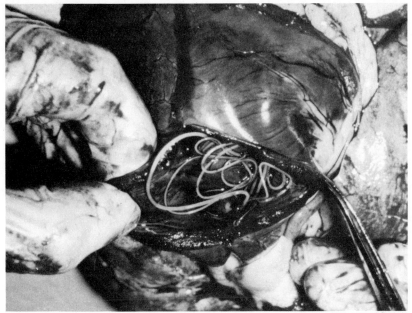

Heart of dog cut open showing adult heartworms.

(the anterior vena cava) which carries blood from the heart to the lungs. The adult worms are shoestring thin but quite long, 8 to 13 inches.

Mature adult female worms, rather than laying eggs, produce thousands of larval forms, called microfilariae, which are shed into the blood and circulate throughout the dog's body. When mosquitoes feed on the blood of dogs the microfilariae are ingested with the blood.

In certain species of mosquitoes, these heartworm microfilariae can survive and develop in the mosquito to an advanced larval stage that is infective to a dog. When the mosquito again feeds on the same or another dog the infective heartworm larvae are transmitted.

Beneath the skin of the dog these infective larvae will grow from less than ⅛ inch to about 2 inches during the first 3 months. Then they move into the heart to complete their development to adult worms in another 3 months.

Earliest signs of heartworm infection are coughing and tiring during exercise. In general, a small dog with but a few worms may show these

Worm Parasites

signs when a larger dog with the same number of worms may not. As the larger dog acquires greater numbers of worms, however, it also will develop clinical signs.

As the disease progresses, a chronic cough develops and a dog has difficulty breathing when exercised. In advanced cases, the legs and abdominal cavity become swollen with fluid, an indication that the heart is failing to function properly.

Diagnosis of infection with heartworms is usually made by finding microfilariae in a sample of the dog's blood. However, in 5 to 10 percent of heartworm cases, microfilariae do not occur (the adult worms may be all males or all females, for example). In such cases, radiographic examination of the heart or a special serology test may help a veterinarian establish a diagnosis of heartworm infection.

Treatment for heartworm infection in dogs involves several steps. First, a drug must be given to get rid of the adult worms. The only available drug for this purpose is an arsenic-containing drug, thiacetarsamide sodium, which is given intravenously twice a day for 2 days.

The adult worms are gradually killed during the

following week and are swept with the blood flow into the lungs where they eventually decompose and are cleared away by natural body defenses. During this 1-month period following treatment, a dog should be confined to prevent any exercising which would overly exert its heart and lungs.

About 6 weeks after treatment for adult worms, treatment can be administered to destroy the microfilarial stage. One of three drugs can be used. Dithiazanine iodide (Dizan) or levamisole (Levasole) are given orally for 7 to 10 days; fenthion (Spot-On) is applied to the surface of the skin or is injected subcutaneously.

All three drugs occasionally cause vomiting and diarrhea. A dog which becomes ill while taking one of the drugs may tolerate another without sickness.

Prevention of heartworm infections is more desirable than having to treat a heartworm-infected dog. Diethylcarbamazine, abbreviated DEC, destroys the infective larval stage that is transmitted from mosquitoes to dogs.

If DEC is given every day throughout the mosquito season (and for 2 months after mosquito season), heartworm infection in a dog can be pre-

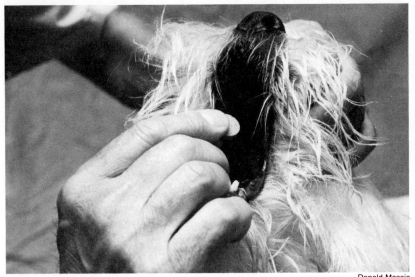

Donald Massie

Heartworms can be prevented by giving your pet the prescribed drug every day throughout the mosquito season and for two months afterwards.

vented. Daily administration of the drug, however, is essential since mosquito transmission may occur at any time. In warmer states like Florida, the mosquito season is nearly year-round; thus, DEC should be given year-round. Dogs that are already positive for heartworm microfilariae should not be given DEC because of a potential adverse reaction. Such dogs should first be treated to get rid of adult worms, then treated to get rid of microfiloriae—before they are started on the preventive DEC.

In areas of the country where heartworm infection is prevalent (Atlantic and Gulf coasts, states along the Mississippi River), pups should be started on DEC as soon as they are weaned. Several commercial formulations are available—syrup, wafers, tablet. Any of these not only serve as a preventive for heartworms but also will prevent intestinal ascarid infection.

A particular syrup formulation, Styrid-Caricide, combines DEC and another drug, styrylpyridinium Cl, and serves as a preventive also for intestinal hookworm infection of dogs when administered daily for the dog's entire life.

Worm Parasites

Fleas, Ticks, Lice, Mites, and Flies

By Lynn P. Schmeitzel and
Peter J. Ihrke

Fleas are wingless, brown, bloodsucking insects that may infest dogs and cats, and other warmblooded animals. Fleas transmit several diseases (for example, plague) and parasites such as tapeworms. Young animals heavily infested with fleas may die from severe blood loss. Fleas prefer certain species of animals but will attack any source of blood if the preferred animal is not available.

The cat flea (*Ctenocephalides felis*) and the dog flea (*Ctenocephalides canis*) both infest dogs and cats. *C. felis* is the most common flea found on dogs and cats. Cat and dog fleas move rapidly on the skin and are most easily found on the rump and in the groin area.

Sticktight fleas (*Echidnophaga gallinacea*) are found on birds (especially chickens) and may attack dogs and cats exposed to infested birds. This flea attaches to the face of the animal and moves slowly.

The human flea (*Pulex irritans*) may attack dogs and cats.

Flea eggs laid on the host are smooth and quickly fall off into the animal's environment. The eggs are oval, white, and glistening.

Small larvae hatch from the eggs and feed on the feces from adult fleas. After several molts, the last larval stage forms a pupal case. While in the case, the larva develops into an adult flea. The adult flea emerges from the pupal case and searches for an animal.

Time required for the flea

Lynn P. Schmeitzel is Assistant Professor of Dermatology, College of Veterinary Medicine, University of Tennessee, Knoxville. Peter J. Ihrke is Assistant Professor of Dermatology and Allergy, School of Veterinary Medicine, University of California, Davis.

Dogs and Cats

to develop from egg to adult may be as short as 16 days during periods of warm temperatures and high humidity.

A small amount of flea saliva is deposited in the skin each time the adult flea bites an animal. This saliva is very irritating and an allergic reaction can cause severe itching, resulting in the skin disease termed flea allergy dermatitis.

Biting and scratching around the rump and groin areas is the most common sign of flea allergy. Hair loss, a red rash, and thickening of the skin are commonly seen. Fleas may be difficult to find in allergic animals since very few flea bites are needed to cause an allergic reaction. In areas of the United States where fleas are common, flea allergy dermatitis is the most common itchy disease of the skin.

Flea feces (flea dirt) in the haircoat confirms the presence of fleas. Flea dirt consists of dehydrated blood from the dog or cat and is reddish-black and comma-shaped.

Successful treatment of flea allergy dermatitis requires the absolute elimination of fleas from contact with the affected dog or cat. If one dog or cat in a household has fleas, it may be assumed that all animals in the household have fleas. Therefore, all animals in the household must be treated. All animals, the house, and premises should be treated with appropriate insecticides at frequent intervals to prevent reinfestation.

Contrary to recent folklore, brewers yeast (a thiamine or B_1 source), garlic, or sulfur are not effective in either repelling or killing fleas.

Ticks, Hard and Soft

Ticks are bloodsucking arthropod parasites of the skin. They transmit many diseases such as Rocky Mountain Spotted Fever to people and animals. Severe blood loss may result from heavy infestation. Tick paralysis is a rare disease caused by a toxic substance in the saliva of some ticks. Recovery is rapid if the ticks are removed.

Ticks have a four-staged life cycle including an egg, a six-legged larva (seed tick), an eight-legged nymph, and an eight-legged adult. Ticks are identified as one-host, two-host, and three-host ticks depending on the number of hosts required to complete their life cycle.

Hard ticks (*Ixodidae*) and soft ticks (*Argasidae*) are the two main families of parasitic ticks.

Hard ticks have a hard shield on their backs distinguishing them from soft ticks which do not. Most hard ticks require three different hosts to complete their life cycle and each stage only feeds once.

Thirteen species of economically important ticks are in the hard tick (*Ixodidae*) family. Most of these ticks are acquired outside except for the Brown Dog Tick (*Rhipicephalus sanguineus*) which can infest buildings.

The Brown Dog Tick is widely distributed in North America. Since this tick survives indoors, it can infest kennels and households. The Brown Dog Tick is a three-host tick but all three stages can parasitize the dog. This tick also parasitizes cats, horses, rabbits, and humans. The Brown Dog Tick has no white markings on the shield on its back.

The American Dog Tick (*Dermacentor variabilis*) is widely distributed in North America but is most common on the Atlantic coast. These ticks, unlike the Brown Dog Tick, live only in grasses and shrubs.

The larval and nymphal stages of the American Dog Tick parasitize field mice. The adult tick usually infests the dog but also can parasitize humans, wild animals, cattle, and horses. Adult American Dog Ticks have white markings on the shield on their backs. Outdoor areas such as fields are the major sources of American Dog Ticks.

Removal. Hard ticks usually are found securely attached by their head to the skin. Before removal, these ticks should be sprayed with an insecticide safe for use on animals, or soaked with alcohol. The head should be grasped with an instrument such as tweezers and pulled on gently until removed. Cigarettes, lighters, gasoline and kerosene can severely injure the skin and should never be used to remove ticks. If the ticks are Brown Dog Ticks, the kennels and household premises may need repeated treatment with pesticides.

Soft ticks (*Argasidae*) have a leathery outer covering. The Spinose Ear Tick (*Otobius megnini*) is the only medically important soft tick. This tick is most common in the southwestern parts of the United States. The young stages (larvae and nymphs) live in the outer ear canal of dogs, cats, cattle, and horses. Adult soft ticks do not feed and do not live on animals.

The Spinose Ear Tick can

cause severe irritation to the ear canal and may occasionally cause paralysis and seizures in some animals. The animal should be taken to a veterinarian for removal of these ticks since the eardrum may be damaged by improper removal of the ticks, especially by sharp instruments.

The Louse

Lice are wingless insects that are uncommon parasites of dogs and cats and are common parasites of livestock and birds in the United States. Lice spend their entire life cycle on the host and are not readily transmitted from one animal species to another (they are host specific). In other words cat lice will not usually infest dogs and vice versa. Lice are spread from an animal to another by direct contact.

Female lice attach their eggs (nits) to the hairs or feathers on their hosts. The young lice undergo several molts before becoming adults. Development from egg to adult takes about 19 to 28 days.

The two main types of lice include sucking lice (*Anoplura*) and biting lice (*Mallophaga*).

Sucking lice are larger than biting lice, have piercing mouthparts for obtaining a blood meal, and have pincer-like claws for clinging to the hairs of their hosts. These lice are grey to red depending on the amount of blood they have ingested. Sucking lice may cause severe anemia in heavily infested young or debilitated animals.

Sucking lice can infest most domestic animals (except birds and cats). Infested animals are usually itchy and often have rough dry coats. Sucking lice move slowly.

Biting lice usually are yellow with a large rounded head and mouthparts adapted for chewing and biting. Some species have legs for clasping, others have legs for moving rapidly. These lice may cause severe hair loss from scratching and rubbing. Biting lice can infest dogs, cats, cattle, sheep, goats, horses, and birds.

Specific identification of lice is difficult and is less important than being able to determine if the louse is a biting species or the more harmful blood-sucking species.

The dog has one common biting louse (*Trichodectes canis*) and one common sucking louse (*Linognathus setosus*). The cat has only one common species, a biting louse (*Felicola subrostratus*).

Adult lice and eggs attached to hair and feathers may be seen with the unaided eye. Lice and nits may be found more readily by using a magnifying hand lens with good lighting.

Many pesticides will kill adult lice but the eggs are quite resistant. Consequently, animals should be treated and then retreated two weeks later to kill the lice that have hatched from eggs not affected by the first treatment.

All About Mites

Demodectic mites (*Demodex* spp.) parasitize many domestic animals. These mites live in hair follicles in the skin. They crawl from the mother to the nursing puppy or kitten during the first few days of life. They do not cause any harm in small numbers and are considered normal inhabitants of the skin. These mites are not contagious from animal to animal, or animal to human. The skin disease caused by an increased number of mites is called demodicosis or demodectic mange.

Demodex spp. are elongated mites with short stubby legs. The life cycle includes an egg, a six-legged larva, an eight-legged nymph, and an eight-legged adult.

These mites can be demonstrated by a veterinarian performing a skin scraping, removing the superficial layer of a small area of skin with a scalpel blade. The debris is placed on a glass slide with mineral oil and examined with a microscope.

Affects Dogs. Demodicosis is a potentially serious disease in the dog. If large numbers of *Demodex canis* mites are found in several skin scrapings a diagnosis of demodicosis may be made.

There are two forms of demodicosis in the dog—localized and generalized. Patchy hair loss on the head, forelegs, and trunk is called localized demodicosis. In generalized demodicosis hair loss, reddening, and crusts may involve the entire body. These animals also may develop severe bacterial infections in the skin.

An inherited defect in the animal's immune system allowing the mites to multiply is believed to be an important factor in development of generalized demodicosis. Since it is believed that the defect of the immune system is inherited, dogs with demodicosis should not be used for breeding. Demodicosis is not a contagious disease. Affected puppies were born with a predisposition to develop demodicosis.

Diagnosis and treatment of localized and generalized demodicosis should be supervised by a veterinarian. Localized demodicosis often does not require any treatment and usually will spontaneously cure in six to eight weeks. Occasionally the localized form will become generalized, so the affected areas and normal skin must be closely observed. No one can predict if a dog with localized demodicosis will spontaneously cure or develop generalized demodicosis.

A veterinarian usually will treat generalized demodicosis with a series of parasiticidal rinses after clipping the hair. Antibiotics may be needed for a secondary bacterial infection that is often present.

Rare in Cats. Demodicosis is a rare disease in cats. There are two types of demodectic mites in the cat: *Demodex cati* and an unnamed *Demodex* spp. In localized demodicosis there is patchy hair loss, reddening, and occasionally crusting on the neck, ears and head. In generalized demodicosis hair loss, reddening, and crusting may involve the entire body.

Generalized demodicosis may develop in cats secondary to suppression of the immune system associated with systemic diseases such as diabetes mellitus or feline leukemia virus infection. Diagnosis and treatment of feline demodicosis should be supervised by a veterinarian.

Sarcoptic Mites
The family Sarcoptidae includes the *Sarcoptes* spp. and *Notoedres* spp. of mites. These mites may affect many species of animals but usually prefer one species. They are spread by direct contact from one animal to another.

This family of mites burrow within the superficial layers of the skin and the entire life cycle is spent on the host animal. The life cycle includes an egg, a six-legged larva, two eight-legged nymphal stages and an eight-legged adult. The development from egg to adult takes about 17 days.

The common skin disease caused by sarcoptic mites is called scabies or sarcoptic mange. The variety *Sarcoptes scabei* is named after a particular host (for example, *Sarcoptes scabei* var. *canis*—the sarcoptic mite of dogs). In all animals, scabies is an intensely itchy disease causing the animal to scratch, chew, and rub constantly.

Canine scabies is a common, contagious skin disease. The most common signs are scaling, crusting, and a red rash on the head, ears, and abdomen. The entire body may be affected. Many of the skin lesions are self-induced since dogs with canine scabies are almost constantly scratching, chewing, and rubbing their skin. Severe itching is induced by very few mites and may be due to an allergic reaction to the mites.

Scabies is highly contagious from dog to dog. Dogs obtained from sources with large numbers of animals housed together such as pounds, large puppy producing establishments, and some pet shops are more likely to be affected by scabies.

Scabies mites may be transmitted to a human, resulting in a red rash. Usually the disease in humans is self-limiting since canine scabies mites apparently cannot complete their life cycle in human skin.

Since these mites often are difficult to find by multiple skin scrapings, response to treatment with parasiticidal rinses is often used by veterinarians to diagnose canine scabies.

Cat Scabies, Mange. Feline scabies or notoedric mange caused by *Notoedres cati* is an uncommon skin disease in many parts of the

United States yet may be common in certain local areas. These mites are highly contagious to other cats and occasionally may be transmitted to people and dogs. In the cat there is hair loss, thickening and crusting of the skin, usually affecting the head and forelegs. These areas are severely itchy.

Notoedres mites have morphologic characteristics similar to *Sarcoptes scabei* mites. These mites may cause a red rash in humans. Usually this rash spontaneously resolves in people since *Notoedres cati* mites cannot complete their life cycle in human skin.

Parasiticidal rinses are used to treat notoedric mange. Since many parasiticides are highly toxic to cats, a veterinarian always should supervise the use of any parasiticides in cats.

Ear Mites. The Psoroptic family of mites usually are parasites of cattle and sheep. The life cycle includes an egg, a six-legged larva, two eight-legged nymphal stages, and an eight-legged adult.

One member of this family, *Otodectes cyanotis,* the ear mite, is a common cause of ear problems in the dog and cat. These mites generally are found in the outer ear canal but may rarely be found on other parts of the body. The mites are readily transmitted between dogs and cats.

Ear mites cause severe irritation and thick, dry, black crusts in the ear canals. The mites may be seen with a magnifying instrument called an otoscope. They are large, white, and mobile. Eardrops usually are prescribed by veterinarians to treat this disease.

Walking Dandruff. *Cheyletiella* spp. or Walking Dandruff Mites are contagious mites that live on the surface of the skin. These mites cause severe scaling, usually on the back. Some itching may be seen but this disease usually is not as itchy as the other skin diseases caused by mites in dogs and cats. The mites commonly affect dogs, cats, and rabbits. They may be seen with a magnifying hand lens or in skin scrapings.

Chiggers are larval stages of the Trombiculid mites. Only the larval stages are parasitic. The nymphs and adults are free living. Chiggers are seen most often in the late summer and early fall and are obtained by contact with heavy underbrush.

The North American Chigger (*Trombicula alfreddugesi*) is the most common chigger that affects animals and people. On animals they cause an itchy, red rash on the belly, face, feet, and legs. Chiggers are orange-red in color. They may be found in the ears of cats.

The larval mites remain attached to the skin for only a few hours, so the larvae often are difficult to find on the animal. Since chiggers leave voluntarily, the only treatment that may be needed is something to stop the itching. Chigger infested areas should be avoided during summer and fall months to prevent recurrence.

Flies. The larvae of *Cuterebra* spp. flies infest cats, dogs, rabbits, squirrels, and small rodents in the summer. Pets acquire the larvae by investigating rodent burrows. Consequently the neck is most commonly affected.

The larva penetrates the skin and forms a cavity under the skin. A breathing pore communicates with the outside. Cuterebra larvae should be removed surgically by a veterinarian.

'Ringworm,' Other Fungus Diseases

By David K. Chester

Disease caused by fungal organisms (mycosis) occurs throughout the world. There are about 100,000 species of fungi, with less than 200 of them involved in fungal infections of animals or humans.

Fungus diseases vary greatly in clinical signs, incidence and geographic distribution. Skin infections such as "ringworm," found worldwide, are the most common. Systemic (internal) fungal diseases are less common overall, but in specific localized areas a disease of this group could be the most serious and common disease seen.

Histoplasmosis and blastomycosis are common in the Ohio and Mississippi river

---

David K. Chester is Professor of Medicine, Department of Small Animal Medicine & Surgery, College of Veterinary Medicine, Texas A&M University, College Station.

valleys, while coccidioidomycosis is common in the desert Southwest—but any of these can be seen elsewhere. Other fungi are found throughout the country, but are more common in hot, humid environments.

The importance of fungal diseases in animals must be kept in mind. "Ringworm" usually is not serious to the animal; however, it is important to diagnose and treat it properly because the animal can be a source of human infection.

Systemic fungal diseases are not directly contagious from animals to humans, but can be fatal to the infected animal or require long and expensive treatment. Some fungi are opportunistic. They are common in the environment but infect animals or humans only under unusual circumstances.

Fungal diseases often look like other diseases, which may

result in misdiagnosis and expensive, ineffective or harmful treatment.

'Ringworm' Infections

Three fungal organisms, *Microsporum canis, Microsporum gypseum,* and *Trichophyton mentagrophytes* cause nearly all the dermatophyte infections ("ringworm") in dogs and cats.

The cat is the preferred host for *Microsporum canis.* This organism will easily infect dogs and people. Infections result from direct contact with infected animals or infected hairs or skin.

Microsporum gypseum normally grows in the soil. Animals develop the disease by digging or otherwise contacting the infected soil.

Many species of animals, especially wild rodents, carry *Trichophyton mentagrophytes.* Their burrows are seeded with the organism and many dogs and cats develop "ringworm" by contact with these rodents or their burrows.

Lesions caused by dermatophytes are confined to the skin or haircoat and appear similar regardless of which organism causes them.

Cat lesions often are so mild they go unnoticed for years. Lesions may consist of broken hairs around the face,

ears or feet, or reddened, scaly skin in areas of broken hair. In severe cases, scales and crusts may accumulate and the skin becomes thickened and itchy.

Dogs More Affected

Lesions in dogs usually are more severe. The hair is broken or gone, papules (small swellings), scales, crusts, and redness are more prominent signs. As the disease spreads from one hair follicle to another, a circular pattern of skin redness develops around a healing center. This looks somewhat like a worm under the skin, resulting in the term "ringworm."

Dermatophytosis is diagnosed by finding typical skin lesions, a history suggesting exposure to the organisms or contagiousness, and laboratory evaluation. Laboratory confirmation of the disease is especially important since the lesions alone can look like so many other diseases.

The most reliable laboratory test is fungal culture. Broken hairs or scrapings from the skin are placed on appropriate culture media and allowed to grow in a dark, moist area. The fungi will usually grow within 4 to 10 days, but cultures generally are held 3 weeks before declaring them negative. The organism can be identified by staining and microscopic examination.

An ultraviolet (Black or Wood's) light may be used to help identify some *Microsporum canis* infections.

Skin scrapings may be cleared of debris with sodium hydroxide and examined under a microscope for spores of fungi. Experienced personnel can identify fungal diseases with this technique, but identification of the specific organism usually is not possible.

Treatment. Dermatophyte treatment aims are: Cure the infected animal and prevent reinfection or infection of others.

Hair in and around the animal's lesion should be clipped off and disposed of. Local treatment with baths, dips, creams or lotions containing antifungal agents are then prescribed. Oral medications such as griseofulvin or ketoconazole may also be used.

Treatment needs to continue 6 weeks or longer in most animals.

Isolating infected animals, cleaning and/or disinfecting the premises, and washing well after treating infected animals are important in preventing human infection and spread to other animals.

Systemic Infections

Three diseases generally are classified as systemic fungal infections because they can involve any or all of the body systems. They are: Blastomycosis, caused by *Blastomyces dermatitidis*, histoplasmosis, caused by *Histoplasma capsulatum*, and coccidioidomycosis, caused by *Coccidioides immitis*.

All these organisms are found in the soil in endemic areas. *Blastomyces* and *Histoplasma* prefer moist soil enriched with bird or bat droppings and *Coccidioides* prefers hot, dry, alkaline soils. All three diseases result from inhaling infective spores from soil. They all grow in the body in a noncontagious yeast form.

Many animals and humans living in endemic areas have had these diseases, developed immunity and recovered without the problem being realized. The diseases start with respiratory signs such as cough, rapid breathing, or pneumonia and fever. When these diseases become severe or chronic, the result may be weight loss, loss of appetite, inactivity and even death.

Each of the diseases has

signs more specific to that disease. Severe diarrhea is common with histoplasmosis but not with blastomycosis or coccidioidomycosis. Nodular draining skin lesions are common with blastomycosis but uncommon in the other two diseases. Coccidioidomycosis frequently affects the bones—resulting in swellings, lameness and fractures—while that is much less common with the other two diseases.

Laboratory confirmation of these diseases is needed even though the diagnosis may be suggested by history and physical findings. The most reliable finding is locating the organism in discharges or body fluids by cytology or in the tissue by biopsy. Blood tests (serology) may be helpful but are not as reliable as finding the organisms.

Treatment of animals for these diseases requires months of therapy with expensive and potentially toxic drugs. Amphotericin-B is considered the most effective treatment. It must be given intravenously and often causes kidney damage.

Ketoconazole is a newer, less toxic drug that can be given orally but has not been as effective in acute illness and is quite expensive.

It is becoming common practice to use both drugs in early treatment and then continue with ketoconazole alone after a few weeks.

Direct infection of humans from infected animals has not been reported. Humans can become infected from the same source as their animals.

Subcutaneous Types
These fungus diseases are so named because the main clinical sign is a nodule or abscess just under the skin. The organism usually is introduced into the body from bite wounds, rose thorns or other foreign bodies, or accidents. The three most common diseases in this group are: Sporotrichosis, phycomycosis and mycetoma.

Lesions of the diseases are nodules or tumor-like masses on the skin. They may have openings which drain reddish or yellowish fluid or which exude granules. Besides the skin lesions, sporotrichosis may become systemic and affect any of the organ systems. Frequently phycomycosis involves only the gastrointestinal tract of the dog, resulting in vomiting, diarrhea, and rapid weight loss.

The diseases are diagnosed by finding the causative

organisms in infected tissue. Sporotrichosis can be cured by several months of therapy with sodium iodide if the disease has not become systemic. Sodium iodide may also be used to treat the systemic disease but results are poor. Mycetoma and phycomycosis lesions can be cured if they can be surgically removed. When that is not possible, treatment usually is not successful.

With the exception of sporotrichosis, humans are not likely to get these diseases from animals. If infected material gets in a wound, any of them have the potential to cause disease.

Other Infections

A number of fungal organisms are present in the environment which can cause disease only when the animal's immune system is compromised. Immune suppression can be a result of drug therapy with cortisone type steroids or anti-cancer drugs, and immunosuppressive diseases.

The most common symptoms associated with these diseases are respiratory (coughing, sneezing, nasal discharge) with cryptococcosis and *Aspergillus* infections, and ear infections with *Candida, Pityrosporum* and *Aspergillus*.

Some animals become severely debilitated.

The diseases are treated with various drugs but most important is to take steps to improve the animal's general health. These diseases are not considered contagious to humans.

Digestive, Hormone, and Autoimmune Ills; Poisonings

By Dennis Blodgett

There are many causes of digestive problems, and in general the causes are similar for dogs and cats. However, prevalence of the various digestive problems differs for each species.

The most common signs of digestive problems are vomiting and diarrhea. Other less common clinical signs of digestive problems include constipation, bloat, abdominal pain, excessive salivation, difficult swallowing, and lack of appetite. Some of the most common causes of vomiting and diarrhea in dogs and cats will be discussed.

Vomiting is produced by stimulation of the vomiting center in the brain stem. Vomiting is not always due to irritation of the gastrointestinal tract, however. Heart, liver, and genitourinary tract irritations, motion sickness, kidney failure, various infections, and particular drugs or toxins may also produce vomiting.

One of the more common causes of vomiting from gastrointestinal irritation is a dietary problem. This may result from a sudden change in diet or from ingesting foreign materials. Foreign materials (such as dirt, plants, garbage, and poisons) are more commonly ingested by dogs, especially puppies, than by cats.

Internal parasites also may induce vomiting but mainly produce diarrhea. Some internal parasites found in dogs and cats are roundworms, hookworms, tapeworms, whipworms, flagellates, and coccidia. Roundworms and tapeworms are the most likely of these parasites to produce vomiting.

Both bacterial and viral infections of the gastrointes-

Dennis Blodgett is Assistant Professor, Virginia-Maryland Regional College of Veterinary Medicine, Virginia Tech, Blacksburg.

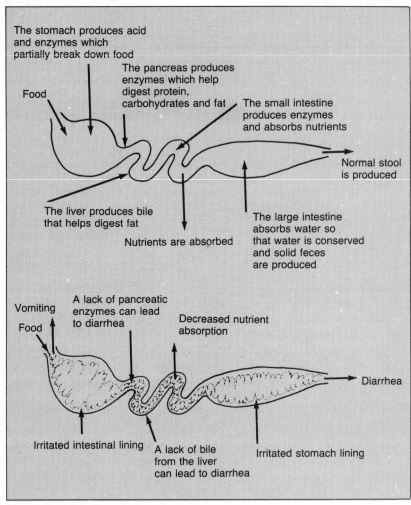

The stomach produces acid and enzymes which partially break down food

Food

The pancreas produces enzymes which help digest protein, carbohydrates and fat

The small intestine produces enzymes and absorbs nutrients

Normal stool is produced

The liver produces bile that helps digest fat

Nutrients are absorbed

The large intestine absorbs water so that water is conserved and solid feces are produced

Vomiting

Food

A lack of pancreatic enzymes can lead to diarrhea

Decreased nutrient absorption

Diarrhea

Irritated intestinal lining

A lack of bile from the liver can lead to diarrhea

Irritated stomach lining

Normal and irritated digestive systems.

tinal tract may induce vomiting. Some of the most common viral infections which cause vomiting and diarrhea in the dog and cat are canine distemper, panleukopenia (feline distemper), and canine parvovirus. Canine parvovirus has

been especially devastating in the last few years.

Digestive tract obstructions are another common source of vomiting. Foreign bodies are one of the most common obstructions. They may be either in the stomach or intestines. Dogs tend to swallow bones, toys, cloth, metallic objects, or stones. Cats are more likely to ingest hair, thread, string, or cloth.

Intussusceptions, when one part of the intestinal tract collapses or telescopes into an adjoining part of the tract, are another common obstruction. They often are associated with vomiting over an extended period of time.

An additional cause of vomiting in dogs and cats is inflammation of the pancreas. This condition usually occurs in obese, middle-aged dogs. Exact cause of the pancreatic inflammation varies, but often an unbalanced diet is involved. Diarrhea also is present in about half the cases.

Diarrhea. Causes of diarrhea in dogs and cats are as extensive as those of vomiting. Although diarrhea often accompanies vomiting, diarrhea may be present by itself.

Diarrhea results from problems in the small or large intestines. Vomiting or weight loss in conjunction with diarrhea is more likely due to a problem in the small intestine than in the large intestine.

Small intestine diarrhea often has markedly increased volume, undigested food, and color variations. Large intestine diarrhea has normal to increased volume, mucus commonly, and usually no undigested food or color variations.

An addition to the causes of diarrhea mentioned under vomiting is pancreatic exocrine insufficiency. The pancreas is unable to produce adequate amounts of the enzymes, lipase and amylase, for the small intestine. This results in an inability to digest fats and starches, which produces a voluminous fatty diarrhea.

Pancreatic exocrine insufficiency affects dogs more commonly than cats. The condition can be inherited or the result of a long-term pancreatic inflammation.

Other causes of diarrhea include overeating, bile deficiency, intestinal tract tumors, lymphatic disorders, and various drugs.

Hormone Disorders
Hypothyroidism is a condition in which inadequate amounts of circulating thyroid hormone are produced. The condition may occur with or without goiter (enlarged visible gland in the neck).

The most frequent hypothyroidism in small animals is without a goiter. The thyroid glands shrink in size. Although the syndrome affects both dogs and cats, it most

Digestive Ills, Poisoning

often is diagnosed in larger breeds of dogs 2 to 5 years old.

Decreased thyroid hormone output results in a decreased metabolic rate. Often the animal has a cold body temperature and seeks out warm places to lie down. The hair frequently is coarse and thinning and the skin may be thickened and pigmented.

Increased body weight often is seen due to the decreased metabolic rate. Mental activity may be decreased or more sluggish. Once a diagnosis of acquired primary hypothyroidism has been made, the animal is given thyroid hormone medication for the rest of its life.

Excessive parathyroid hormone (PTH) occurs in primary disease of the parathyroid glands, accompanying longstanding kidney failure, and due to nutritional imbalances of calcium and phosphorus or not enough vitamin D_3.

Excessive PTH can be found in both dogs and cats. When due to kidney failure there is decreased blood calcium and decreased intestinal absorption of calcium. When due to nutrition it often is the result of feeding all meat diets high in phosphorus and low in calcium. Clinical signs with both forms of excess PTH are related to excessive loss of cal-

cium from the bones. Animals may be lame, paralyzed, or have rubbery jaws. Calcium is supplemented in the diet for both forms.

Eclampsia (*Puerperal Tetany*) is due to reduced calcium in the blood of dogs or cats which recently have had litters. It results from an inability of the body to immediately compensate for the loss of calcium in the milk.

Most frequently eclampsia is seen in small breeds of dogs and only occasionally in the cat. Usually the syndrome appears 1 to 3 weeks after birth of the litter when milk production is at its peak.

Clinical signs associated with eclampsia include nervousness, trembling, staggering, muscle tremors, and seizures. Intravenous injection of a calcium solution results in rapid improvement of the animal.

Diabetes mellitus is most often due to decreased insulin output by the pancreas. Insulin is the hormone responsible for the utilization of sugar in the body. A deficiency of insulin results in increased blood glucose concentrations.

This endocrine disorder affects both dogs and cats. Affected animals lose high amounts of sugar in the urine, which carries excessive amounts of water with it. An increase in the loss of water is accompanied by increased water consumption. Because of the high loss of sugar calories in the urine, animals often eat more but nevertheless lose weight. Further complications may result in vomiting, dehydration, and coma.

Insulin is injected daily to treat animals, just as it is for human diabetics.

Autoimmune Ills

The body has an immune system which defends it against foreign substances such as bacteria and viruses. An important factor in the immune response is the production of antibodies against these foreign substances.

Usually antibodies are formed only against foreign substances and not against cells normally found in body tissues. However, on rare occasions an individual produces antibodies against cells in its own body (that is, autoantibodies). This is an immune response against oneself or an autoimmune response.

Autoimmune responses occur in various species of animals and in humans for a variety of reasons which are not totally understood. A few of the most common autoimmune diseases in the dog and

cat will be discussed.

Autoantibodies are formed against red blood cells in the body during autoimmune hemolytic anemia (AIHA). Although both dogs and cats can be affected. AIHA is more common in dogs. The disease most frequently is diagnosed in middle aged female dogs, 2 to 8 years old.

The clumping of autoantibodies with red blood cells results in anemia. The anemia may arise very suddenly or over a longer period of time. Although hemolysis (destruction of red blood cells) sometimes occurs, usually the altered red blood cells are removed by the spleen. AIHA may occur by itself or in association with other autoimmune diseases.

Autoantibodies are formed against blood platelets during immune mediated thrombocytopenia (IMT). Although the disease occurs in both dogs and cats, IMT is more common in dogs. It is most frequently diagnosed in female dogs.

Platelets play an important role in blood clotting. Alteration of the platelets in IMT results in hemorrhage. The bleeding can be massive over a short time or fairly minimal over an extended time. The massive hemorrhages often occur from the nose or in the urine or feces.

Autoantibodies against many components of the blood may be formed during systemic lupus erythematosus (SLE). Although the disease is found in both dogs and cats, SLE most frequently occurs in female dogs. The disease affects many of the body's systems. Autoantibodies from lupus may produce the two autoimmune diseases (AIHA and IMT) previously discussed.

Autoantibodies against complex chemicals of the blood are deposited in the kidney, joints, or skin.

Dogs with SLE may show lameness, fever, anemia, hemorrhage, skin problems, or kidney problems. Usually not all of the clinical signs are found in any one animal.

Skin Diseases. A number of autoimmune skin diseases occur in both dogs and cats, although the dog is most commonly affected. The most frequent are *pemphigus vulgaris* and *pemphigus foliaceous*. Pemphigus diseases arise from autoantibodies against substances in the skin. This undermines the outside layer of skin. The skin separations resemble blisters.

Pemphigus vulgaris in dogs shows no breed, sex, or age predilection. Affected dogs have ulcerations at the borders of the mouth, eye, or nose; or in the mouth, ear, or nail beds of the feet. Usually the dogs do not feel or eat well. Response to therapy generally is poor.

Pemphigus foliaceous does not involve the junctions of the skin and mucous membranes as does *pemphigus vulgaris*. Often *pemphigus foliaceous* starts on the head and ears and may spread over the entire body. Affected dogs have scaly skin and don't feel or eat well. Response to therapy is often favorable, however.

Numerous other autoimmune diseases have been diagnosed in the dog and cat. These include thyroid and kidney diseases, *myasthenia gravis,* and rheumatoid arthritis. Other autoimmune disease syndromes will probably be found as immunological techniques are improved.

Poisonings

The incidence of dog and cat poisonings (toxicoses) has increased with the greater abundance of drugs and chemicals in our environment. Dog poisonings are reported and diagnosed much more frequently than cat poisonings.

Cats do not seem to ingest poisons as readily as dogs. However, cats are more sensitive than dogs to certain types of chemicals because of a deficiency of a particular enzyme in their bodies and other possible inherent differences.

The various types of drugs and chemicals which produce most of the poisonings in dogs and cats can be put into a few classes. These classes include insecticides, plants, household products, rodenticides, herbicides, human and veterinary medications, metals, and miscellaneous compounds.

Selected chemicals in each class which produce most of the dog and cat poisonings will be discussed. Many toxic compounds will not be included, since poisonings produced by them are seen less frequently.

Insecticides. Organophosphate and carbamate insecticides act similarly in animals, and as a group produce most of the insecticide poisonings in dogs and cats. Chlorinated hydrocarbon insecticides (for example, DDT) have to a great extent been discontinued due to their persistence in the environment, and thus produce fewer insecticide poisonings then the organophosphate/carbamate insecticide group.

Cats can be easily poisoned by careless use of insecticides.

Boric acid used in roach baits and arsenic used in ant traps produce a significant number of poisonings in both dogs and cats.

Plants. Both cats and dogs are fond of chewing on plants. Many of the plants which are eaten are listed as nontoxic. But even "nontoxic" plants can produce intestinal upsets in animals.

A large proportion of plant poisonings in cats and dogs involve plants containing insoluble calcium oxalate crystals (for example, philodendron, dieffenbachia, pothos, and caladium). These plants can produce severe irritation of the mouth and intestinal tract.

Poinsettia plants are frequently ingested by dogs and cats, but usually cause only mild intestinal upsets. Other toxic plants ingested include aloe vera, mistletoe, mushrooms, Japanese yew bushes, rhododendrons, azaleas, oleanders, lily of the valley, castor beans, and flower bulbs (iris, tulip, and daffodil).

Several groups of chemicals fall under the category of household products. Poisonings in dogs and cats from detergents and cleaners are most common in the household products classification. Cleaners which produce poisonings include those with bleach, ammonia, borates, hydroxides, pine oil, and phenol. Cats seem especially sensitive to pine oil and phenol type cleaners.

Rodenticides. Dogs and cats are often poisoned by baits designed to kill rats and mice. Strychnine is a rodenticide which sometimes is used maliciously by people to kill dogs. Strychnine poisonings in cats are much less common than in dogs.

Another major group of rodenticides which produces more poisonings in dogs than in cats is the antocoagulant group (for example, warfarin, brodifacoum, and diphacinone). These rodenticides cause bleeding in animals usually more than 2 days after ingestion.

Dogs and cats are not exposed to herbicides as often as large animals. However, herbicide poisonings do occur in small animals, especially dogs. Dogs are unusually sensitive to the herbicide 2, 4-D, used to kill broadleaf weeds in lawns. Other herbicides which cause poisonings in dogs and cats include glyphosate, paraquat, and arsenic-based herbicides.

Medications. Both dogs and cats have been known to ingest the contents of prescription bottles when the owner isn't watching. The result depends on the type and amount of medication ingested.

Poisonings also can result when owners give animals medications not prescribed by veterinarians. This type of poisoning is most common in cats given aspirin or acetaminophen pain killers. One acetaminophen tablet can kill an adult cat.

The most common metal poisoning in small animals is lead poisoning. It is much more common in dogs than in cats. Common sources of lead include old paint chips, fishing and drapery weights, roofing shingles, and used motor oil.

Antifreeze used in car radiators is a common source of poisoning for both cats and dogs. It has a sugary taste and is ingested readily. Animals may appear drunk, depressed, and die fairly rapidly—or several days later— due to kidney failure.

Another common poisoning in small animals, especially dogs, is food or garbage poisoning. Garbage poisoning may be very mild or in some cases lethal.

VIII. RABBITS AND OTHER SMALL ANIMALS

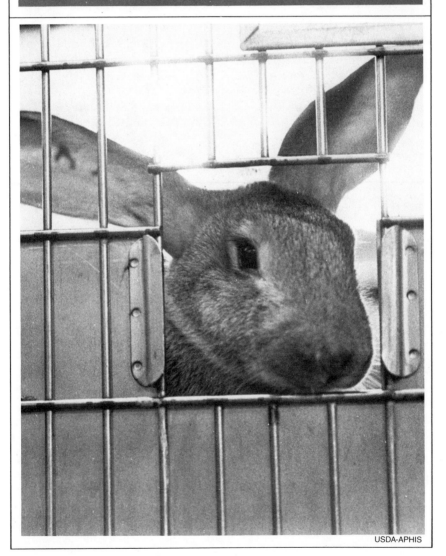

USDA-APHIS

Fundamentals

By Robert J. Russell and
Jim A. Stunkard

Rabbits, gerbils, hamsters, guinea pigs, mice, rats, and ferrets—the subjects of this section—are quite popular animals. Although they trail dogs and cats in popularity, significant and growing numbers are kept as pets. These animals are interesting and friendly, require little space, maintenance, or attention, and generally fit easily into the busy schedules of people in today's urban environment.

Because these small animals have made unique contributions to biomedical research, they have been extensively studied in the laboratory. Considerable information is available on their diseases, proper care and husbandry, reproductive performance, normal physiology, and behavior.

Husbandry advances in the laboratory also have resulted in the availability of a variety of housing systems, support equipment, etc., that can be used with individual pet animals and by people wishing to maintain small colonies of these animals. This introductory chapter briefly describes the husbandry requirements (housing, nutrition, reproduction, etc.) and disease conditions of the animals.

Health Evaluations

Make routine health evaluations and inspections of all animals at least once each day, and keep a history of individual animal or colony health and procedures. Evaluate the following factors:

–Age, sex, body weight, activity (lethargic, aggres-

Robert J. Russell is Director, Laboratory Animal Sciences Program, Program Resources Inc., Frederick, Md. Jim A. Stunkard is Director of the Bowie Animal Hospital, Bowie, Md.

sive), appetite (none, reduced, increased), skin and coat (hair loss, coat luster, scaly skin, open lesions).

–Ears (erect, drooping, discharge, swelling, inflammation or redness), presence of nasal and/or eye discharge (sneezing, eyelids closed), respiration (rate, difficulty).

–Mouth (odor, color, bleeding), teeth (overgrown, broken, missing), salivation (drooling—wet chin or cheeks).

–Abnormal enlargement or shape of body areas (neck, head, chest, abdomen), feces (diarrhea, sticky stools, mucus, tail staining, blood, parasites), limbs (abnormal limb movement, abnormal joint movement, paralysis, swelling, loss of toes, toenail length), breeding status (pregnant, bred, nursing).

Evaluate Environment

Besides examining the animal, carefully evaluate the animal's environment because many diseases and abnormal conditions directly relate to environmental factors. Monitor the following:

–Sanitation, ventilation, light, temperature, relative humidity, cage population (avoid overcrowding), type of housing and state of repair.

–Feed supply (source, type, cleanliness, condition of feeders, supplements, recent changes); water supply source (type of supply, treatment—chlorination or acidification); condition of support equipment; and recent husbandry changes.

Be sure to provide ample food, fresh water in a clean container, and a roomy, clean home.

Feed, bedding, and water supplies can be a source of pathogenic organisms (for example, bacteria, parasites), chemicals, and/or toxins. Purchase feed and bedding from reputable dealers and manufacturers.

Certain contact beddings (wood with high oil content: for example, untreated pine and cedar) have been shown to stimulate liver microenzymes in laboratory-housed animals. However, their effect on the pet animal has not been thoroughly studied. Water also can be a source of toxic contaminants. Therefore, clean, potable water always should be available.

When problems are noted, keep a record of the clinical signs of individual animals, the numbers of dead (if any), the time of onset of the problem, the rate of spread to other animals, the number of animals exposed and affected,

Fundamentals

Small Animals—Physiological Data

	Rabbit*	Gerbil†	Syrian Hamster†	Guinea Pig†	Mouse†	Rat†	Ferret#
Life expectancy (years)	5-13	2-4	1-3	4-8	1-3	1-3	5-10
Adult weight (grams)							
Range	2,000-7,000	85-100	100-150	600-900	20-60	250-500	500-2,100
New Zealand White	4,000-5,000						
Dutch Belted	1,500-2,000						
Average	3,000	90	125	750	40	350	2,000 (male) 700 (female)
Gestation period (days)							
Range	30-35	24-26	15-18	59-72	17-21	20-22	40-44
Average	31	25	16	63	19	21	42
Litter size							
Range	1-18	1-12	1-12	1-6	1-23	2-20	2-15
Average	8	4	7	4	10	9	7
Weaning age (days)	35-56	21	20-25	14-28	21-28	18-28	56-70
Breeding age (days)	180-210	70-90	48-56	90-150	42-49	90-110	252-364
Daily feed consumption, adult (grams)	100-150	5-10	10-15	30-35	5	20	80-120
Daily water intake adult (milliliters)	200-850	4-5	7-10	100-250	6	35	100-250

*Lagomorph (two pairs of incisor teeth in upper jaw)
†Rodent (one pair of incisor teeth in upper jaw)
#Mustella

Rabbits and Other Small Animals

and the ages and sexes affected.

Accuracy and completeness of this information is extremely important—and usually essential—to enable the veterinarian to arrive at a rapid, accurate diagnosis.

Human Allergy

Many people have developed allergies to rabbits and rodents, particularly rats and guinea pigs. This factor must be considered before bringing these animals into your home environment. Proteins excreted in the urine, skin dander, and hair are the primary causes of human allergies.

Most affected people develop runny eyes and nose, coughing, and sneezing. Others develop itchy skin and skin lesions or the most serious of the symptoms of the condition—asthma.

Good ventilation and good sanitation practices—for example, frequent cage cleaning—are very important. Additionally, protective clothing, including gloves and masks, may be needed. Treatment by a physician is often required, and in many cases removal of the animals from the affected person's environment becomes necessary.

Further Reading

The Biology and Medicine of Rabbits and Rodents. J.E. Harkness and J.E. Wagner. Lea and Febiger, Merchandising Department, 600 South Washington Square, Philadelphia, PA 19096. $16.00.

The Guide for the Care and Use of Laboratory Animals. Superintendent of Documents, U.S. Government Printing Office, Washington, DC 20402. $4.50.

A Guide to Diagnosis, Treatment and Husbandry of Pet Rabbits and Rodents. R.J. Russell, D.K. Johnson, and J.A. Stunkard. Veterinary Medicine Publishing Company, 690 South 4th Street, Edwardsville, KS 66111. $7.00.

ILAR News. Institute of Laboratory Animal Resources, National Research Council, 2101 Constitution Avenue, NW, Washington, DC 20418. Free.

Introductory Laboratory Animal Science. L.R. Arrington. Interstate Printers and Publishers, 19-27 North Jackson, Danville, IL 61820. $10.50.

Lab Animal. United Business Publications, Inc., 475 Park Avenue, South, New York, NY 10016. $11.75 per year.

Our Domestic Rabbits

By Robert J. Russell and
Jim A. Stunkard

Rabbits are the only lago-morphs that have been domesticated. Lagomorphs include primarily rabbits and hares; other members of the group are pikas and coneys. Our domestic type is *Oryctolagus cuniculus*.

Wild *Oryctolagus* rabbits do not exist in the United States except for a few islands near the coast of California, although they are numerous in the wild in other continents—for example, Europe and Australia. Wild rabbits (cottontails) found in the United States belong to the *Sylvilagus* genus.

Domestic rabbits are easy to breed and therefore have been domesticated very successfully by humans. Adult fe-

Robert J. Russell is Director, Laboratory Animal Sciences Program, Program Resources Inc., Frederick, MD. Jim A. Stunkard is Director of the Bowie Animal Hospital, Bowie, Md.

males are called does, and adult males bucks. Rabbits are unique animals in that they are kept as pets, raised for fur production, used in research, and serve as a human food source. There are about 100,000 rabbit producers in the United States, who produce over 10 million rabbits per year.

A number of specific breeds and varieties of these breeds—based on type, color, and size—have been developed, and several associations were formed to assist in organizing breeding efforts. Some of the more popular breeds are the New Zealand White (8 to over 12 lbs. body weight), the Dutch or Dutch Belted (less than 5 lbs.), the Polish (less than 5 lbs.), the Flemish (over 10 lbs.), the Checkered Giant (over 10 lbs.), the Chinchilla, the Lop, and the Rex. Smaller breeds are becoming more popular as pets.

Kevin Shields

Rabbits are unique animals in that they are kept as pets, raised for fur and food production, and used in research.

Marie T. Sebrechts

Domestic rabbits are easy to breed. There are about 100,000 rabbit producers in the United States, who produce over 10 million rabbits per year.

Domestic Rabbits

491

Marie T. Sebrechts

Rabbits make good house pets and can be trained to use a litter box.

Rabbits often make good house pets and can be trained to use a litter box. They rarely bite, but their powerful hind legs can cause severe scratches if they are not restrained properly. Most rabbits will live to 5 or 6 years of age, and some may live 12 to 15 years. Many publications discussing rabbit raising are available in libraries and bookstores.

Nutrition

Rabbits are monogastric (single stomach) herbivores (plant eaters). They have a very large, well-developed cecum, in which bacterial fermentation occurs, producing night feces (soft fecal pellets) that contain B vitamins, essential amino acids, and other nutrients.

The rabbit practices coprophagy (pseudorumination), that is, eats the nutrient-containing night feces. Fecal eating also permits further digestion of some foodstuffs by this second passage through the digestive tract.

Good quality pelleted rabbit diets are available commercially. Growing rabbits generally require a diet containing 15 percent protein, pregnant does 15 percent, lactating does 18 to 21 percent, and adults on a maintenance diet 12 percent.

Adult rabbits should be fed a high-fiber diet (fiber approximately 20 to 25 percent of the diet) to aid in preventing digestive tract problems. Switching from a low-fiber to a high-fiber diet should be done gradually over a week or more to prevent the rabbit from going off feed.

Adult rabbits (8 to 10 lbs. body weight) consume 125 to 150 grams (4 to 5 ounces) of feed per day, but feed intake should be limited to lower amounts in inactive rabbits. It is best to feed half the daily diet twice each day to help prevent boredom and obesity.

A moderate amount of good quality hay, fruits, and vegetables (kale, carrots, apples) can be fed sparingly as a treat. Greens should be rinsed in a chlorine solution and then rinsed in freshwater before feeding, to aid in disease control.

Housing

Providing adequate housing is extremely important in maintaining good sanitation practices and disease control procedures, and providing for the animals' physiologic and behavioral well-being.

Rabbits usually are maintained indoors, but they also

Marie T. Sebrechts

It's best to feed rabbits twice a day, to help prevent boredom and obesity.

can be held outdoors throughout the year in many parts of the United States if they have adequate shelter. Rabbits housed indoors generally do better at a lower room temperature than most other animals, 65° to 70° F.

Rabbits should be housed outdoors, provided draft-free enclosed areas as protection from cold temperatures (less than 40° F), and provided with adequate ventilation, shade, and/or water sprinklers for temperatures over 85° F. High temperatures may cause overheating and death in rabbits of all ages, and also sterility in breeding animals. It is im-

Kevin Shields

Wire floors are very popular and recommended because they permit droppings and hair to fall out of the cage into a dropping pan or ledge which can be easily cleaned.

Marie T. Sebrechts

J-type feeders and water bottles with sipper tubes are recommended because they keep feed and water clean.

portant to protect rabbits housed outdoors from predators (dogs, foxes), and also to prevent contact with wild rodents and insects which can transmit disease.

Cages can be constructed from steel, galvanized metal, aluminum, and wire. Rabbits often will chew on wood cages, and therefore these are not recommended unless the wood is protected by wire.

Wire Floors. To assist in sanitation, most cages are provided with a wire floor (1/2" to 1" mesh) to permit urine, feces, and hair to fall out of the cage into a dropping pan, which should be cleaned at least 3 times each week.

Hutches can be purchased commercially from farm supply and feed companies. Construction plans also are available from a variety of sources if you wish to build your own.

Housing units should be structurally strong, free of sharp edges, easy to clean, with J-type self feeders, provided with water bottles with sipper tubes and/or automatic water valves, and the housing units should be large enough for exercise space. Water bowls are not recommended as they readily become contaminated and may serve as a source of skin and systemic disease.

Cages should be thoroughly cleaned at least every 2 weeks. Water bottles should be cleaned and sanitized at least 2 times each week (daily is preferred).

Adult rabbits of 4 kg (9 lbs.) body weight require about 3 square feet of floor space; rabbits over 5 kg need 4 square feet. A doe with a litter should have at least 6 square feet. Cages should be at least 14" high.

Reproduction

Rabbits generally breed throughout the year. Pregnancy (gestation period) is 30 to 35 days in length, and the act of giving birth is called kindling. The usual breeding life is between 4½ months and 3 years of age.

In a natural mating system, the doe (female) is taken to the buck's (male) cage. One buck usually is required for each 15 breeding does. However, if artificial insemination is used, one buck can support almost 500 does.

Does normally will start to pull their fur and make nests 28 to 30 days after mating. A condition called pseudopregnancy (false pregnancy) may be indicated if the doe tries to make a nest 18 to 22 days after mating; this condition occurs because the rabbit is a reflex ovulator, and mechanical stimulation may cause ova (eggs) to be released from the ovary and the false pregnancy condition to develop.

The litter size averages 8 babies (30 to 100 grams body weight each) and they are born hairless and with their eyes and ears closed. Does usually feed the young only once each day.

Diseases. Pet rabbits can be affected by a variety of infectious diseases and conditions that cause serious problems and/or death losses in large herd operations.

Pasteurella multocida, a bacterium, is responsible for one of the most common diseases (pasteurellosis) seen in rabbits. The respiratory form ("snuffles") is most frequently seen. The most frequent sign is a watery to thick discharge seen around the eyes and nose. Many animals sneeze, and accumulations of nasal discharge can be found on the inside of the front feet from wiping and rubbing their nose and eyes.

The disease can be acute (rapid onset); however, it generally takes a chronic course (long duration with a low death rate). The disease is spread by direct contact or by droplets produced by sneezing.

Infection can progress from the upper respiratory tract to the lungs and cause pneumonia and death. Middle ear infections with twisting of the head and neck (torticollis) and abscesses anywhere in the body also occur. Abscesses seen in the testis of the buck can be spread to the uterus of the doe during breeding.

Pasteurellosis probably occurs in the majority of rabbit colonies in the United States. However, a number of commercial and laboratory colonies have been specifically developed and maintained to exclude this disease by deriving animals by cesarean section and maintaining them in barrier holding facilities—limited personnel access and sterilized feed, bedding, and water supplies.

Respiratory symptoms usually can be alleviated by antibiotics and sulfonamides (penicillin, tetracycline, ampicillin, sulfamethazine). Abscesses are treated by local therapy. Unfortunately, organisms are rarely eliminated from infected animals, and signs usually recur.

The best means of control is to purchase young, clean animals, inspect the parents, evaluate the colony history if possible, and then maintain clean animals in an environment apart from other rabbits. A *Pasteurella multocida* resistant rabbit has been developed at the Rabbit Research Center, Corvallis, Oreg. Vaccines may be available in the future.

Pseudomonas aeruginosa, Bordetella bronchiseptica, and *Staphylococcus aureus* may also cause respiratory disease.

Pseudomonas usually is spread through a contaminated water supply. *Pseudomonas* commonly causes skin infections, which are characterized by a green color due to a pigment produced by the organism as it grows. Generalized disease and pneumonia can occur when stress is present. *Bordetella* and *Staphylococcus* rarely cause pneumonia.

Skin, Other Ills

A number of bacteria, viruses, fungi, and parasites can cause skin disease. Bacteria are among the most common causes of skin disease, for example, *Staphylococcus aureus, Pseudomonas aeruginosa, Fusobacterium necrophorum,* and *Streptococcus* species. Swellings, areas of hair loss (alopecia), redness (inflammation), ulceration, and skin growths may be seen.

Rabbits seem particularly sensitive to both abscess formation and systemic disease caused by *Staphylococcus* species. Swellings develop under the skin (abscesses) and may ulcerate (rupture or open) and discharge pus. Nursing does can develop inflammation of the mammary gland (mastitis). Young nursing rabbits may develop systemic disease with multiple abscesses and high death losses.

Local treatment—cleaning, draining, applying antibacterials, and use of specific systemic antibiotics—often is effective.

A condition called *sorehocks*, which can occur on the rear sides of both the front and hind legs, is asssociated generally with dirty housing and/or skin abrasion. Inherited factors also are involved, as some strains of rabbits are more susceptible because they have inadequate fur covering of affected parts of the legs.

Mastitis due to *Staphylococcus* and *Streptococcus* species is usually seen as an acute disease. Affected animals will go off feed, have high fever, crave water, and develop one or more red, swollen, firm mammary glands. The condition often is associated with dirty bedding, but milk retention and injury from nursing young and/or nest boxes frequently initiate the condition.

Antibiotics and local therapy often are effective. Young rabbits from affected does should be isolated and hand-fed to prevent transmission to other does.

Hutch burn is a superficial skin infection occurring around the genital area. The condition is due to prolonged contact of the skin with urine, and often is associated with poor husbandry.

Moist dermatitis develops in folds of the skin of the head and neck and usually is associated with continued exposure to water when the animals drink from open pots or bowls. Use of water bottles will reduce incidence of this condition.

Infection with *Treponema cuniculi* occurs occasionally and causes erosive ulcerated lesions on the genital area (penis, prepuce, vaginal opening) with spread to the legs, feet, lips, ears, and face.

The condition is called *rabbit syphilis*, and the organism—specifically infectious for rabbits—is spread during breeding. The organism is related to the agent of human syphilis, *Treponema pallidium*. Serologic tests are available for diagnosis, and penicillin is an effective and specific therapy.

Virus Lesions

Several viruses can be responsible for skin lesions in rabbits.

Myxomatosis, a disease caused by a pox virus, is seen primarily in the Western United States, Europe, and Australia. The virus causes subcutaneous (under the skin) swellings and skin hemorrhages around the eyes, nose, lips, ears, and genital area. Affected rabbits may develop conjunctivitis, with eye discharge.

Outbreaks of this disease can result in high death rates in exposed rabbits. Death can occur as early as 2 to 5 days after the first skin lesions are noticed.

The disease is transmitted by biting insects—for example, mosquitoes, fleas, flies. There is no specific treatment for the disease. Rabbits should be housed indoors or in screened outdoor hutches to aid in prevention.

Shope fibromatosis, caused by a pox virus related to myxomatosis virus, is a rare disease in domestic rabbits but very common in wild rabbits. The virus causes single or numerous subcutaneous nodules. Death has occurred in young *Oryctolagus* rabbits. Mosquitoes and other biting insects are responsible for spread of the disease. Housing systems should be designed to protect rabbits from insect exposure.

Rabbit pox virus is an uncommon disease. Several outbreaks with high death rates have occurred in the research laboratory. These outbreaks may have been due to accidental exposure to human pox virus (Vaccinia virus).

Cutaneous papillomatosis, caused by a papovavirus, is characterized by wart-like skin growths that can develop into squamous cell carcinomas (cancer) if they persist for over 6 months. The disease is seen primarily in wild cottontail rabbits and is spread by both direct contact and by ticks. The growths can be surgically removed.

Another papovavirus causes the disease called oral papillomatosis. White growths are seen on the membranes of the mouth, especially the undersurface of the tongue. These growths usually disappear without treatment.

Ringworm
Fungal skin infections (ringworm) are rare and are caused primarily by the fungus *Trichophyton mentagrophytes.* Irritation and inflammation of skin areas occur, with crusts, scabs, and hair loss.

USDA

Ringworm infection, showing loss of fur and scaling of skin on ear.

Affected animals should be isolated, and since the organism can cause disease in humans, the rabbits should be handled carefully. Local and systemic treatments with antifungal agents—for example, griseofulvin—generally are effective.

Flies, Mites
Larvae of certain flies (bot flies) cause local swellings and abscesses below the skin (warbles). The lesions are found primarily around the head and ears and along the back.

Surgical removal and local therapy can be used to eliminate individual lesions,

Domestic Rabbits

and the condition can be prevented by housing animals indoors or by providing screened outdoor housing. The lesions commonly are encountered in pet rabbits.

The mite *Cheyletiella parasitovorax* can cause hair loss and skin inflammation. The mites can be easily identified, and treatment with standard insecticides will eliminate them.

Ear mites, *Psoroptes cuniculi,* are the most common parasites of rabbits. The mites can be readily found in the external ear canal but skin lesions can extend from the ears over the head and neck areas. Local treatment with standard miticides will correct the condition.

Digestive Diseases

Diseases of the digestive tract are probably the major health problem in rabbits today. Outbreaks of diarrhea with high death losses, especially in young rabbits, commonly occur.

Usually the condition appears to result from a number of different organisms and factors working together (the normal function of the rabbit digestive tract and the dietary needs of rabbits are not fully understood).

Disease outbreaks can be initiated by changes in feed or feeding practices, changes in sanitation, stress due to weaning, overcrowding, environmental temperature fluctuations, and transportation stress. The disease often is associated with the presence of bacterial toxins in the intestinal tract (enterotoxemia).

Some of the agents involved in producing diarrheal disease are *Clostridium spiroforme, Clostridium dificile, Clostridium perfringens, Escherichia coli, Bacillus piliformis* (the agent of Tyzzer's disease), *Salmonella* species, *Vibrio* species, intestinal coccidia of at least four strains of *Eimeria,* and one coccidium—*Eimeria steidai*—that also affects the liver. Viruses also may be involved, although a direct relationship has not been proven.

Most of the concern today centers on the *Clostridium* species because these organisms produce toxins that have been found in a number of disease outbreaks in young rabbits.

Death losses (30 to 95 percent) can occur within 12 to 72 hours after the initial signs of disease are noted. Affected animals have acute massive diarrhea, go off feed, lose weight rapidly, become debilitated and dehydrated, are lethargic, have a hunched posture, may have abdominal straining (appear constipated), often have an unquenchable thirst, generally appear to be in pain, frequently develop abdominal swelling, and often grind their teeth.

Dead animals on examination may be found to have blocked intestines (impactions) or blood (hemorrhagic necrosis) and fluid (edema) in the gut wall. The intestinal contents may contain bloody fluid and massive accumulations of gelatinous mucus. Some animals will not have any internal signs of disease except for accumulations of mucus in the intestines.

Diagnosis is based on evaluation of clinical signs, isolation of causative bacteria, identification of parasites, demonstration of the presence of toxins, and evaluation of gross and histopathological lesions.

Treatment often is not very effective. However, supportive therapy and the use of antibiotics and coccidiostats (if coccidia are present) may help. Sulfaquinoxaline and oxytetracycline are approved by the Federal Government for rabbits used in meat production.

Preventive Steps

The greatest success against digestive diseases usually is based on prevention—that is, maintain a clean, dry environment, use high-quality feed, provide high-fiber diets, lower dietary carbohydrate by reducing the amount of cereal grains because they have a high starch content, and reduce stress as much as possible.

Reduction of dietary fines (small particles of grains) also aids in prevention. Remove feces from cages daily, assure good ventilation, and increase feed amounts slowly in young animals.

Antibiotics (for example, penicillin, ampicillin, clindamycin, and lincomycin) have caused gut flora alteration with enterotoxemia, diarrhea, and death in rabbits. Take care to ensure that feed supplies are not accidentally contaminated with antibiotics. Future success involves greater understanding of the normal function of the rabbit's digestive tract and its specific nutritional and dietary needs.

Hazard to Man. While they usually do not cause diarrhea in rabbits, the presence of *Salmonella* species is a serious concern because of possible disease transmission to humans. Affected rabbits may not show clinical signs, or they may be off feed, weak

Domestic Rabbits

Marie T. Sebrechts

Marie T. Sebrechts

Preventive steps are the best way to avoid digestive diseases—clean out rabbit cages daily, provide a clean, dry environment and adequate ventilation.

Kevin Shields

Rabbits and Other Small Animals

and emaciated with hunched posture, and have diarrhea. Lesions may be found in several internal organs.

Salmonellosis does not occur often in rabbits. The most common source of infection is contamination of feed, bedding, or water supplies by wild rodents. Treatment is not recommended, because some animals can become permanently infected (carriers) and spread the disease after treatment. Euthanasia (humane killing) is recommended.

Rabbit roundworms—that is, stomach worms (*Obeliscoides cuniculi, Graphidium strigosum*), pinworms (*Passalurus* species), and whipworms (*Trichuris* species)—and the tapeworms (flat worms) (*Cittotaenia* and *Raillietina* species) usually are not associated with clinical disease.

Hair Balls

Rabbits continually lick their fur, and most rabbits have some accumulation of hair in the stomach (hair balls, *gastric trichobezoars*). In some animals, these accumulations may cause clinical problems— off feed and water, no production of feces, lethargy, death. Diagnosis can be confirmed by palpation or by radiographs (x rays).

Fresh pineapple juice

(contains an enzyme which helps break down hair balls), mineral oil, and intravenous fluids including glucose may help. Surgical removal of the hair ball, although not always successful, can be accomplished. Good quality hay fed occasionally to increase fiber content of the diet and/or use of a high-fiber diet help in prevention.

Other Problems

Pregnancy toxemia (ketosis) has been associated with the presence of gastric hair balls by some investigators. Reduced feed intake by affected rabbits results in appearance of the condition close to kindling. Affected animals develop a fatty liver, an enlarged gall bladder, acetone odor to the breath, ketones in the urine, and have a high death rate. Treatment, as outlined in the previous paragraph, may help.

Overgrowth of incisors of both the upper and lower jaw is quite common. The teeth of rabbits grow throughout life (about 2 mm in length per week), and if improper alignment prevents the teeth from wearing on each other, overgrowth can rapidly occur.

The improper alignment results from a recessive genetic defect. Affected rab-

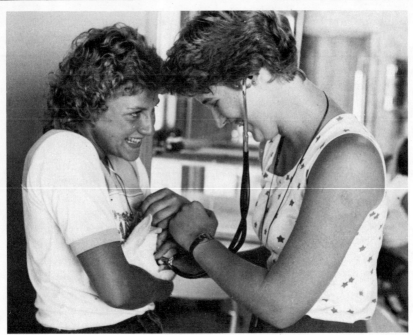

Cooperative Extension Service

Rabbits should be held with two hands with particular care to support the hind legs and prevent struggling.

bits and their parents should not be used for breeding. Teeth of affected rabbits must be trimmed on a regular basis to enable the animal to eat normally and to prevent lip, cheek, or gum punctures, which result in abscesses.

The intermediate stages of tapeworms of dogs and other carnivores can be found in the abdominal cavity of rabbits. These tapeworm stages do not cause problems, but their presence can be disconcerting, especially if the animals are going to be used for food. Rabbits should be prevented from exposure to the tapeworm eggs found in carnivore feces.

Encephalitozoon cuniculi is a commonly encountered protozoan parasite that causes kidney lesions consisting of small pits or dents or scars on the surface of the kidney. Its presence usually is not associated with clinical disease.

Fractures of the lumbar spine (broken back) are commonly encountered. Rabbits have a low ratio of skeletal mass to muscle mass, and

Rabbits and Other Small Animals

their strong hind legs can exert enough pressure on the spine to cause fractures when they are improperly handled. Rabbits should be held with two hands at all times with particular care to support the hind legs and prevent struggling.

Animals with lumbar fractures will be unable to move their hind legs and will usually sit in an upright position, supporting their weight on their front feet. Radiographs will confirm the diagnosis. There is no treatment and animals generally have to be euthanized.

Bupthalmia, commonly known as ox eye, is due to a genetic defect. The eyes appear enlarged and bulge from the sockets. Affected eyes can become secondarily infected. There is no treatment, and surgical removal is occasionally required.

The most common tumor of the rabbit is *adenocarcinoma* of the uterus. The tumor frequently metastasizes to the lungs and other organs. Altered reproductive function often is seen in does several months before recognition of the tumor, and there is a possible correlation with previous episodes of false pregnancy.

Surgical removal of the affected uterus may prevent spread to other organs if the tumor is recognized at an early stage of development. However, early diagnosis is difficult.

Hunters Take Care. Tularemia, caused by *Francisella tularensis,* is primarily a disease of wild rabbits and not commonly seen in pet or commercial rabbits. Blood-sucking insects act as vectors. Clinical signs usually are not seen. Hunters and others should take precautions such as wearing gloves when working with wild rabbits. Infected animals should be euthanized.

Rabbits rarely are exposed to or infected with rabies, but cases have occurred in rabbits housed outdoors. Take precautions to prevent contact with wild animals by providing secure, protected housing systems. Vaccination of rabbits for rabies is not recommended.

Further Reading
Biology of the Laboratory Rabbit. S.H. Weisbroth et al eds. Academic Press, Order Department, Orlando, FL 32887-0015. $85.00

Domestic Rabbit Biology and Production. L.R. Arrington et al. The University Press, 15 Northwest 15th Street, Gainesville, FL 32603. $11.25.

The Gentle Gerbil

By Robert J. Russell and
Jim A. Stunkard

Pet gerbils usually belong to the species commonly known as Mongolian gerbils (*Meriones unguiculatus*). They are very inquisitive, clean, gentle animals and much less agressive than other rodents. They are native to desert regions of northeastern China and eastern Mongolia.

The most common color is a mixed brown, but black and white mutations also occur. Because of the lack of variety in their coat colors, little interest has been shown by breed fanciers.

Gerbils are naturally desert animals, and they excrete very little urine, therefore producing only a slight odor. They are monogamous (usu-

ally one mate for life), and mature animals generally will not accept another mate. The male and female are best paired at 9 to 10 weeks of age prior to sexual maturity to insure successful mating. Gerbils practice coprophagy (as do rabbits; see previous chapter) and obtain B vitamins and probably other nutrients in this manner.

Gerbils have a hairless sebaceous gland, approximately ½″ in diameter, located in the skin of the abdominal midline. The gland is used for territorial marking and should not be considered abnormal.

Gerbils are not naturally found wild in the United States, and there is concern that they might establish themselves and become pests. It is illegal to maintain gerbils as pets in some States— California, for example.

Robert J. Russell is Director, Laboratory Animal Sciences Program, Program Resources Inc., Frederick, Md. Jim A. Stunkard is Director of the Bowie Animal Hospital, Bowie, Md.

Rabbits and Other Small Animals

Marie T. Sebrechts

Gerbils, which are very inquisitive, clean and gentle animals, make fun pets that are easy to care for. A variety of plastic and metal solid-bottom cages are available and wood shavings, wood chips, ground corncobs and shredded paper are all okay for bedding.

Cages

A variety of plastic and metal solid-bottom shoe box cages are available commercially. Glass fish tanks with tightly fitting covers that provide adequate ventilation are also acceptable. Wire bar cages and exercise wheels often are the cause of broken legs, and their combined use should be avoided.

Enough bedding (1″ deep) to permit nest building should be provided; wood shavings, wood chips, ground corncobs, and shredded paper are all acceptable. Provide an enclosed space within the cage as a hiding space.

A breeding pair can be maintained in a cage providing 200 square inches (10″ × 20″) of floor space and a minimum height of 6″.

Dietary Guide

Standard, commercially available, pelleted rodent diets generally are adequate. However, many people supplement these diets with mixed grains and seeds (corn, oats, wheat, barley, sunflower seeds) and vegetables (cabbage, lettuce, carrots). If you do not use a pelleted ration, be sure to feed a mixed ration, as the use of

Gerbils

only one seed—for example, sunflower seeds—can result in nutritional deficiencies.

Although gerbils have a low water requirement, they should be provided with a continuous supply of fresh, clean water. The animals can be maintained at temperatures between 65° and 85° F. Cages usually require changing only every 2 weeks.

Diseases

Generally, gerbils are afflicted by few spontaneous diseases.

Often seen is a condition commonly called *red nose*, causing hair loss and red, swollen areas of the skin of the nose and muzzle. *Staphylococcus* generally is the cause. But other bacterial organisms, trauma due to burrowing, or as yet undetermined factors may be involved.

Animals generally recover spontaneously. Sometimes removal of metal feeders and other objects from the cage, and the use of local and systemic antibiotics, are required.

Bite wounds, especially on the tail and tailhead, occasionally occur, and animals may require separation.

Gerbils usually are not affected by external parasites except for the microscopic mite *Demodex*. Lesions due to its presence are rare.

High death rates can result from the bacterium *Bacillus piliformis*, the cause of Tyzzer's disease. Affected animals have rough hair coats, become lethargic, go off feed, and suffer weight loss. Diarrhea does not usually occur. Lesions are found in the liver and the intestinal tract.

There is no specific treatment, although antibiotics can produce limited success. Control of stress may be beneficial in prevention.

Incisors

As in other rodents, overgrowth of incisor teeth can occur and trimming may be needed.

Gerbils are rarely infested with intestinal parasites. Pinworms (*Syphacia obvelata*) and tapeworms (*Hymenolopis diminuta*) can occur, but clinical signs usually are not seen.

About 20 percent of gerbils develop recurring bouts of spontaneous, convulsive seizures. The seizures commonly are of short duration and usually seen after handling. Treatment generally is not necessary.

The antibiotic streptomycin should not be used in gerbils, as it has been associated with high death rates.

Those Cheeky Hamsters

By Robert J. Russell and
Jim A. Stunkard

Marie T. Sebrechts

Handling a hamster frequently makes these cheeky animals more gentle pets.

Hamsters often are pugnacious animals; however, many of them make gentle pets when handled frequently. The hamster commonly seen as a pet is the Syrian or golden hamster, *Mesocricetus auratus*. They are a light golden brown color.

Robert J. Russell is Director, Laboratory Animal Sciences Program, Program Resources Inc., Frederick, Md. Jim A. Stunkard is Director of the Bowie Animal Hospital, Bowie, Md.

Two species of hamsters are rarely seen as pets: 1) the European hamster, *Cricetus cricetus,* light brown with a black belly and white areas on the face; and 2) the Chinese hamster, *Cricetulus griseus,* characterized by a black dorsal strip and a light brown to gray and white coat color.

Hamsters are nocturnal, their gestation period is extremely short (14 days), and they have extensive cheek pouches to carry food and move their babies from one location to another. The ham-

Hamsters

Marie T. Sebrechts

USDA-APHIS

Hamsters are escape artists, so get a secure, solid cage. Clean, fresh water should be available continuously. Hardwood chips, ground corncobs and shredded paper all make good bedding materials.

Rabbits and Other Small Animals

ster uses pigmented flank organs (sebaceous glands), located high on the thigh, for territorial marking.

Escape Artists

Hamsters are extremely adept at escaping from their cages. So it is extremely important that lids and doors have secure latches and that cages are solidly constructed.

Generally, wire bar, plastic, metal, or glass solid-bottom shoe box cages are used, and most have clip-on wire bar or solid metal tops. Many people equip their cages with tunnels and exercise wheels; however, exercise wheels are often the cause of broken legs, especially when used in wire bar cages.

Hardwood chips, ground corncobs, and shredded paper are acceptable as bedding materials. Adult hamsters require a floor area of at least 20 square inches with a cage height of 6″. A female hamster should have 150 square inches of floor space.

May Hibernate

Environmental temperatures between 65° and 75° F generally are acceptable. Hamsters will hibernate at temperatures below 48° F and also if the daily period of light is very short—less than 2 hours

a day. Pelleted rodent feeds, available commercially from major feed suppliers, generally are readily available and acceptable. Mixed seeds can be used as a treat. Clean, fresh water should be available continuously.

Hamsters occasionally are difficult to breed successfully. Both hand mating and monogamous mating systems can result in fighting.

Cannibalism can be a serious problem. The incidence may be reduced by providing sufficient nesting materials, a dark hiding place free from disturbance, prevention of sudden noises, and separation of males from pregnant and lactating females. Generally the young should not be handled during the first week of life.

Hamsters frequently fight with each other. Severe bite wounds, occasionally resulting in death, are often inflicted. To reduce fighting it is best to house animals together early in life, at weaning rather than at several months of age.

Diseases

Hamsters generally are quite healthy animals, and disease outbreaks usually are rare.

The most important disease seen in hamsters has been given a variety of names:

Hamsters

Marie T. Sebrechts

Keeping hamsters healthy is relatively easy as long as good sanitation and good quality food are provided.

hamster enteritis, wet tail, proliferative enteritis, ileal hyperplasia. A specific etiology has not been found. An as-yet-unidentified intracellular bacterium may play an important role, although several different causes—bacteria, viruses, diet, poor sanitation—may be involved.

Affected animals go off feed, have rough hair coats, become debilitated, and have a mild to severe watery diarrhea. Rectal prolapse, seen as a red protrusion from the anus, may occur. High death rates often occur within 1 to 2 days after the initial clinical signs.

All ages of hamsters can be affected, but animals 3 to 8 weeks old are the most susceptible. Intestinal lesions often appear as enlargements or growths, hence the name proliferative ileitis and ileal hyperplasia.

Systemic antibiotics (tetracycline, gentamicin, tylosin,

Rabbits and Other Small Animals

neomycin) and supportive therapy (oral administration of whole milk, buttermilk) may be beneficial, although response to treatment is often poor. Good sanitation and good quality food help in prevention.

Both *Salmonella* and *Bacillus piliformis* cause disease in hamsters. The lesions are found in the liver and intestinal tract.

Parasites

Pinworms *(Syphacia obvelata)* and tapeworms *(Hymenolepis nana)* are found occasionally in hamsters, but clinical signs usually do not occur with either parasite. It is important to remember that *Hymenolepis nana* can directly infest man. Anal tape tests and fecal examinations will demonstrate the ova of pinworms, and tapeworm ova may be found on routine fecal flotation examinations.

Hamster intestines generally contain a number of different protozoan parasites— such as *Giardia, Spironucleus, Trichomonas*—but these parasites usually do not cause clinical disease in hamsters.

The use of several antibiotics (for example, penicillin, streptomycin, lincomycin, and erythromycin) has been associated with an occasionally fatal *toxic syndrome* in hamsters. Broad-spectrum antibiotics such as tetracycline, chloramphenicol, and sulfonamides are usually safe.

Demodex species (hair follicle mange mites) are generally the only external parasites found in the hamster. Microscopic examination of skin scrapings will reveal the parasites. Skin lesions are not seen usually.

Staphylococcus can cause abscesses and joint infections. Hamster cheek pouches can become infected due to foreign bodies and trauma and may ulcerate through the skin. Local therapy and systemic antibiotics are generally effective.

Several outbreaks of the viral disease *lymphocytic choriomeningitis* have occurred in humans and been traced directly to spread by hamsters. This virus also occurs in guinea pigs, mice, nonhuman primates, dogs, and pigs.

The disease in humans varies from an absence of clinical signs to an influenza-like (flu) syndrome, although encephalitis occasionally occurs. In hamsters clinical signs generally are absent, and specific testing is required for diagnosis. A number of commercial diagnostic laboratories provide this testing service.

Guinea Pigs

By Robert J. Russell and
Jim A. Stunkard

The guinea pig, (*Cavia porcellus*) or cavy originated in South America and was first domesticated by Andean Indians.

Guinea pigs are very docile, nonaggressive animals that appeal to many individuals, although their larger size is not as amenable to urban living as the smaller rodents. Their bodies are bullet-shaped with very short limbs. They have a number of different and attractive coat colors, patterns, and hair textures that appeal to breeders and fanciers.

Guinea pigs usually are housed in plastic, stainless steel, or galvanized metal cages, large bins, or pens.

Robert J. Russell is Director, Laboratory Animal Sciences Program, Program Resources Inc., Frederick, Md. Jim A. Stunkard is Director of the Bowie Animal Hospital, Bowie, Md.

Both solid bottom and wire mesh floors ($1\frac{1}{2}'' \times \frac{1}{2}''$) are used, although foot problems are more common on mesh floors.

Open bins with 7" to 12" high sides often are used, as guinea pigs rarely try to escape. You should insure that other animals (dogs, cats) do not gain access to the open cage. Adult animals need at least 101 square inches of floor space and breeder females 180 square inches.

Wood chips, shredded paper, or hay bedding is used. Wood chips and ground corncob bedding occasionally interfere with breeding by lodging in the prepuce and vulva and may also lodge in the anus and under the eyelids. Poor appetite is seen occasionally in animals housed on cedar chip and pine bedding. The cause is unknown, although switching to another bedding may stimulate the appetite.

Control of temperature

USDA

fluctuations and drafts is particularly important in guinea pigs. Temperatures between 64° and 75° F are acceptable if fluctuations are minimal. Guinea pigs are quite susceptible to overheating. Control

Since guinea pigs have a number of different and attractive coat colors, patterns and hair textures, they hold a special appeal for breeders and fanciers. From top to bottom: Short-haired, rough-haired and long-haired guinea pigs.

Guinea Pigs

515

of ventilation and indoor temperatures and provision of shade for animals housed outdoors are essential.

A Little Messy

Generally, water bottles with sipper tubes and suspended feeders are used. Guinea pig cages and equipment require frequent cleaning, as guinea pigs are quite messy animals. They often will spit food back into their water bottles, kick food out of the cage, scatter feed, and defecate in feed bowls.

Good quality guinea pig feed is available commercially and will meet the animals' needs if stored away from heat and direct sunlight and used within 90 days of manufacture.

Guinea pigs—like man, nonhuman primates, and several other species of animals—require a dietary source of vitamin C. If they do not receive this vitamin, they develop **scurvy.**

Initial clinical signs of this disease are dehydration, poor appetite, diarrhea, rough hair coats, lethargy, and weight loss. Small pinpoint hemorrhages develop on the gums, and joint swellings with lameness also occur. The animals have severely reduced resistance to other infectious agents, especially those causing respiratory disease.

The guinea pig's daily vitamin C requirement is 16 milligrams (mg) per kilogram (kg) body weight for maintenance and 30 mg/kg during pregnancy. Scurvy can be treated by administering high levels of vitamin C.

Guinea pig diets can be supplemented, either in the food or water, with vitamin C. Vegetables and fruits—such as kale, parsley, spinach, cabbage, green peppers, mustard greens, collard greens, oranges, apples—and high quality hay can be used daily. Lettuce is not a good source of vitamin C.

Ascorbic acid can be added to the water at a level of 200 mg/liter of drinking water. The vitamin C activity is lost quite rapidly, and solutions should be prepared daily.

Gestation of guinea pigs is particularly long (average 63 days; range 59 to 72 days) when compared to other rodents. Guinea pig young are born fully haired with their eyes open and teeth erupted. They can eat solid food within a few days after birth.

Breeding usually is accomplished by housing 1 boar (male) with 1 to 10 sows (females) in a large pen. Guinea pigs do not build nests. They should be bred before 7 months of age to insure that the pubic symphysis of the female will open normally and not block the birth canal. The pubic symphysis space (½″ to 1″) can be palpated 24 to 48 hours before birth.

Diseases

Respiratory disease is common, and a number of bacteria can be involved—*Bordetella bronchiseptica, Streptococcus pneumoniae, Pseudomonas aeruginosa, Klebsiella pneumoniae,* and *Streptococcus pyogenes.*

Affected animals will have nasal discharge, sneezing, twisting of the head and neck (torticollis), and weight loss. Broad-spectrum antibiotics and supportive therapy are indicated, including substantial doses of vitamin C. Prevention should be directed toward good sanitary practices and provision of vitamin C in the feed and/or water.

Guinea pigs frequently develop grossly visible swellings on the undersurface of the neck (*cervical lymphadenitis*). These swellings usually are due to enlarged, abscessed lymph nodes, caused by the bacteria *Streptococcus zooepidemicus* and *Streptobacillus moniliformis.* Other lymph

nodes also may get involved.

Affected animals become lethargic, go off feed, and lose weight. The initiating factor may be abrasions or punctures of the cheeks and/or gums. Systemic antibiotics, surgical drainage, and/or surgical removal may help. In a herd situation, affected animals should be isolated or euthanized to prevent spread to other animals.

Drug Hazards. Guinea pigs can develop a toxic syndrome that results in high mortality from the use of a number of antibiotics—for example, penicillin, chlortetracycline, oxytetracycline, lincomycin, bacitracin, erythromycin, streptomycin, and tylosin. However, tetracyclines can be used safely on occasion at lower dosage levels.

Take particular care also in the use of other antibiotics that are primarily effective against gram-positive organisms. Only broad-spectrum antibiotics—those equally effective against both gram-positive and gram-negative bacteria—should be used in the guinea pig.

Obesity in Sows

Healthy, well-nourished sows develop a toxic syndrome in late pregnancy (*pregnancy toxemia*), characterized by severe lethargy, loss of appetite, difficult breathing, weight loss, and death often within 24 hours after development of initial clinical signs. The condition occurs much more frequently in obese animals.

Although the exact cause remains obscure, the condition may be due to a reduction in the normal blood supply to the uterus. Systemic supportive therapy is indicated, but the prognosis is usually poor and death of the sow and the fetuses often results. A good-quality diet is essential, especially during the latter half of pregnancy. Female guinea pigs should not be permitted to become obese.

Pregnant females often will develop patchy or generalized hair loss (*alopecia*) during pregnancy. The specific cause is unknown, but it may be a normal physiologic reaction to pregnancy. The skin appears normal except that the hair follicles are in an inactive stage. Affected animals usually recover spontaneously.

Barbering

Hair loss due to hair pulling or barbering is not uncommon and is usually seen when a group of animals are housed together. One or more individuals often will pull hair from their cagemates. Separation of the "barber(s)" from the other animals will prevent hair loss.

The mites *Chirodiscoides caviae* and *Trixacarus caviae* and the biting lice *Gyropus ovalis* and *Gliricola porcelli* are the most frequent external parasites of guinea pigs. *Chirodiscoides* mites usually cause the most severe lesions, and hair loss may occur over the entire body. Standard insecticide preparations, as used in cats, generally are effective.

Malocclusion, especially affecting the premolars, is quite common. Animals go off feed and lose weight. The condition probably has a genetic basis, and affected animals and their parents should not be used for breeding. Trimming of both the molars and incisors can be accomplished, although often it is difficult to trim the molars because of the small mouth cavity.

Guinea pigs can be infected by intestinal coccidia (*Eimeria caviae*) and by an intestinal roundworm (*Parapsidodera uncinata*), but clinical disease is rare.

Further Reading
Biology of the Guinea Pig. J.E. Wagner and P.J. Manning eds., Academic Press, Order Department, Orlando, FL 32887-0015. $75.00

Mice Can Be Nice

By Robert J. Russel and
Jim A. Stunkard

The ancestor of the pet or laboratory mouse is the house mouse. Mice (*Mus musculus*) are not the most popular pets. They do, however, have a variety of coat colors and patterns that are of interest to breeders, and they can be maintained in a very small space. Unfortunately, their smell (feces, urine) is unacceptable to many people.

Pet mice generally are quite tame, although they will bite quickly if mishandled. Housing systems similar to those used for gerbils and hamsters are used, and a variety of diets are available commercially.

Robert J. Russell is Director, Laboratory Animal Sciences Program, Program Resources Inc., Frederick, Md. Jim A. Stunkard is Director of the Bowie Animal Hospital, Bowie, Md.

Fast Breeders

Mice breed rapidly, and once they reach sexual maturity (4 to 8 weeks of age), they can produce a new litter every 3 to 4 weeks. The number of new babies soon can overwhelm the inexperienced owner.

The most common pet mouse is the white or "Swiss," an outbred mouse. Because of the extensive use of mice in research, numerous inbred strains have been developed. An inbred strain is produced by 20 generations of brother to sister mating, and results in animals that have essentially the same genetic makeup.

Respiratory Ills

Several organisms can cause respiratory disease in mice: *Mycoplasma pulmonis*, Sendai virus, Pneumonia Virus of Mice, *Pasteurella pneumotropica*, *Pseudomonas aeruginosa*, *Klebsiella pneumoniae*, and *Bordetella bronchiseptica*.

Infection with Sendai virus is the most common. Certain inbred strains are particularly susceptible to Sendai virus, and sickness and death rates can be high. Some affected animals will not show clinical signs; others will exhibit respiratory chattering or clicking sounds, labored breathing, and cyanosis (blue color). Some animals will walk continuously in circles and/or develop a head tilt due to middle and inner ear infections.

Diagnosis often requires evaluation of clinical signs, cultures, serological tests, and pathology. Systemic antibiotics can be of benefit when there is a colony outbreak; however, therapy alone usually will not eliminate the causative organisms. A vaccine that protects against Sendai virus is available commercially.

Chlorination and/or acidification of the water supply is especially helpful in the control of *Pseudomonas*.

It is very difficult to prevent exposure to the agents of respiratory disease in the pet environment. In the laboratory, the development of physical barriers—for example, isolator cages, isolator racks, barrier buildings, filter top and microisolator cages, cesar-

ean rederivation—have been successful. The use of filter top cages and/or microisolator cages can help in the maintenance of pet animals.

Barbers and Fighters

A number of different skin conditions are seen in mice. Mice will chew on the hair of cagemates (barbering) during establishment of social groups, and affected mice will have patchy or generalized hair loss. Isolation of the "barber" (the fully haired animal in a cage containing several animals with hair loss) will eliminate the condition. The condition is seen fairly commonly in certain strains of mice, for example C57BL and C3H, but usually is rare in white mice.

Mice, especially males of certain strains, fight frequently. Bite wounds, generally on the tail and tail head, are seen.

The wounds can become contaminated with bacteria—for example, group G *Streptococcus* and *Staphylococcus aureus*—and high death rates can result. *Staphylococcus* can also cause abscesses of the face, and preputial gland infections which are seen as swellings on the posterior ventral abdomen.

Animals that fight should be separated, and mice should

be placed in cages together at weaning rather than later in life.

Mouse pox (ectromelia), caused by a pox virus, is not commonly seen in the United States. However, several outbreaks have occurred in research colonies in the past few years. The disease is extremely serious, and high death rates can occur. Affected animals become lethargic, go off feed, lose weight, develop skin papules or pustules, and may lose their limbs, feet, and tails or die suddenly without lesions.

Diagnosis is based on serological testing and histopathologic and electron microscopic evaluation of affected tissues. The skin lesions require differentiation from fight wounds, trauma, and bacterial and fungal infections.

Treatment is not recommended, and affected animals should be euthanized to prevent spread of the disease to other mice. Prevention is based on quarantine and serologic testing, especially for animals coming from outside the United States.

Mites and Mice
Mice are very commonly infected with a variety of mites (*Myobia musculi, Myocoptes musculinus, Myocoptes rombutsi, Radfordia affinis, Ornithonyssus bacoti*) that can cause severe irritation and inflammation due to self-trauma and hair loss. Repeated use of any of a number of insecticides is generally effective in controlling these parasites. Lice (*Polyplax*) are rare, and lesions generally minimal.

Intestinal disease can be caused by several different infectious agents. Mouse hepatitis virus is widespread and a cause of diarrheal disease and high death rates in young mice prior to weaning.

Certain inbred strains of mice are particularly susceptible. Older mice may die, but usually no clinical signs or only mild diarrhea or stunted growth is seen. Reovirus Type 3 can cause diarrhea and an oily hair coat in mice around 10 to 14 days of age.

A specific strain of the bacterium *Citrobacter freundii* causes a severe disease in suckling and newly weaned animals called colonic hyperplasia.

Affected animals are debilitated and have ruffled hair coats and arched backs, and diarrhea may or may not be present. Death can occur 3 to 5 days after initial signs. Sulfonamides have been used with some success, and other antibiotics may be beneficial. The condition often resolves spontaneously as the animals become older.

Internal Parasites

Mice can be infested with pinworms (*Syphacia obvelata, Aspiculuris tetraptera*) and tapeworms (*Hymenolepis nana* and *Hymenolepis diminuta*). These parasites rarely cause clinical disease. *Hymenolepis nana* can have a direct life cycle— that is, no intermediate host required—and can directly infest man.

The protozoans *Spironucleus muris* and *Giardia muris* are capable of causing high death rates in mice between 3 and 5 weeks of age when other stress is present. Affected animals become lethargic, have hunched posture, do not gain weight, develop sticky stools, and have gas- and fluid-filled intestines due to the presence of large numbers of parasites. Dimetridazole is effective in reducing the death rate.

Toxins, Tumors, Defects

Low doses of streptomycin and procaine have caused deaths in mice. Exposure to low levels of chloroform causes high death rates, especially in some strains of male mice, for example C3H.

The two most common types of tumors in mice are lymphomas (leukemia) and mammary gland tumors. Viruses are responsible for many of these tumors. Enlarged lymph nodes, enlarged spleen, and general lethargy and debilitation are seen with leukemia.

Mammary gland tumors occur on the abdomen, chest, and back, as normal mammary gland tissue has extensive distribution in the mouse. Metastasis (spread to other organs) of mammary gland tumors is not very frequent. The virus is transmitted to nursing young in the milk.

Because of the numerous strains of inbred mice that have been developed, a variety of genetic defects are seen commonly in pet mice, for example, hydrocephalus, hydronephrosis (kidney disease), and missing limbs and eyes. This fact is important to remember when evaluating health problems in mice and other rodents.

Further Reading

The Mouse in Biomedical Research. Edited by H.L. Foster and others. Academic Press, Order Department, Orlando, FL 32887-0015. Volume I, $65.00; Volume IV, $90.00.

Rats Friendly, But Not High on Pet List

By Robert J. Russell and
Jim A. Stunkard

Pet and laboratory rats are derived from the wild brown or Norway rat (*Rattus norvegicus*). Rats are not one of the more popular pets, probably because of their social/historical impact on man than for any other reason.

Most rats become very friendly, are quick to learn, and respond positively to handling and attention. They are generally friendlier than mice, but they will bite if provoked.

Rats with brown hair coats are usually less friendly than the white-haired varieties. All tend to lose their trust if handled roughly on a recurring basis or if several injectable treatments are required. Feed and housing systems are similar to those used

Robert J. Russell is Director, Laboratory Animal Sciences Program, Program Resources Inc., Frederick, Md. Jim A. Stunkard is Director of the Bowie Animal Hospital, Bowie, Md.

for gerbils, hamsters, and mice, although larger in size.

Diseases

Respiratory disease is the most common disease seen in rats. *Micoplasma pulmonis* is the primary cause and is responsible for a chronic disease that occurs in almost all rats held outside barrier facilities.

Affected animals produce a snuffling sound when they breathe, rub their eyes and nose, develop nasal discharge, have rough hair coats, become lethargic, and lose weight. Some animals develop middle ear infections that cause circling or head tilt.

Acute Pneumonia. A variety of secondary invaders—for example, *Streptococcus pneumoniae, Pasteurella, Bordetella, Pseudomonas aeruginosa*—can cause acute pneumonia in animals also infected with *Mycoplasma*. Increased respiratory difficulties and sudden deaths can occur.

Rats

Streptococcus pneumoniae is a particularly frequent secondary invader. A sudden high death rate is seen, and the majority of animals develop rapid shallow breathing and have eye and nasal discharges. Animals have rough hair coats and become rapidly debilitated.

Systemic antibiotics may help control clinical signs, but many animals develop a fibrinous pneumonia that results in either permanent lung damage or continued death losses. Isolation of the causative organism is required for definitive diagnosis, although clinical signs and gross and histopathologic lesions often are characteristic.

Treatment of respiratory disease with systemic antibiotics may be helpful. Infected animals should be isolated. However, eliminating infected colonies followed by repopulation with clean animals is often the only way to eliminate the problem.

High ammonia levels have been shown to exacerbate respiratory disease; therefore, good sanitation and ventilation are extremely important. Barrier systems are used in the laboratory environment to control the disease effectively.

Sialodacryoadenitis virus, a coronavirus, causes inflammation of the conjunctiva, discharge from the eyes, inflammation of the lacrimal (tear) gland with excretion of a dark to red pigment around the eye and the nose, swelling of the salivary glands in the ventral neck area, and weight loss. Affected animals usually recover spontaneously within 7 to 10 days, except that some may have permanent eye damage.

Susceptible animals should not be brought into infected colonies for at least several months after the last clinical case, to prevent continued outbreaks of the disease in incoming animals.

Skin, Tail Problems

Staphylococcus aureus has been responsible for a variety of skin infections including ulcerative dermatitis and pododermatitis (foot infections). Toenail clipping has been successful in some cases. Ringworm lesions are similar to those seen in rabbits and are caused by *Trichophyton* and *Microsporum*. Local and systemic treatments are effective.

Ringtail, usually seen only in young rats, is observed as constrictions of the tail and even loss of the tail distal (posterior) to the constriction. Usually the condition is seen in winter months in periods of low humidity (20 to 30 percent) when the heating system is in use. The relative humidity should be maintained around 50 percent in indoor rodent housing areas.

Lice (*Polyplax*) and, particularly, mites (*Dermanyssus, Notoedres, Radfordia ensifera*) can cause skin irritation and hair loss. Local treatment is generally effective except for *Dermanyssus*, which spend a portion of their life cycle away from the rat. In these cases the entire room must be treated. *Dermanyssus* mites occasionally will attack humans.

Mammary gland tumors are the most common tumors seen in the rat.

Progressive kidney disease is a frequent cause of death in old rats. Affected animals become lethargic, go off feed, and become severely debilitated. No treatment is available.

Healthy rats commonly carry the bacterium *Streptobacillus moniliformis* in their mouths and throats. This organism can be transmitted to humans and is responsible for the disease commonly known as rat-bite fever. Another organism, *Spirillum minor,* occasionally carried by both rats and mice, also can cause rat-bite fever in humans.

Further Reading
The Laboratory Rat. Edited by H.J. Baker and others. Academic Press, Order Department, Orlando, FL 32887-0015. Volume I, $67.50; Volume II, $63.00.

The Masked Ferret

By Robert J. Russell and
Jim A. Stunkard

Ferrets are carnivorous animals in the same family (Mustellidae) as skunks, weasels, mink, and badgers. They make good pets and usually are quite easy to handle.

They have been domesticated for over 2,000 years in Europe, where they have been used to hunt rabbits and kill rats and snakes. Ferrets are banned in some States, and you should check with local and State officials regarding legality of ownership.

Mustella putorius furo, the common ferret or polecat of Europe, North Africa, and Asia, is called the fitch ferret in the fur industry. It is pale yellow-buff with black mask, limbs, and tail. An albino va-

Robert J. Russell is Director, Laboratory Animal Sciences Program, Program Resources Inc., Frederick, Md. Jim A. Stunkard is Director of the Bowie Animal Hospital, Bowie, Md.

riety, white fur and pink eyes, also is seen. Male ferrets are called "hobs," females "jills," and the offspring "kits" or "puppies."

Breeding season in the Northern hemisphere usually is March through August. Place female in the male's cage for breeding.

The pen should provide a dark, quiet nesting box. A female can produce one to two litters per year. Separate pregnant females from males. Cannibalism may occur if the females are disturbed during the first few days after birth.

Kits are born hairless and blind. Their eyes open around 4 weeks of age. They usually are weaned between 8 and 10 weeks of age, and they reach their adult weight at 4 months of age and sexual maturity in the spring after their birth (36 to 52 weeks of age).

Onset of Estrus

Heat or sexual receptivity (es-

Marie T. Sebrechts

trus) is signalled by an enlarged, swollen vulva. The female will remain in estrus up
to 4 months if not bred. The
vulva will remain swollen until after being bred.

In many instances of pro-
longed estrus, the jill becomes
lethargic and emaciated and
develops aplastic anemia.
Treatment often is started too
late to reverse the disease
process.

Therefore, it is a good
idea to breed jills until no

*Ferrets make fun pets and usually
are easy to handle.*

more kits are wanted, and
then have your veterinarian
surgically spay (ovariohysterectomy) the jill. Hormone injections have been used to
control prolonged estrus, but
the effects are unreliable and
only temporary at best.

Estrus can be artificially
induced in the female by
lengthening the photoperiod
(period of light). Unfortu-

Ferrets

Marie T. Sebrechts

A good cage is made easily from large mesh-wire, with exterior-grade plywood or cement block for the base.

nately, this can be accidentally accomplished in pet ferrets when the family keeps the house lights on for several hours after sunset in the winter months.

Descenting

Male ferrets make better pets and have less odor if they are castrated (testes removed). Ferrets frequently are descented (surgical removal of scent glands), as many people find the ferret's odor offensive.

Housing

Generally, large mesh-wire, exterior plywood, or cement block solid-bottom cage boxes are used. Bedding is shredded paper, corncobs, straw, wood shavings, or hardwood chips.

Metal or fiberglass cat and dog cages can be used if all cage openings are small. Cages should be provided with an enclosed area for sleeping.

Open-sided sheds with wire cages and attached nest boxes are used outdoors. Cages should be carefully constructed to prevent escape. Ferrets are good burrowers, and outdoor enclosures should be designed to prevent escape by digging.

Boxes should measure at least $30'' \times 30'' \times 17''$ high and large boxes should be used if group housing animals. Animals can be group housed in

Rabbits and Other Small Animals

the winter months if males and females are not housed together. Temperatures in indoor facilities should be kept below 75° F.

The housing environment should provide an outlet for the ferret's normal active behavior. The use of tunnels and pools of water or dust provides environmental variety, and aids in preventing abnormal behavior (tail chewing, circling). You probably will enjoy spending time playing with your ferret loose in the house.

Dietary Needs

Ferrets require complete, good-quality diets. Commercial dry cat food supplemented with canned dog or cat food mixed with hot water and milk or dried milk replacements (for example, Esbilac) and supplemental vitamins provides a substantial, well-balanced diet.

Ferrets usually can be fed as much as they will eat. They rarely become obese, although ferrets normally can have large variations in body weight over the course of a year. Many ferret fanciers give cod liver oil as a hair coat conditioner. Small quantities should be used (less than 0.25 milliliters per day) to avoid development of fatty liver.

Handling

Ferrets usually are quite tame and generally can be handled without gloves. However, new animals and females with young should be handled with care.

Ferrets rarely struggle when held by the nape of the neck, which is the way they carry their offspring. As a general rule, they may be carried, examined or immunized more easily in this manner than any other way. They also may be held with two hands, by grasping over the neck and shoulders with one hand, and the pelvis with the other hand.

Vaccinations

Ferrets are extremely susceptible to the virus that causes canine distemper, and almost 100 percent of unvaccinated animals exposed to the virus will die. Discharge from the eyes and nose, breathing difficulty, and diarrhea occur. The virus also may affect the nervous system.

Treatment, if attempted, must be intensive and include general supportive therapy and injections of vitamins and antibiotics. The prognosis is very poor.

To prevent the disease, ferrets should be vaccinated, using a series of two or more

Ferrets

Marie T. Sebrechts

Ferrets rarely get fat; usually you can feed them as much as they will eat. Commercial dry cat food is the basis of a good diet, but must be supplemented to make it complete.

injections with modified live virus vaccines manufactured for use in dogs. Reactions to the vaccine are rare if leptospirosis vaccine combinations are not used. Anaphylactic shock (fatal reaction) may occur when using leptospirosis vaccine in ferrets.

Some controversy exists as to whether ferrets should be vaccinated for feline enteritis (feline distemper, panleukopenia). To be on the safe side at this time, it appears that animals should be vaccinated with feline enteritis or canine parvovirus virus. Definitive research needs to be accomplished in this area.

Aleutian disease, caused by a parvovirus, results in severe pelt damage and, in some cases, death. A diagnostic test for this disease is available and is used by many breeders. Canine parvovirus vaccine or feline enteritis vaccine may help prevent the condition.

Diarrhea Ailments

Hemorrhagic enteritis (bloody diarrhea) of unknown cause is a frequent disease in some areas. Acute cases have bloody diarrhea, go off feed and die within 3 to 4 days. In chronic cases diarrhea may come and go, and the animals gradually become emaciated and die within a month. Antibiotics and supportive therapy are successful in some cases.

The bacterium *Campylobacter fetus* subspecies *jejuni* has been shown recently to be responsible for diarrhea and body weight loss. Healthy ferrets also can carry this organism without showing any clinical signs of disease.

C. fetus subspecies *jejuni* is known to cause diarrhea in people, and ferrets could be a source of human infection. Consideration should be given to culturing pet ferrets for the presence of this organism. See your veterinarian when you first get your animal and also if any animals develop diarrhea. Treatments to successfully eliminate the organism from carrier animals have not been described.

A bacterium, *Pasteurella multocida*, is a cause of severe disease in ferrets. Affected animals are lethargic and off feed, develop breathing difficulties, and occasionally have locomotor problems. Sudden death without clinical signs also may occur. At death, abscesses may be found in many organs, especially the lung, liver, and spleen. Systemic antibiotics and aggressive supportive treatment are helpful

if started early in the disease.

Botulism. Ferrets are very susceptible to botulism caused by the toxin produced by the bacterium *Clostridium botulinum*. Clinical signs include breathing difficulty and paralysis; death may occur without prior clinical signs.

The disease is due to contaminated food and is seen more frequently in large colony operations than in singly maintained pet animals. Commercially raised ferrets are vaccinated for botulism at weaning and annually thereafter. Pet ferrets do not require vaccination if they are given fresh food.

Ferrets can be infected by a variety of intestinal parasites that can cause disease, and routine fecal examinations should be performed.

Other Problems

Ear mites, caused by *Otodectes cynotis,* is a very common problem and causes discomfort, scratching, head shaking, and a buildup of debris in the external ear canal. Standard therapy as used for cats and dogs will kill the mites and correct the condition.

Other external parasites are rare, but hair loss and skin lesions can be caused by *Sarcoptes scabei.* The fly lar-

Ferrets

vae *Cuterbra* may occur occasionally in ferrets housed outdoors.

Cataracts (eye opacities) are frequently seen in young ferrets. Because the condition may be inherited, affected animals should not be bred, to prevent this serious, debilitating condition from occurring in future generations.

Tartar accumulates in the teeth of animals fed soft food, and should be removed to prevent gum disease.

The anal glands occasionally become impacted, and manual expression of the glands by a veterinarian is required to reduce pain and prevent abscesses.

Fight wounds can be common in group housed animals. Separation of animals and provision of a larger and a more interesting housing environment may be needed. Bacteria—for example, *Streptococcus* and *Staphylococcus*—may cause single or multiple abscesses under the skin. The abscesses may be initiated by fight wounds. Local treatment, drainage and the use of antiseptics—and occasionally the use of systemic antibiotics—are indicated.

Sore feet (pododermatitis, foot rot) occurs commonly from bacterial infections, such as *Staphylococcus aureus,*

when ferrets are kept in a wet, filthy environment. Grass and dirt become matted on the toenails, toes, and feet causing sores, scabs and swelling of the feet two to three times normal size. Tails also may become affected.

Cleaning contaminated cages and keeping the animals dry will often eliminate the condition.

During the breeding season, jills and hobs may develop *alopecia* (hair loss, "blow their coats") and lose up to one-half their body weight.

Mycotic (fungal) dermatitis, usually caused by *Trichophyton mentagrophytes,* occurs fairly frequently in commercially raised ferrets and causes severe pelt damage.

Tumors of internal organs, especially the spleen, occur sporadically and often result in death. The first clinical signs usually are not specific but may consist of poor appetite, lethargy, and weight loss.

Although the ferret is highly susceptible to rabies and capable of transmitting it if infected, the risk of rabies usually is negligible as most pet ferrets are kept in cages and rarely exposed to rabid animals. A rabies vaccine has not been approved for use in ferrets; therefore, rabies vaccination is not recommended.

IX. HORSES

USDA

Respiratory Diseases

By R. D. Scoggins

The principal use for most horses is related to their athletic ability. This necessitates physical soundness, with horses traditionally sound in "wind and limb". Any disease that affects the respiratory system may potentially inter-fere with the horse's soundness of wind.

Even animals used very little physically or only for breeding need to be free of respiratory disease. Horses not worked, but kept only as pets, may cause their owners distress if chronic respiratory disease causes the horse apparent difficulty.

A number of disease conditions may interfere with respiratory health. Respiratory disease can affect horses of any age, and chronic problems may seriously reduce the usefulness of horses at maturity.

Respiratory diseases may be due to infectious agents, mechanical problems, allergic responses, or a combination of these. Mechanical problems may create breathing difficulties for horses, while bacterial, viral and allergy producing agents can all cause respiratory disease.

Respiratory disease reduces usefulness of the affected animal, since the horse is unable to tolerate vigorous exercise. A discussion of some of the more frequently seen problems of the respiratory system follows.

Sinusitis. In this condition, sinuses of the horse's head become inflamed. Causes include infectious agents, mechanical problems, and tumors.

Sinusitis rarely is a contagious disease unless it is caused by a specific virus or bacteria. The person who

R.D. Scoggins is Equine Extension Veterinarian, College of Veterinary Medicine, University of Illinois, Urbana-Champaign.

cares for the horse may notice a discharge from one or both nostrils. It may be quite thick in consistency and tinged with blood, and frequently has a strong unpleasant odor. Occasionally, the side of the horse's face may appear swollen. There are no geographical limitations to the occurrence of sinusitis.

Veterinarians diagnose sinusitis by physical examination, cultures of the discharges, x ray examination, and sometimes by surgery accompanied by biopsy or the removal of a small piece of the involved tissue.

Prevention includes periodic examinations for apparent abnormalities, an active immunization program to prevent infectious diseases, and periodic dental exams to prevent tooth disease from affecting the sinuses.

Palate Elongation. With this mechanical condition the soft portion of the roof of the mouth extends too far back into the upper throat or pharynx, where it may interfere with breathing during strenuous exercise. Veterinarians diagnose the condition by examining the horse's throat with an endoscope, a flexible instrument with lights that allows them to look into body cavities or spaces.

Horses cannot breathe through their mouths due to the physical design of their pharynx. Elongation of the soft palate reduces normal airflow to the point that horses are unable to tolerate hard exercise.

Because this is a developmental problem of the horse's anatomy, there is no effective prevention. Treatment consists of surgically removing the excess portion of the palate.

Bleeders
EIPH—Exercise Induced Pulmonary Hemorrhage (or bleeding) is a serious condition in equine athletes. Racehorses are most frequently affected. The more strenuous the exercise, the more frequently bleeding occurs. Some studies indicate that over 60 percent of horses being raced may exhibit some degree of bleeding after racing.

The hemorrhage occurs from minute vessels in the lungs. Although seldom fatal, bleeding can interfere with the horse's breathing and result in what appears to be choking or difficulty in obtaining air.

Since blood does not always appear at the nostrils, owners may not be aware that bleeding is occurring. Some

Respiratory Diseases

horses show visible blood when they lower their head and blood flows from the nostril.

Considerable controversy surrounds the origin and treatment of bleeders. Diuretics have been utilized with mixed success. Some hormonal therapy has been attempted using conjugated estrogens. Use of various types of fumes to "smoke" a horse's head had some temporary popularity among horsemen.

Various other chemical agents have been used unsuccessfully to prevent EPIH.

Proponents of interval training suggest that more rigorous conditioning programs resulting in horses in better physical condition would reduce EPIH. Considerable research is needed to determine the specific cause of bleeding among equine athletes.

"Heaves"

Allergic equine respiratory disease is primarily seen clinically as a condition termed "heaves" by horsemen or pulmonary emphysema by veterinarians.

This resembles asthma or emphysema in humans. It has several components of its clinical condition including reduced exercise tolerance, a frequent soft cough, a distinct push with the abdominal muscles when air is being expelled, and a crackling or squeaking sound over the lung fields when listened to with a stethoscope.

The condition frequently follows a bout of respiratory disease accompanied by severe coughing. It sometimes appears suddenly with severe respiratory distress in bronchial asthma-like attacks. The condition usually is progressive. It frequently is associated with feeding of roughage that contains a high content of dust, pollen or mold spores.

Preventive steps include a vigorous vaccination program against infectious respiratory disease, along with prompt treatment and adequate rest until complete recovery occurs from any attack of respiratory disease. Avoid feeds with dust, pollen or mold. Allow horses to live in a fresh air environment as much as possible.

Treatment is a combination of several procedures. Non-allergenic, dust-free feeds and as much green pasture turnout as possible is needed. This may be combined with antihistamines, bronchial dilators and/or regularly decreasing doses of corticosteroids. Sometimes atropine or atropine-like drugs help in

Horses

Lots of fresh air is as important to the prevention of respiratory problems as it is easy to provide. Other important preventive steps include: Vaccination, prompt treatment, and adequate rest after any disease has been treated.

Marie T. Sebrechts

Marie T. Sebrechts

Marie T. Sebrechts

Respiratory Diseases

537

acute cases. Followup nursing care will be needed to some degree for the remaining life of the horse.

Dealing With EVR
Equine Viral
Rhinopneumonitis (EVR).

Equine Herpes Virus-1 is the cause of EVR. In susceptible horses, especially foals, it causes an acute upper respiratory infection. A severe nasal discharge occurs, particularly in foals. Direct contact spreads the virus between horses.

After exposure, susceptible horses may develop a temperature of 102° to 107° F for up to a week. Other signs include depression, loss of appetite, a watery nasal discharge, and a mild cough. Immunized horses usually develop a milder or inapparent infection. Occasionally, the virus may enter the central nervous system and cause mild to severe incoordination that can progress to total paralysis.

Pregnant mares without immunity to EHV-1 may abort. Abortions usually occur from the 8th through the 11th month of pregnancy. Occasionally, weak live foals are born but die shortly. Mares abort without warning and breed back without difficulty. Although some specific signs may occur in aborted foals, laboratory diagnosis is best.

Prevention via immunity from either natural exposure or vaccination is relatively short lived. Repeated exposure or repeated immunizations appear to enhance protection.

Vaccination programs vary in usage but in general include vaccinating with either a modified live virus vaccine at 2- to 3-month intervals year-round or using the killed product at the 5th, 7th, and 9th month of pregnancy. No effective treatment is known at present. Vaccinating foals at 60 days of age and repeating at 60 to 90 day intervals reduces the clinical signs in foals.

Horse farms must isolate pregnant mares and foals from contact with transient stock. Show and race horses returning to the farm or visiting mares for breeding are sources of infection. No other animals or humans are known to be affected by this virus.

Equine Influenza

This is an acute, highly contagious disease that causes a high fever and persistent cough. "Flu" is caused by at least two distinct myxoviruses—A equi 1 and A equi 2. These viruses are widely spread throughout the horse population. Exposure occurs at shows, sales, races, trail rides and other events where horses come together from different areas.

Following exposure to nasal discharges containing influenza virus, the susceptible horse develops a fever up to 107° F within 3 to 5 days. The high temperature may persist for up to 3 days. A hard persistent cough develops early and persists for up to 2 to 3 weeks.

Secondary bacterial infections sometimes develop as a complication. Muscle soreness occasionally is seen in some horses with stiffness being apparent.

Good nursing care is indicated as treatment. This includes providing a soft, palatable, dust free diet and fresh, clean water, while preventing drafts. Bandaging of legs and blanketing may be indicated.

Controlled hand walking exercise during a rest and rehabilitation program after recovery is essential. If the horse returns to work too soon, recurring bouts or other complications usually result. Horses should not return to work of any kind for 10 to 14 days after complete cessation of all flu symptoms.

Use of antibiotics or fever controlling drugs are seldom needed. They should only be given following a veterinarian's advice. Serious complications occur when a horse's symptoms are masked by medication, since the horse returns to work too soon.

Reports of chronic lung disease or serious pleural pneumonia complications are heard following the use of corticosteroids, phenylbutazone, and other anti-inflammatory drugs without proper supervision.

Prevention is provided to some degree by a vaccine containing two inactivated viruses, A-1 and A-2. An initial vaccination followed by a booster in 4 to 6 weeks is recommended. Followup boosters are given at 3 to 6 month intervals. The more likely the horses are to be exposed, the more frequent the boosters are recommended.

Pinkeye

Viral Arteritis (Pinkeye) is a separate viral disease that can cause respiratory symptoms along with swelling of the legs and abortion in pregnant mares. This usually is a sporadic disease spread by contact with infective nasal discharges.

Few horses die unless complications occur. Young or very old horses are most se-

Respiratory Diseases

verely affected. Up to 80% of the pregnant mares may abort. Severity of the infection apparently varies greatly between outbreaks.

Following exposure, the symptoms can occur 1 to 8 days later. Swelling and redness occur around the eyes with flowing of tears and squinting. Horses are dull and go off feed. Eyelids, legs, and the underside of the body become swollen. Some yellowing or jaundice may be noticed. Pregnant mares abort during or shortly after the fever occurs.

Complications can include fatal lung disease due to accumulation of fluid. This is especially dangerous if the horse already had lung disease. The virus attacks the small blood vessels and the changes seen are due to damage to these structures.

Veterinarians diagnose Viral Arteritis by clinical signs and differentiating it from several other virus diseases.

Treatment in general consists of very careful nursing care. The specific treatment depends on the individual case. Vaccines are not commercially available at this time. Prevention is best accomplished through good sanitation and isolation.

Strangles

This is a highly contagious abscess-producing infection caused by a specific streptococcus bacteria, *Streptococcus equi*. Pus from the ruptured abscesses can contaminate the environment including mangers, fences and water tanks. This material remains infective to other horses for months and is a major means of prolonging a disease outbreak on a farm.

Young horses are most frequently affected. Susceptible horses of any age may develop the disease following exposure. Stress such as hauling, weaning, weather changes, hard work and poor nutrition all weaken a horse's defense. Outbreaks tend to be prolonged and may follow introduction of an apparently healthy carrier.

Only horses, mules, ponies and related equidae (zebras, etc.) are susceptible. Other domestic animals and humans do not develop the disease.

Three to 6 days following exposure, susceptible horses stop eating. They may extend their heads and drool, as it is painful for them to swallow. A temperature of 106° F is not unusual.

Swelling between the jaws and near the base of the

ear may occur. These enlarge, become soft, burst and drain a creamy, blood-tinged pus within 5 to 7 days.

Once the abscesses drain, the temperature frequently returns to normal or near normal. During the period when the temperature is high, the horse appears very depressed and may lose considerable weight.

The entire course of the disease in an uncomplicated case may take 4 to 6 weeks. Complicated cases may be prolonged for months with failure of lesions to heal, severe weight loss, and extensive abscess formation throughout the animal's body.

Recurrence of the disease in cycles is not uncommon if new horses are added regularly to the herd. The infection rate is high, with over 80% of the horses showing signs of the disease. Death losses usually are low if no complications occur.

Death may occur either from abscesses rupturing within internal organs, or choking due to large abscesses blocking the horse's ability to breathe or breaking into the horse's airway, resulting in suffocation.

After apparent recovery of an affected horse, allow considerable rehabilitation time to avoid a flareup of infections in the throat (gutteral pouches), internal abscesses, swelling of the legs, head, ventral abdomen (*Purpura hemorrhagica*) and joint infections, especially with foals and yearlings.

One form that consists of multiple abscesses throughout the body is "Bastard Strangles". These usually result from an incomplete immune response by the animal, vaccination in the face of an outbreak, or insufficient treatment of a case of strangles.

Veterinarians diagnose strangles by its clinical appearance plus culture and identification of the organism *Streptococcus equi*. Other streptococci can cause a similar but milder disease that resembles strangles.

Vaccination. Prevention is accomplished by the use of commercially available vaccines. Three injections at 2-week intervals are given deep in heavy muscles. An annual booster is indicated. However, vaccination of horses in the face of an outbreak or while recovering from the disease can be disastrous. Only healthy, uninfected, unexposed horses should be vaccinated.

Treatment is best determined by a veterinarian. Hot

Respiratory Diseases

The best prevention for pleuropneumonia is prevention of all respiratory diseases. A clean, healthy environment, a complete immunization program, internal parasite control, and avoiding unnecessary stress will greatly reduce the odds that your horse will have problems with his "wind" . . . and "limb."

USDA-APHIS
Chuck Herron, USDA- APHIS

Horses

packs on forming abscesses, cleaning of abscesses, and providing easily eaten feed and fresh, clean water are essential. Prevent the contents of abscesses from widespread contamination by isolating infected animals in one spot and leaving them there until completely healed.

Streptococcus equi bacteria is highly penicillin sensitive, but vigorous and prolonged treatment is necessary. Recommended doses of penicillin should be administered daily, and for several days after the temperature returns to normal. This usually requires treatment for a minimum of 10 to 14 days.

Discontinuing treatment too soon, reducing dosage, skipping days of treatment, or using inappropriate drugs or dosage are the most frequent causes of treatment failure. Some horses may require treatment for as long as 30 days to obtain a cure.

Pleuropneumonia

This disease condition usually is the aftereffect of an earlier respiratory problem. A number of different organisms can cause the condition. Inflammation develops in the tissues that line the chest cavity and surround the lungs. This space fills with fluid, debris and infective bacteria.

Pleuropneumonia results from incomplete or improper treatment of previous lung disease. In most cases, corticosteroids or other anti-inflammatory drugs have been used. Occasionally, inadequate dosages of antibiotics or sulfa drugs have been given. At other times, treatment has not been carried out long enough.

This usually is considered a contagious disease. The condition is painful, with the horse being reluctant to move. Pressure over the chest area causes discomfort, and some horses act as though they have colic or abdominal pain.

The veterinarian diagnoses the disease by listening to the horse's chest with a stethoscope for abnormal lung sounds, by the horse's painful attitude, by sounds of increased density on percussion, and finally by performing a chest tap. A chest tap is placing a drain in the chest wall to draw fluid for examination.

Prevention is best accomplished by avoiding respiratory disease in horses. This includes a clean, healthy environment, a complete immunization program, internal parasite control, and avoiding undue stress. If respiratory disease occurs, prompt, appropriate treatment is necessary

Respiratory Diseases

for the indicated length of time.

Treatment may consist of chest drainage by tubes surgically implanted in the chest, specific antibiotic treatment, and good nursing care. Vigorous appropriate treatment can frequently result in a return of the animal to usefulness.

Abscess Pneumonia

This is becoming an increasingly serious disease of foals. The bacteria *Corynebacterium equi* causes heavily encapsulated abscesses to develop in the lung. These abscesses displace lung tissue. In severe cases extensive destruction of lung tissue occurs. The bacteria seem to be very irritating to tissue and cause severe tissue reaction.

Symptoms seldom are evident until the disease has progressed to a critical stage. In the early stages, only a dry persistent cough is present.

As the disease progresses, the foal develops severe breathing difficulty. Any exercise worsens the condition. Foals may reach a state where pumping movements with the abdominal muscles are almost diagnostic. Rectal temperatures generally are in the 102° to 104° F range.

Death is usually due to asphyxiation as lung tissue is destroyed. Foals that recover may show no after-effects as adults, despite the severity of symptoms during the disease's course.

Veterinarians diagnose the disease in foals by the symptoms, cultures of the trachea (windpipe) and age of the foals, usually 4 to 8 weeks when the disease is first noticed.

Abscess pneumonia appears to be increasing in frequency, and several colleges of veterinary medicine are studying the disease.

At present no effective commercial vaccine is available for use in horses. Prevention is best accomplished by superior management, especially internal parasite control, dust control, avoiding overcrowding, increased use of pasture and minimizing enclosed housing.

Treatment should be vigorous and prolonged. Foals that respond must be treated for extensive periods of time. Twice daily for up to 4 to 6 weeks is not an uncommon treatment schedule.

Hot, dry, dusty conditions tend to result in an increase in this condition. The disease is not felt to be highly contagious as large numbers of foals in a group usually are not affected.

Further research in all areas of this disease is needed to obtain more information about its spread, method of infection, treatment and development of an effective vaccine.

When respiratory disease complications occur, problems can become more serious or even fatal. These complications occur due to a number of causes. Among them are:

—Use of corticosteroids. These drugs cause horses to appear to feel better, but they suppress the horses' own defenses. As a result, the infection is spread and the condition worsens.

—Secondary bacterial infections following a virus infection. Cultures and identification are necessary to treat these conditions specifically.

Adequate time for complete recuperation is absolutely essential. This is the most difficult aspect of treatment for persons handling the horses. Green grass, fresh air and being outside are all beneficial to recovery.

Several infectious diseases of horses affect their respiratory system, but may also cause problems within other areas of the body. Some bacteria also cause abscesses within the abdomen or joints.

Respiratory viruses may enter the nervous system and cause paralysis, while others may cause severe inflammation and soreness in the muscles. One strain of the Herpes virus can cause pregnant mares to abort their foals.

Equine respiratory disease also may be a mixed infection of more than one organism. Surveys of owners and veterinarians indicate that stress, hauling, shows, sales, and racing all predispose horses to respiratory disease.

Isolation or culture of the causative organism, or blood serum samples drawn two or more weeks apart, help specifically to identify the causative agent.

Digestive Diseases

By R.D. Scoggins

Digestive diseases are a frequent problem of horses, and insurance companies cite colic as the most frequent cause of death in horses insured against loss. The following is a discussion of some of the more frequently seen causes of digestive disturbance.

Problems in the mouth—the beginning of the digestive tract—can result in improper chewing of food which can then hamper swallowing and digestion.

Malformed mouth parts on newborn foals should always be evaluated. Some abnormalities may be repaired surgically, while others may be impossible to successfully repair. Because many of these conditions are considered her-

itable, use of these animals as breeding stock should be discouraged.

Wry muzzle, cleft palate, overshot or undershot jaws are all conditions affecting horses. Their importance in animals depends on their severity. These problems not only affect eating, but can seriously interfere with a horse properly wearing bits for control when it becomes old enough to train for riding or driving.

Since dental disease may occur at any age, horses should have their mouths examined twice yearly for dental abnormalities. Although caries or cavities are uncommon, abnormal or uneven wear is frequently observed and needs correction.

Young horses lose their baby teeth from 2 to 5 years of age. At times, these are not shed normally, and it becomes necessary to assist in their removal. When sharp points de-

R.D. Scoggins is Equine Extension Veterinarian, College of Veterinary Medicine, University of Illinois, Urbana-Champaign.

velop along edges of the grinding or jaw teeth, they irritate the inside of the lips and edges of the tongue. These sharp points are filed down with specially designed files called "floats."

Horse owners can recognize possible dental problems when horses begin chewing abnormally, twist their heads sideways, drop excessive feed from their mouth, or refuse to eat hard grains or pellets.

Foreign bodies in the mouth cause similar problems. Grass awns, pieces of wood or metal, corncobs, and other items may lodge in the mouth and interfere with eating.

Prevention of foreign bodies is best accomplished by care in feeding practices. Use only clean feed boxes and avoid hay with foxtail or similar type awns in it.

Throat Problems

Choke is a condition in horses that occurs when feed becomes lodged in the esophagus. While choke seldom is life threatening, it is uncomfortble to the horse. Many horses become excited and lunge about trying to dislodge the material causing the choke. In the process, they may injure the handler or themselves.

Choke usually occurs when horses attempt to eat too fast, or are fed very finely ground or very dry feed. Grass clippings from lawns also can cause choke.

Horses with choke should be placed in a stall and allowed free movement of their head. Veterinarians usually attempt to remove the choke with a naso-gastric tube and lavage or flushing with water. Sedation may be necessary to accomplish this.

Owners should not attempt to dislodge a choke themselves as injury to the esophagus or lungs may occur.

Since horses that choke are prone to do it repeatedly, such horses should be denied access to the type of feed or circumstances that may cause choking to occur.

Use of large flat bottomed feed troughs or the placing of large rocks (softball size) in the grain box will slow down gluttonous eaters. Do not feed extremely dry or finely ground grain. Allow adequate eating space when horses are fed in groups. These procedures should reduce the possibility of choking.

Colic Calls for Action

Colic is a broad term that describes a horse showing abdominal pain. This can be caused by a number of conditions but common usage indicates it is pain in the digestive tract.

When colic occurs, it is important to determine the exact cause if possible. Successful treatment often depends on a correct diagnosis.

A distended stomach, acute inflammation of the small intestine, parasites that cause a decrease in blood flow to the intestine, dry food impaction, or gas distention of the large bowel are all types of colic that can occur and will vary in degree of severity as well as treatment required.

Any colic, no matter how mild, is an emergency. The potential for the condition to worsen is too great to risk delay in treatment.

Owners first notice horses that have colic when they stop eating and drinking. The horse may curl its upper lip, paw at the ground and turn its head toward either side. More severe pain causes colicky horses to sweat, to get up and down, and to attempt to roll. The horse with colic indicates it is in severe discomfort.

Rapid breathing, profuse sweating, violent activity and a cold clammy feeling may indicate the horse has gone into shock and is in need of immediate professional attention.

Veterinarians attempt to diagnose the specific type and cause of colic. They use medication to control pain and the horse's response helps evaluate the severity of the condition. Reducing the pressure in the stomach is important and oral medication may be needed to lubricate the mass or prevent further gas distention.

Medication given orally by owners may be dangerous since it can accidentally enter the lungs and cause pneumonia.

In some cases, surgery is the treatment of choice. This means moving a very hurting, sick horse to a veterinary hospital that has surgical facilities. The decision needs to be made as soon as possible and necessary supportive treatment must be provided until the horse arrives at the surgical hospital.

The most frequent causes of colic are internal parasites and sudden drastic changes in the feeding schedule, either in the amount or kind of feed. Nearly 90 percent of the horses that die from colic have related lesions due to internal parasites at autopsy. Diarrhea, especially in young horses, can result in colic due to telescoping of the bowel.

Any severe digestive up-

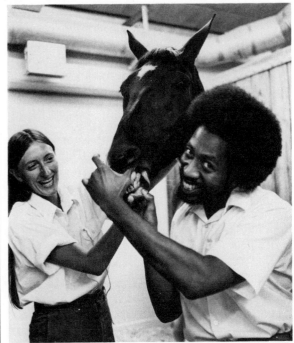

Regular check-ups are as important to horses as they are to you. Although horses rarely get cavities like people, abnormal or uneven wear is frequently observed and needs correction. So their mouths should be checked twice a year.

Marie T. Sebrechts

Marie T. Sebrechts

Allowing adequate eating space when horses are fed in groups helps reduce the possibility of choking.

Digestive Diseases

set has the potential to result in colic symptoms.

Prevention is best accomplished by:

1) An ongoing parasite control program, especially for young animals

2) Maintaining a regular feeding schedule using only quality feeds

3) Avoiding sudden dietary changes in kinds or amounts of feeds

4) Providing salt and clean fresh water free choice at all times

Treatment of this emergency condition is best left to professional veterinary care.

Potomac Fever

Acute Infectious Diarrhea Syndrome or Potomac fever is a severe diarrhea condition of horses. Most affected animals are adults that may have recently been under stress. About 30 percent of horses with Potomac fever die, so both owners and veterinarians are quite concerned.

Researchers at several veterinary colleges are attempting to identify the causative agent. At the present time, a virus transmitted by a biting insect is the primary suspect.

The majority of cases have occurred in Maryland, Virginia and southeastern Pennsylvania. Similar cases have been reported from other areas of the country, but until a specific agent can be identified, it is difficult to verify that they are all caused by the same organism.

Infected horses become depressed, stop eating and develop a profuse watery diarrhea. Some horses will have a fever of up to 105° F before the diarrhea starts. With continued diarrhea, the affected horses become weaker and develop signs of shock. The disease does not seem to be contagious and does not affect humans.

Treatment must begin as soon as possible and is intended to replace fluids and control the diarrhea. Large volumes of intravenous fluids and antidiarrheals are necessary. Time required for almost constant treatment becomes extensive and therefore fairly expensive.

At present, no vaccine is available. Horses should be handled in a manner that minimizes stress. Insect control, particularly ticks, is important.

Further research hopefully will provide more adequate answers concerning prevention and control of this disease.

Horses

Other Diarrheas

Other causes of acute diarrheal disease in horses include colitis X, salmonellosis and other diarrheal syndromes. Most of these are related to or follow stress, such as hauling, respiratory disease, or surgery. In some instances, such as salmonellosis, the diarrhea is contagious between horses and may infect humans.

Most of these diarrheas respond to vigorous treatment, although laminitis or founder frequently occur following a severe diarrheal episode.

Specific treatments or preventions are not available at this time. Salmonellosis can be vaccinated against with an autogenous bacterin. On occasion a horse will recover and be left with chronically soft stools.

Foal Heat Diarrhea

Most newborn foals develop diarrhea at 7 to 12 days of age. At about the same time the mare comes into what is called foal heat.

Affected foals usually show no problems due to the diarrhea, but occasionally the foal becomes ill or the diarrhea persists. Some may even develop serious intestinal problems and colic.

The cause is felt to be related to larvae of the intestinal threadworm, *Strongyloides westeri*. The immature larvae locate in the mare's udder and the foal acquires an infection by nursing. Within 8 to 10 days the parasites are established within the foal's intestinal tract. They irritate the gut wall, which results in the foal diarrhea.

Prevention is best accomplished by deworming pregnant mares during the last 30 days of pregnancy with drugs effective against the *S. westeri* larvae.

Affected foals may respond to intestinal protectants, appropriate deworming agents, and—if needed—fluids. Oral antibiotics seldom are of much value.

A secondary problem is the scalding of the foal's rear quarters, with resultant burning and irritation and hair loss. To prevent this, horse owners must clean the foal's rear parts and place some protective ointment on the area. Vaseline or zinc oxide ointment on the foal's tail helps, as it becomes a self-made applicator.

Seemingly harmless diarrheal conditions can rapidly become critical. Horse owners need to keep a close watch on any animals with diarrhea. Proper treatment and aftercare are essential to minimize resultant problems.

Other Common Diseases

By R.D. Scoggins

Clostridial diseases as a group are due to a family of bacteria that grow in the gut or tissue and produce gas and very powerful toxins that affect the nervous system.

Tetanus, a frequently seen disease of horses, is caused by a neuro-toxin produced by *Clostridium tetani.* This nerve tissue poison causes spasms and rigidity of the skeletal muscles. Affected horses cannot eat and have difficulty drinking, thus the term lockjaw. Over half of affected horses die due to suffocation, starvation or dehydration.

Due to the large number of *Clostridium tetani* in the horse's digestive tract, people working around horses should consult their physicians concerning tetanus immunization for themselves.

Infected horses acquire the problem through puncture wounds or other deep wounds. Within 10 to 14 days following injury, horses become increasingly nervous, then stiff or rigid and as a result have difficulty moving. The more rapid and severe the onset of symptoms, the less chance of recovery.

Persistent treatment and much nursing care are needed. Affected horses need to be protected from light and sound that can stimulate nervousness. Horses are placed in darkened stalls and their ears plugged with cotton to reduce stimuli from sound.

Veterinarians usually administer tetanus antitoxin, antibiotics, and sedatives repeatedly for several weeks. One third to one half of affected horses may recover if diagnosed early and treated vigorously.

R.D. Scoggins is Equine Extension Veterinarian, College of Veterinary Medicine, University of Illinois, Urbana-Champaign.

Prevention is twofold. Unvaccinated animals should receive tetanus antitoxin within 24 hours following injury or surgery. This provides temporary protection for 10 to 14 days. If healing is not complete at that time, then tetanus antitoxin should be repeated at 2-week intervals until healing is complete.

Vaccination with tetanus toxoid provides a very stable immunity. All horses should be vaccinated against tetanus and receive annual boosters on a regular basis and following an injury.

Botulism: Two Types

Botulism is due to *Clostridium botulinium* and can occur in adults as "forage poisoning" or in foals as the Shaker Foal Syndrome.

With "forage poisoning", adult horses become weak and stagger, have difficulty swallowing, and may go down and be partially or completely paralyzed. Silage, incompletely cured hay, or forage with spoiled areas are usually the cause. A commercial vaccine is not available at present. Prevention is best accomplished by careful selection of hay, silage or other harvested forage for horses.

The Shaker Foal Syndrome appears as a problem in young foals nursing mares being fed high energy, high protein diets. Experimental vaccination of pregnant mares prior to foaling has prevented the condition, and vaccine may become available commercially.

Care in nutritional management of mares nursing foals may control or prevent Shaker foals from developing. Affected foals become uncoordinated, develop jerky movements, and eventually become paralyzed and die. Once symptoms are apparent, treatment has little effect in improving the foal's condition.

Clostridial Myositis

Infections of muscle masses by one or more of several clostridial bacteria families can occur. These organisms usually enter through wounds, needle injections, or other muscle injury.

The bacteria grow rapidly, form gas pockets, create severe pain, and cause shock from the toxins produced. Hand pressure causes both crackling sounds and sensation due to the gas formed under the skin. Often, cattle are or have been present when a problem occurs.

Veterinarians treat this condition by promptly establishing drainage and using adequate dosages of appropriate antibiotics. Despite vigorous treatment, some cases fail to respond.

Appropriate injection techniques, avoiding the use of irritating drugs, and not injecting excessive volumes at one site are all important in preventing clostridial myositis. Prevention of injuries and prompt attention to any wound are helpful in preventing this disease. No approved vaccines are available.

Sleeping Sickness

Three forms of this disease are caused by viruses that affect the nervous system. Wild animals and birds act as reservoirs; the viruses also can affect humans. With the Eastern and Western forms, horses are dead-end hosts and the virus does not spread from them.

Venezuelan encephalitis spreads between horses and from horses to humans. Mosquitoes are the principal means of virus transmission between victims. Thus horses at pasture are more susceptible than stabled horses.

Infected horses initially develop a fever, act as though they have problems seeing, wander aimlessly, stagger, grind their teeth, and have a drooping lip. The disease may progress until paralysis occurs. Mild cases recover slowly over several weeks.

From 25 to 50 percent of those infected with the Western form may die, over 90 percent of those infected with the Eastern form die, and 75 percent die with the Venezuelan virus.

No specific treatment is available, but veterinarians can provide supportive care. Mosquito control is an important preventive measure, as is annual vaccination. The Venezuelan form has not been a problem in the United States since 1971, but could enter this country from Latin America.

Highly effective vaccines are commercially available and should be administered annually, before the mosquito season. They may be combined with other vaccines as well.

Swamp Fever

Equine Infectious Anemia (EIA) or swamp fever is a viral disease. In the acute form, it causes severe red blood cell destruction and resultant anemia. An inapparent carrier state occurs upon recovery. The virus is spread by bloodsucking insects and repeated use of needles or instruments without adequate sterilization between patients.

The disease causes severe anemia, fever, weakness, weight loss, edema, and sometimes death. Inapparent infections show few if any symptoms. Horses with inapparent infections that receive regular hard physical work or some other stress frequently become clinically apparent cases.

Clinical diagnosis of EIA is by a positive "Coggins Test". Titers causing a positive test occur 2 to 4 weeks after the initial disease.

No effective treatment is available. Prevention is best accomplished by maintaining Coggins Test negative horses only where other negative tested horses are maintained. Fly control and use of disposable needles among horses is an important aspect of control. Any horse that has a positive Coggins test should be maintained away from uninfected horses, especially during the insect season.

Rabies

Rabies (Hydrophobia) is a universally fatal viral disease of the central nervous system of all mammals. The virus is transmitted in saliva and infects humans, as well as other mammals. Wild animals, especially raccoons and skunks,

appear to be important reservoirs of the disease.

When horses come in contact with rabid wild animals, their curiosity often results in being bitten on the muzzle. Symptoms of rabies usually occur within 2 weeks following the bite.

A sudden change in behavior is the first indication of rabies. Drooling may or may not occur. After 1 to 3 days horses may suddenly become vicious, attempting to bite without provocation. Some roll extensively, as though with colic. The size and strength of horses makes them dangerous and potentially unmanageable. Self-mutilation is not uncommon.

Treatment is not considered effective nor feasible nor safe for the humans involved. Suspect animals should be confined for 2 weeks. If the horses are then destroyed, care should be taken not to damage the brain. Have a veterinarian remove the head and prepare it for submission to a laboratory for examination at once.

Horses may be protected against rabies by vaccination with an approved product properly administered by a licensed veterinarian.

Foreign Diseases

By Edwin I. Pilchard

Horse owners of the United States enjoy the freedom of this country's $12 billion equine industry from over 13 highly destructive diseases affecting horses in many other parts of the world.

Among the most important of these diseases are Venezuelan equine encephalomyelitis, dourine, surra, African horsesickness, glanders, and contagious equine metritis.

Cooperative efforts by industry and government succeeded in eliminating glanders from the United States by 1934 and dourine by 1942.

A sudden incursion of Venezuelan equine encephalomyelitis (VEE) into Texas in 1971 was promptly eradicated by a well-coordinated program of vaccination and aerial spraying of thousands of acres of land with pesticide to destroy the vector mosquitoes.

The virus causing VEE attacks the central nervous system, causing sleepy or depressed behavior, difficulty in walking, and sometimes a braced stance with feet placed widely apart in an apparent effort to avoid falling.

As the disease advances, swallowing becomes difficult. Most unvaccinated horses then rapidly lose consciousness and die.

Humans are susceptible to VEE and sometimes may develop fever, stiff neck, severe headache, and other signs, after being bitten by mosquitoes carrying the virus. Most humans recover.

Dourine and surra are caused by different members of the same group of microscopic parasites, *Trypanosoma equiperdum* and *T. evansi,* and they differ widely in their effects on infected animals.

Edwin I. Pilchard is a Principal Staff Officer, Veterinary Services, Animal and Plant Health Inspection Service.

Horses

Dourine is transmitted by infected stallions to susceptible mares during breeding, and is seen as soft swelling of the underside of the body and the legs, sometimes lameness, and abortion. In contrast, surra is transmitted principally by tsetse flies to horses, cattle, and camels, resulting in fever and anemia.

. Perhaps the most dramatic and destructive of the foreign diseases of horses is African horsesickness. Spread by biting midges, the virus of this disease first produces restlessness, then colic, then a rapidly fatal pneumonia in which foamy fluid fills the lungs and airways. Horses that survive a few days may show soft swellings of the head above the eyes, underside of the chest and abdomen, and lameness. Also, pregnant mares may abort.

Caused by the bacteria *Pseudomonas mallei,* glanders produces coughing, severe irritation of the inside of the nose—often resulting in nosebleed, and skin ulcers. Another foreign disease affecting the nose is schistosomiasis, caused by the microscopic parasite, *Schistosoma nasalis.*

Contagious equine metritis appeared for the first time in the United Kingdom and France in 1977, and has since spread to several other countries. It entered the United States but was quickly contained and has been eliminated, largely through diligent industry action and compliance with government requirements to prevent spread, or reintroduction from abroad.

This disease can prevent pregnancy in mares. Bacteria causing contagious equine metritis irritate tissues of the infected mare's reproductive tract, producing an outpouring of thick, white or yellowish fluid from the vagina a few days after breeding by a contaminated stallion.

Besides Venezuelan equine encephalomyelitis mentioned earlier, at least three other foreign diseases can attack the equine nervous system.

Borna disease can produce loss of muscular control of the legs and body, and paralysis of the tongue in horses, sheep, and goats. It is caused by a virus.

Japanese encephalitis in horses may be seen as a fever accompanied by violent behavior and death. In areas where vector mosquitoes transmit the virus, it can also cause sickness in swine and humans.

Equine encephalosis,

U.S. horses are free of over 13 highly destructive diseases found in other parts of the world. One of these, the mosquito-spread virus VEE, was introduced into Texas in 1971 and was promptly eradicated by a cooperative program that included the vaccination of 2.8 million horses.

Jim Strawser, USDA

USDA

To protect the $12 billion American equine industry, a large assortment of regulations exist to assure that horses brought into the country are free of disease. Anyone transporting horses, other animals and animal products into the United States should be aware of these rules well ahead of time, so all necessary health testing and certification can be completed.

Horses

caused by a virus that has been reported only from Africa, has been described as a rapidly fatal disease characterized by fever, excited behavior, and incoordination. In any discussion of diseases of the nervous system, it is well to remind the reader that rabies virus can cause signs like those just described, and that contact should be avoided with the sick animal, its saliva, or other body fluids.

Other Diseases

Several other foreign horse diseases should be mentioned because of their potential to spread to new geographic areas, and lack of an effective treatment. One of these is Getah disease, a mosquito-transmitted viral disease reported from Japan in recent years. Infected horses develop soft swellings of the lower legs that interfere with locomotion. A vaccine has been developed to prevent Getah.

Melioidosis, described in the *Foreign Diseases* chapter of Section IV—Sheep and Goats, can produce a variety of signs in horses by damaging the internal organs and lymph system.

Vesicular stomatitis occurs in the United States from time to time, and some strains or types of the virus that causes it are foreign. Vesicular stomatitis gets its name from the appearance of blisters (vesicles) and raw ulcers in the mouth *(stoma)* of infected horses, swine, cattle and humans. More is said about it in the *Foreign Diseases* chapter of Section V—Swine.

Preventing foreign disease outbreaks in horses and other livestock and poultry requires cooperation by all who transport horses or other animals or animal products from affected countries into the United States.

Parasites

By Robert K. Ridley

Parasitism can best be considered a farm or herd problem and not a problem of individual horses. To control equine parasites, it is necessary to understand that not only are horses parasitized but that pastures, currycombs, blankets, horse trailers, etc., may be involved in the infection and reinfection of horses with some parasites.

To survive and propagate themselves, well-adapted parasites live in harmony with their hosts. If a parasite were always to kill its host, it would be responsible for its own demise, since by definition parasites are organisms which live in or on another organism of a different species for the purpose of obtaining food.

Robert K. Ridley is Associate Professor of Parasitology, College of Veterinary Medicine, Kansas State University, Manhattan.

Implicit in this definition is the notion that the parasite harms its host to some extent. However, sometimes it is only when parasites "get out of control" that we become aware of their harmful effects, and seek to rid our horses of their unwelcome guests. Although parasites affect horses of all ages and are found in all parts of the country, they most commonly occur in young animals in temperate regions.

Internal parasites are those which are found on the inside of the horse and are single-celled animals (protozoa), roundworms (nematodes), or flatworms (flukes and tapeworms). These parasites usually are found in the gastrointestinal tract, but may be found in other internal organs. External parasites (lice, ticks, mites, etc.) are found on the skin, in the ears, etc.

Signs associated with

both internal and external parasites depend on the type and number of parasites present and can range from no apparent effects to general unthriftiness, weakness, debilitation, and ultimately to death of the host.

According to our definition, many organisms satisfy the definition of a parasite, including bacteria, viruses, rickettsias, and yeasts, as well as more traditional "parasites" which as noted above include protozoa, nematodes, cestodes, trematodes, and acanthocephalans (spiny-headed worms).

Most of the parasites affecting horses are nematodes, or roundworms. Indeed, because the horse is infected with so many species of roundworms it is said to harbor more helminth (worm) parasites than any of our domestic animals. Fortunately many of these are similar and we can group them in order to discuss the effects they have on horses and the way horses become infested with them.

Protozoans are single celled animals which occur in the bloodstream and intestinal tract of horses. These organisms multiply by dividing and may be transmitted from horse to horse by an arthropod vector or simply by being ingested in food or water as a result of fecal contamination.

Most equine nematode parasites have a direct life cycle. This type of parasite does not require any other organism except the definitive host to complete its life cycle.

Typically, females which live in the digestive tract lay eggs which are passed to the outside with the horse's feces. The eggs hatch in 2 to 3 days, depending on temperature and humidity, into small worm-like organisms called first-stage larvae (L_1). First-stage larvae develop and molt to second-stage larvae (L_2) which molt to third-stage larvae (L_3).

It is the L_3 stage that is infective to the final host. They migrate up blades of grass and the horse ingests them when grazing. These so-called preparasitic stages are much the same for most of the strongyle parasites of the horse.

When the horse ingests the third-stage larvae, it develops into a fourth-stage larvae which may wander extensively through the body of the horse before becoming an adult in the intestinal tract ("large strongyles"), or it may develop into an adult in the gut with no migration through other organs ("small strongyles").

Other nematode parasites require a second host in order to complete their life cycles. This second host is an invertebrate and is called the intermediate host. Typically the intermediate host eats the egg or first-stage larvae, which then undergoes its development in the intermediate host instead of on the ground. The definitive host then becomes infected when the intermediate host (flies, ticks, etc.) injects the infective stage of the parasite while it is taking a blood meal. Sometimes the host gets the infective stage by eating the infected intermediate host.

All cestodes (tapeworms) which occur in horses use pasture mites as intermediate hosts. The host becomes infested while grazing by ingesting the mite containing the infective cysticercoid. Mites become infected by ingesting tapeworm eggs which are deposited on the pasture with the host's feces.

Flukes also require an intermediate host, most often a snail. Although flukes do occur in horses, they are of minor significance and will not be considered here.

Roundworms are by far the most serious and economically important of the worms which occur in horses. These,

as their name implies, are elongated, cylindrical worms ranging in size from 2 to 3 mm to 12 to 14 inches in length. Although the large worms cause significant problems, the small worms are far more important both from an economic and health point of view.

Some roundworm parasites damage the host by sucking blood, others cause damage by migrating through body tissues such as the lungs, and still others can cause severe colic in horses simply by forming a mass of worms in the intestine which interferes with intestinal motility and to some extent absorption of nutrients.

The tapeworm which occurs in horses is a large worm consisting of a head, which attaches to the intestine of the horse, and a long ribbon-like body with many similar segments called proglottids. In the nematodes the sexes are separate—there are males and females and mating occurs to produce the next generation. In the tapeworms, both sexes are contained within the same worm.

Nematodes have a complete digestive system, that is, they have a mouth through which they suck blood or intestinal juices and excrete

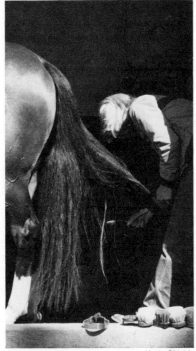

Kevin Shields

Some parasites can be spread from one horse to another through many items regularly used on the farm. To reduce the chance of this, it's a good idea for each horse to have its own equipment and to clean items between usings if they must be used on several horses.

Kevin Shields

Marie T. Sebrechts

their waste through an anus. Tapeworms absorb nutrients through their skin, having no mouth or anus.

Large Strongyles

The most important parasites, as far as horses and horse owners are concerned, are nematodes comprising a group called the "large strongyles." These are the most damaging of all the parasites which occur in horses. Adult worms range in size from approximately ½ inch up to about 1¼ inches in length, and the adults live in the large intestine and cecum where they feed by eating plugs of the mucosal lining.

Far more damaging than the adult, however, are the larvae which migrate through internal organs of the host. Some prefer to live in one of the large arteries supplying the small intestine of the horse. These larval strongyles damage the artery's lining causing it to react and become very thickened, producing an aneurysm.

Often blood clots form and are carried by the bloodstream to smaller vessels where they can block the blood supply to a part of the intestine. If there are other vessels supplying this part of the intestine, no real damage is done. However,

if there is no other blood supply, this part of the intestine in effect dies, and unless corrected surgically the condition can be life threatening. Sometimes these blood clots find their way back to the arteries which supply the hind legs, and can cause rear limb lameness.

The parasite causing these problems is called *Strongylus vulgaris*. Other large strongyles *(S. edentatus* and *S. equinus)* migrate through different organs, notably the liver and pancreas, and inflict damage in their own particular way.

Small Strongyles

As their name implies, small strongyles are much smaller than the large strongyles, usually about ½ inch in length although some are smaller. These parasites are present in much larger numbers than the large strongyles. There may be hundreds of large strongyles in a horse, but usually there are thousands of small ones. While the small strongyles don't produce the damage or present the danger that large strongyles do, they can cause colic due to decreased intestinal motility, in addition to producing ill thrift, diarrhea, rough hair-coat, and other signs associated with heavy parasitic infections. These parasites usually are clumped into one or two genera (*Triodontophorus* spp. or *Trichonema* sp.).

As with the large strongyles, horses become infested by these parasites through ingesting the infective third-stage larva while grazing. Unlike the large strongyles, these parasites require less time to reach maturity and start producing eggs and further contaminate pastures. Consequently, they quickly build up large numbers of larvae to reinfest horses and assure their propagation. Like the large strongyles, small strongyles inhabit the large intestine and the cecum.

Hair-Like Worms

Smallest of the nematode parasites which occur in horses is the stomach hair worm, *Trichostrongylus axei*. It is about 4 or 5 mm in length and very thin and hair-like. As with the large and small strongyles, the life cycle is direct. Eggs are passed in the feces, hatch and develop into third stage infective larvae in 4 or 5 days. Horses become infested by eating the larvae on the grass.

This parasite occurs in the stomach as well as the small intestine and damages the lining of these organs, sometimes causing bleeding into the gut. That is associated with dark, fetid diarrhea and can cause a rapid loss of condition with heavy infections.

The equine intestinal threadworm, *Strongyloides westeri*, is somewhat unique. These small hair-like worms are 8 to 9 mm long and only the adult female is parasitic.

To add to the uniqueness of this parasite, the adult males and females can exist outside the host in a free-living state. When conditions become unfavorable for existence on the outside, the females produce eggs which hatch into third-stage infective larvae and either are eaten by the horse or penetrate the skin. If they penetrate the skin, the larvae migrate to the lungs, penetrate the alveoli, and after reaching the trachea are coughed up and swallowed where they continue to undergo development to adulthood in the gut.

Some of these migrating larvae do not develop, but remain dormant in muscle tissue of mares until they foal. Then they migrate into the mammary gland and infest nursing foals via the colostrum. *S. westeri* has been thought to contribute to foal heat diarrhea which occurs 12 to 13 days after birth.

Tapeworm

The most common tapeworm in horses is in the genus *Anoplocephala*. This worm, *Anoplocephala magna,* is called the "large horse tapeworm" and occurs most often in the large intestine. It also is found in the stomach and sometimes in the cecum.

This is a fairly robust tapeworm about 10 inches long, with very short segments. It retains its position in the host by attaching to the small intestine lining by four suckers located on the head (scolex). Like all tapeworms, there are no males and females, but instead both sexes are contained in each individual proglottid.

The eggs are passed in the host's feces and are eaten by pasture mites. These are the intermediate hosts and consequently this worm has an indirect life cycle. After the horse eats the oribatid mite containing the infective cysticercoid (larva), the larva develops into an adult in the small intestine in 6 to 10 weeks. Typically these worms don't live very long in their host.

With light infestations, there are no signs associated with tapeworms. Heavy infestations cause horses to suffer colic and diarrhea, and possibly go off feed. They often are depressed, may be dehydrated, and spend a lot of time lying down. When many worms are present, sometimes there is little feces passed because the worms cause an intestinal obstruction. Heavy infestations with this parasite can produce complications which result in death.

Horse tapeworm infection is diagnosed by finding the eggs in the feces, and because many horses do not pass eggs—especially with heavy infestations—tapeworms may not be diagnosed when present.

Anoplocephaliasis in the horse is usually a disease of yearlings at pasture.

Lungworms

Although most common in donkeys, horses also harbor worms *(Dictyocaulus arnfieldi)* which live in their lungs. This is another nematode, or roundworm, parasite. The females are much larger than the males; females are about 60 mm long and the males can be a little over half that. The adults live in the lungs of horses where they mate and the eggs produced by the females are coughed up, swallowed and passed with the feces.

Dictyocaulus sp. has a direct life cycle. Horses become infected by ingesting the L_3, or third-stage larva. In horses, the adults may never produce eggs, while in donkeys they may start producing eggs in 3 to 4 months. Although lungworms cause very little clinical problem in donkeys, in horses they may cause coughing, an increased respiratory rate, and some nasal discharge. Because the eggs often are not produced in horses, diagnosis becomes difficult since veterinarians cannot find eggs in the feces and must rely on history—including whether donkeys are grazing with horses—and clinical signs to diagnose the disease.

Stomach Worms

The Habronemas, which consist of *Habronema muscae, H. majus,* and *H. megastoma (Draschia megastoma)*, are the equine stomach worms and cause two rather distinct diseases in horses called gastric and cutaneous habronemiasis. The Habronemas have indirect life cycles, with house and stable flies serving as intermediate hosts.

Habronema eggs which pass with the feces are eaten by fly maggots and mature with the fly as it becomes an adult. Infective larvae are deposited around the horse's lips and nostrils where the flies feed, thereby gaining entrance into the horse's mouth. Horses may also become infected by ingesting infected adult flies which become entrapped in food or water. The larvae are freed in the horse's stomach and develop into adults in about 2 months. In the stomach of horses these parasites produce fibrous tumors, or numerous nodules which if close together form a tumor.

Another type of disease caused by this parasite is cutaneous habronemiasis or "summer sores." This also is caused by *Habronema* spp., but is due to the larvae which the intermediate host deposits in existing wounds in the skin. (Some parasitologists think that the larvae can penetrate healthy skin.) Cutaneous habronemiasis occurs during the summer, and is most common on areas where horses can't switch flies, such as the inside of the legs, over the withers, the penile sheath, the canthus of the eye, and fetlocks.

These lesions are brownish-red, angry-looking sores which may ooze serum tinged with blood. They seem to itch very badly, and often disappear when cold weather sets in—only to reappear when the weather warms up again. The appearance of cutaneous skin lesions in the summertime when flies are numerous would suggest summer sores.

The gastric form of habronemiasis is more difficult to diagnose since few eggs are passed, and because the larvae don't float very well they are sometimes missed during routine fecal flotation examination. Adult females are about 1 inch long; males are somewhat smaller, usually about ⅔ to ¾ the size of the female.

Roundworms

Parascaris equorum is the horse roundworm, or more properly the horse ascarid. This is a very large, robust roundworm. Females are up to 14 inches long; the males are somewhat smaller. The life cycle is direct, but instead of ingesting the larvae on the pasture, foals ingest the infective eggs which have larva within. Because it takes about 2 weeks for the eggs to become infective, a foal could ingest freshly passed feces (a common habit) and not become infected.

After infective eggs are ingested, they hatch and penetrate the wall of the intestine, migrate in the bloodstream to the lungs where they may cause some respiratory problems, and are then coughed up, swallowed, and mature in the small intestine.

The adults start producing eggs about 12 weeks after the foal becomes infected. Because of a developing immunity, foals often shed the infection at about 7 months of age.

Clinical signs of ascarid infection in foals include a dry hair coat, potbelly, abdominal discomfort (sometimes these foals will be kicking their flank), they will be undersized for their age and breed, and very often they have dry stools covered with mucus, although diarrhea sometimes is present. It should be noted that ascarid eggs are very resistant and can survive for years in the soil.

Because some anthelmintics render these parasites unable to move, impaction due to a large mass of immobile worms sometimes can occur following deworming. Your veterinarian can suggest an appropriate anthelmintic to use in the face of a heavy ascarid infection.

Pinworms

Horses, like people and unlike dogs, have pinworms. There

are two kinds of pinworms which occur in horses. A rather large one, the females of which can be up to 2½ inches long, is *Oxyuris equi*. The minute horse pinworm, *Probstmayria* sp., is only about 2 mm long and is of little consequence.

The life cycle of *Oxyuris* sp. is direct, and like horse ascarids the egg is the infective stage. It is infective 3 to 5 days after being laid, and is ingested by the horse with food or water. The parasite matures in the mucosa of the cecum, colon, and rectum and starts producing eggs in 120 to 150 days.

Because the females migrate out of the anus to lay eggs and then return to the colon, this disease causes an intense itching around the anus of horses. Owners will see horses rubbing their hind quarters, often resulting in all the hair being rubbed off over the tailhead.

It is common for these horses to become restless, go off feed, and lose condition. Sometimes young mares may appear to be in heat. Although adult female pinworms occasionally can be seen around the horse's anus, diagnosis is by finding the eggs, usually with a Scotch Tape swab.

Babesiasis. Equine piroplasmosis, or equine babesiasis, is a protozoan disease occuring in horses, mules, and donkeys in the southeastern part of the United States, particularly Florida and Georgia.

Two species of Babesia— *B. caballi* and *B. equi*—are known. These are small, protozoan parasites which occur in red blood cells. The life cycle is indirect; the tropical horse tick *(Dermacentor nitens)* serves as intermediate host. The brown dog tick *(Rhipicephulus sanguineus)* may be able to serve as an intermediate host for *B. equi*.

Equine babesiosis causes horses to have a fever, become listless and depressed. They may go off feed, and may develop central nervous system disturbances causing rear leg weakness or perhaps even paralysis. The limbs may become swollen ("stocked-up").

This disease usually lasts 8 to 10 days and can cause death, although most horses recover and return to normal.

Onchocerciasis

Onchocerca spp. are nematodes which occur as adults in connective tissue of horses, mules, and donkeys. This is a fairly common parasite; about three-quarters of horses surveyed in the Midwest were infected with *Onchocerca cervicalis.* Adult females are quite long, up to 30 cm in length, but the males are small, 6 to 7 mm long. The females of *Onchocerca cervicalis* occur in the ligamentum nuchae of horses and mules.

Onchocerca reticulata occurs in the flexor tendons and suspensory ligaments. This nematode also requires an intermediate host and uses midges *(Culicoides* sp.) as an arthropod vector. Biting midges pick up the microfilarie which occur in the skin of horses and these develop to an infective stage in the midge in about 3 weeks. When the midge takes a blood meal from a horse, the infective stage is injected—thus completing the cycle.

In addition to the dermatitis which this organism can cause, it sometimes causes eye problems. *O. reticulata* causes occasional lameness. *Onchocerca* spp. does not cause fistulous withers (Poll-evil) as formerly believed. Because the new parasiticide, Ivermectin, kills onchocerca microfilarie very quickly, horses sometimes mount an immune response to these dead microfilarie—resulting in tissue edema. This resolves spontaneously in about 7 days.

Eye Worm

The equine eye worm, *Thelazia lacrymalis,* is about ¾ of an inch long and lives in the tearduct and conjunctival sac of horse's eye. The female worms give rise to living larvae; they don't lay eggs. These L_1 larvae wander into the eye secretions and are picked up by face flies which serve as the intermediate host. In the fly the larvae develop into the infective stage and can be transferred to another host when the face fly feeds on eye secretions.

Although most eye worm infections go undetected, heavy infections cause mild eye irritation and can, on rare occasions, result in blindness, probably due to secondary bacterial infection.

Diagnosis is made by observing adult worms in the eye. Treatment is best achieved by removing the adults from the conjunctival sac under opthalmic anesthesia and tranquilization. Decreasing the prevalence of eye worms is best achieved by controlling face flies.

Sometimes the abdominal worm, *Setaria equina,* develops in the eye and causes damage. Normally these nematode parasites, which utilize mosquitoes as intermediate hosts, occur in the

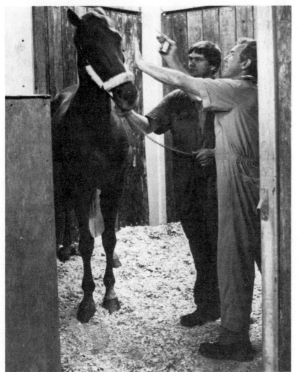

Horses with drooping ears which shake their heads a lot may have ear ticks. Several preparations are available for treatment.

Marie T. Sebrechts

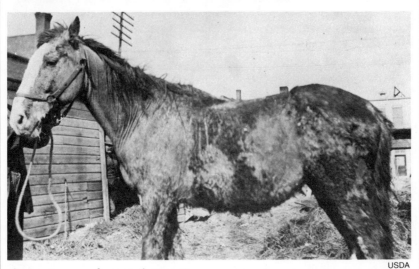

USDA

An acute case of sarcoptic mange.

Parasites

abdominal cavity and are of little or no consequence.

Ticks. There are three kinds of ticks which occur commonly on horses. Each has a preferred location on the horse. Sometimes they are more common in different parts of the country.

The winter tick, *Dermacentor albipictus,* has become widely distributed because horses now are commonly transported from one part of the country to another. Although this tick occurs primarily on the horse, it is found on other farm animals, such as cattle, sheep, and goats, so these animals can be involved in its spread.

Ticks differ one from another in that some utilize only one host as they develop from egg to larvae, nymphs, and adults, while other ticks utilize more than one host. The winter tick is one of the ticks which utilizes only one host; the entire life cycle takes place on the horse.

Tick infestations, like those of lice, are more common in the winter than in the warm seasons. Large numbers of winter ticks can cause horses to become weak, lose their appetite and become thin, and—because of the blood loss—sometimes develop an anemia which makes them more susceptible to other diseases. Ticks can cause death, especially in foals.

As its name implies, the Pacific coast tick, *Dermacentor occidentalis,* is found chiefly in coastal areas of the West. Unlike the winter tick, this tick drops off the host to lay its eggs and the larvae and nymphs feed on small mammals before becoming adults and parasitizing horses.

The Pacific coast tick can transmit diseases, such as Rocky Mountain spotted fever, Colorado tick fever, and other diseases affecting rabbits and cattle. It also can produce a condition called Tick Paralysis which can affect humans, dogs and calves. Consequently, horses should be inspected for ticks in areas where they occur after trail rides or cross-country pleasure rides.

The ear tick, *Otobius megnini,* like *Dermacentor albipictus* is a one-host tick. It is common on horses but is also found in the ears of cattle, sheep, dogs, cats, and occasionally people. These ticks do not occur on the horse as adults; only the larvae and nymphs are found in the ears.

Ear ticks on horses cause irritation as evidenced by excessive head tossing or rubbing of the ears. Horses with drooping ears and that shake their heads a lot may have ear ticks. Ear ticks also predispose to secondary bacterial infection of the middle and inner ear and can, consequently, cause serious problems. This tick, unlike Dermacentor, does not transmit any diseases. Several topical preparations are available for treating ear ticks.

Mange Mites

Mites are ectoparasites closely related to ticks and cause a skin condition called mange. The entire life cycle of mange mites occurs on the horse; mating occurs on the skin or in burrows which the mites make in the skin. The eggs hatch on the host after about 4 days and are mature, egg-laying adults 12 to 14 days later.

Sarcoptic mange (*Sarcoptes* sp.) causes lesions usually found on the neck, shoulders, head, chest, and flank of horses. These mites burrow under the skin and produce severe irritation and itching. In trying to relieve the source of itching, horses will bite and rub the affected area so the hair is lost and large scabby areas often result.

Chorioptic mange (*Chorioptes* sp.) produces lesions like Sarcoptic mange, but the mites occur more commonly on the lower extremities, and this mange often is called foot mange. Horses affected with these mites will paw, lick and bite at their lower legs in an attempt to relieve the itching.

Psoroptic mange occurs primarily on the poll or the tail. This mange mite (*Psoroptes* sp.) also causes intense itching, with hair loss and scabs if the horse traumatizes itself extensively.

Mange mites can live off the host for a short time and can be transferred from one host to another on combs, blankets, and so forth. In the past mange has been extremely difficult to control, but with the new Ivermectins mange should be less of a problem.

Chiggers and Lice

Chiggers affect horses in much the same way as they affect people. Chiggers are the larval stage of harvest mites (*Trombicula* sp.) and affect horses' feet and muzzles as they walk and feed on infested pastures.

Lice can be a very serious problem in horses. There are two kinds of lice: Biting lice (*Damalinia* sp.) which feed on skin and hair, and sucking lice (*Haematopinus* sp.) which pierce the skin and suck blood and tissue fluids.

As opposed to ticks and to some extent mites, lice are very host specific—they will not pass from horses to cows, sheep, goats, dogs and so forth.

Infestation with both sucking and biting lice can be debilitating to horses. Biting lice cause skin irritation and itching and horses will rub, bite and kick at themselves in an attempt to relieve the source of irritation. This results in a rough coat with loss of hair, and if serious enough, secondary bacterial infection can cause major skin lesions. In addition, heavy louse infections can produce serious unthriftiness and weight loss.

Sucking lice are perhaps more significant than biting lice. However, a heavy biting louse infestation can remove enough blood to cause a horse to become seriously anemic, in addition to producing irritation and debilitation because of itching.

Louse infestations usually are more severe in late winter and early spring. Frequent grooming and applications of topical pesticides are helpful in louse control.

Flying Insects
Although not permanently associated with their host like worms and mites are, flies, mosquitoes, gnats, and other flying insects are important to horse owners not only because of the worry and loss of condition, but also because some of these insects are vectors of disease.

Fly control depends to a great extent on sanitation, good grooming and common sense. Flies breed in manure and sometimes spilled grain, especially if it's wet. Removing spilled grain and manure from stalls on a regular basis, and changing bedding as it becomes soiled with feces and urine, will aid in fly control. As noted above, some flies serve as vectors of some helminths, in addition to viral diseases.

Mosquitoes, besides causing worry, transmit equine encephalomyelitis. Black flies and "no-see-ums" very often cause intense itching and attendant lesions in horses' ears, although they will bite other thin-skinned areas of the horse as well.

Bots are fly larvae which are parasites in the stomach of horses. *Gastrophilus intestinalis,* the common horse bot, and *G. nasalis,* the throat botfly, are the two common botflies found in this country.

Adult flies look somewhat like bees and are not seen often. These adult flies lay eggs on the hair of the legs or around the chin and throat of horses.

G. intestinalis lays its eggs on the forelegs and shoulders of horses. The eggs hatch when the horse licks itself—so the larvae quickly gain entrance to the horse's mouth. *G. nasalis* lays its eggs around the chin and throat and they hatch spontaneously; that is, the horse doesn't need to lick the eggs for them to hatch. *G. nasalis* eggs hatch and burrow under the horse's skin into the mouth.

Both species remain for about a month in the lining of the tongue and cheeks where they may cause severe ulcers around the teeth and cause horses to go off feed. After about a month the larvae are found in the stomach where they produce a condition called gastric myiasis. Although in small numbers bots cause virtually no clinical signs, in heavy infections there may be virtually no part of the horse's stomach wall which does not have a bot attached.

These botfly larvae are fairly large, about 2 cm long, and have large oral hooklets with which they attach to the stomach wall. Sometimes they completely penetrate the stomach wall, causing peritonitis and subsequent severe problems.

Significance of the adult flies is perhaps more profound than that of the larvae in that these flies seriously annoy horses when depositing their eggs on the legs and chin. Washing the legs and chins of horses with warm water containing an organophosphate insecticide every week during botfly season will aid greatly in control.

Warble flies which cause "cattle grub" can affect horses, but seldom are a problem except in cow ponies used to work range cattle.

Drug Resistance

Drugs used to treat worms in horses are called anthelmintics. Many anthelmintics introduced over the last several years are benzimidazole analogs to which nematode parasites are starting to develop resistance.

Resistance develops when a wormer does not kill a certain population of the worms which survive to contaminate pastures. Over time, pastures are contaminated with a high proportion of larvae that, when eaten, will develop into adults able to tolerate doses of anthelmintics normally administered.

Before concluding that

Parasites

lack of response is due to benzimidazole resistance, note that there may be other reasons why horses have eggs in their feces after worming. Among them might be a low plane of nutrition, rapid reinfection, inappropriate anthelmintic or an inappropriate dose, faulty administration, or use of an anthelmintic which does not affect the developing larvae.

There are two schools of thought now on how best to overcome the anthelmintic resistance problem. One is to use a given class of anthelmintic—for instance a benzimidazole—for a year, and then use a different compound—such as pyrantel, an organic phosphate, or Ivermectin—for a year. It should be noted that by simply changing from one benzimidazole to another is not changing anthelmintics.

Another school of thought says it's best to change classes of anthelmintics each time horses are wormed.

A prime objective of any strongyle control program should be to keep pasture contamination of larvae to a minimum. The worming protocol needed to accomplish this objective will depend on worm burden, stocking rate, and climatic condition, and so will vary from farm to farm. The horse owner with 50 acres to support two horses will have far fewer problems than one who is trying to keep two horses on two acres.

Further Reading

Principal Parasites of Domestic Animals in the United States. Biological and Diagnostic Information. Special Publication 52. V.R. Ivens, D.L. Mark and N.D. Levine. College of Agriculture and Veterinary Medicine, University of Illinois at Urbana-Champagne, Urbana, IL. 61001. $10.

Parasitology for Veterinarians. 3rd Edition. J.R. Georgi. W.B. Saunders Company, 210 West Washington Square, Philadelphia, PA 19105. $35.

Horses

Nutrition

By Harold F. Hintz

Proper nutrition is essential for the health of horses. Deficient or imbalanced rations or poor feeding management can cause deficiency diseases, decreased resistance to infectious diseases, predisposition to lameness, decreased performance, and digestive problems such as colic and enterotoxemia.

Digestion—the process which releases nutrients from feeds for use by the body—begins in the mouth where food is ground and mixed with saliva. Proper dental care such as floating of teeth is necessary so food is chewed properly. Food then travels to the stomach where the chemical breakdown starts.

The horse's stomach is relatively small and horses

seldom vomit. Overfeeding can cause distention of the stomach and signs of colic (a general name for abdominal pain). Horses fed large amounts of grain should be fed two or more times daily, to reduce the incidence of colic.

The small intestine is a major site of digestion and absorption of many nutrients. Good parasite control is necessary for optimum function of the small intestine. Parasites not only reduce feed utilization, but can cause colic.

The large intestine consists of the cecum and colon. It has a large population of micro-organisms (bacteria and protozoa) which digest the fiber in plant materials. If feed changes are made rapidly, the micro-organisms do not have time to adapt. Excessive gas production, colic, and diarrhea may result; so make changes gradually. A change period of 10 days is best, but 5 may suffice.

Harold F. Hintz is Professor of Animal Nutrition, New York State College of Veterinary Medicine, Cornell University, Ithaca.

Nutrition

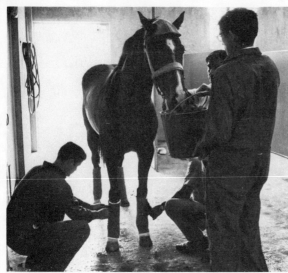

A hard-working race horse may require more grain than average to meet its energy requirements.

USDA

Nutrient Guidelines

The horse requires energy, protein, vitamins, minerals, and water. Overfeeding and underfeeding of energy are two of the most common feeding mistakes. Forages—such as hay and pasture—and grains are the most frequent sources of energy.

Grains usually contain 40 to 60 percent more energy per pound of dry matter than do forages. But forages may contain adequate concentrations of energy to supply the energy needs of some classes of horses.

A non-pregnant, non-lactating mature horse that is not working hard could maintain body weight if fed 1½ to 2 lbs of hay per 100 lbs of

body weight. A pregnant mare (last third of gestation) may require some grain, perhaps ¼ to ¾ lb per 100 lbs of body weight in addition to hay. The intake of hay may also slightly decrease because the fetus fills up some of the body cavity. But some pregnant mares can obtain all the energy needed from good quality hay.

The amount of energy required by the lactating mare depends on the amount of milk she is producing. An average mare may require ¾ to 1 lb of grain per 100 lbs of body weight in addition to hay or pasture.

A hard working horse such as a racehorse at the track may need 1½ lbs of grain and 1½ lbs of hay per 100 lbs of body weight. Rapidly growing foals may eat ¾ lb of hay and 1½ lbs of grain per 100 lbs of body weight.

The above guidelines are only rough estimates. There is considerable variation in energy metabolism among horses. The energy content among hays varies greatly. Energy requirements differ according to environmental temperature.

The eye of the feeder is important. If the horses are too fat, decrease the amount of grain; if too thin, feed more grain.

Keeping records of body weight obtained from scales or by estimating with tapes around the heart girth can be very useful when evaluating a feeding program.

Protein is needed for maintenance and for production of new tissue. A deficiency of protein decreases rate of gain, causes a rough hair coat, and decreases appetite.

The young horse requires the greatest concentration of protein in the ration. The National Research Council recommends that horses weaned at 3 months of age be fed diets containing at least 16 percent protein and horses weaned at 6 months need 14.5 percent.

Calcium and Phosphorus Requirements[a] of Horses

	Ca	P
	Percent	Percent
Maintenance	.3	.2
Pregnant or lactating mare	.45	.3
Weanlings	.7	.5
Yearlings	.5	.35

[a]Percent of air dry feed

Mature horses at maintenance need only 8 percent protein. Pregnant or lactating mares need 11 to 12.5 percent protein. Work does not greatly increase the protein requirement.

Proteins are composed of smaller units called amino acids. Feed protein is digested in the intestine, and the amino acids are absorbed and used to form protein in the animal's body. Feed proteins that contain a good mixture of amino acids are called "high quality" proteins, those with a poor mixture are called "low quality" proteins.

Soybean meal is a reasonable source of amino acids for horses. Other vegetable protein sources such as cottonseed meal and linseed meal contain a lower concentration of the amino acid lysine than that found in soybean meal.

Horses: Requirements, Functions, and Deficiency Signs of Some Minerals

Mineral (Requirement)	Some functions	Some deficiency signs
Calcium (see first table)	Bone mineral; blood clotting; nerve, muscle, and gland function	Rickets, osteomalacia, NSH, osteoporosis, bones may be soft and easily deformed or broken
Phosphorus (see first table)	Bone mineral, part of many proteins involved in metabolism	Bone disease, decreased growth, reproductive problems, low blood phosphorus
Iron (50 mg/kg)[a]	Part of hemoglobin and some enzymes, oxygen transport	Anemia: lack of stamina, poor growth
Copper (9 mg/kg)	Iron absorption, hemoglobin synthesis, skin pigments, collagen metabolism	Anemia; hair pigment loss; bone disease: swollen joints, deformed thin bones
Magnesium (.1%)	Bone mineral, enzyme activator: energy metabolism	Nervousness, muscle tremors, ataxia, convulsions, mineralization of blood vessels, low serum magnesium
Sodium, potassium, and chloride	Tissue fluid pressure and acid-base balance, passage of nutrients and water into cells, nerve and muscle function	Craving for salt, hyperexcitability, decreased growth rate, loss of appetite
Zinc (36 mg/kg)	Activator of many enzymes	Hair loss, scaly skin, poor wound healing; reproductive, behavioral, and skeletal abnormalities

Iodine (.1 mg/kg)	Thyroid function	Goiter, poor growth, low body temperature, impaired development of hair and skin, foals weak at birth
Manganese (36 mg/kg)	Synthesis of bone and cartilage components, cholesterol metabolism	Reproductive problems: delayed estrus, reduced fertility, spontaneous abortion, skeletal deformities in the newborn
Selenium (.1 mg/kg)	Removal of peroxides from tissues, enzyme activation	White muscle disease, low serum selenium and serum glutathione peroxidase concentration

[a]Units per kg of air dry feed

Minerals are required for many functions. Two minerals that are required in greatest amounts are calcium and phosphorus. One of their primary functions is the formation of bone, but they have many other important roles.

An excess of phosphorus decreases calcium utilization and may result in nutritional secondary hyperparathyroidism (NSH) if the diet has a low level of calcium. Horses with NSH have weak bones, become lame, and may have an enlarged head because of invasion of fibrous connective tissue.

Legume hays may contain 1 to 1.5 percent calcium, but grass hay may contain only .3 to .4 percent calcium. Grains contain almost no calcium.

Limestone is an excellent source of calcium for horses. Dicalcium phosphate contains calcium and phosphorus.

Vitamins are also required for many functions. Good quality forage is an excellent source of many vitamins. Excess vitamin A and vitamin D can be toxic.

Water is frequently neglected. Clean, fresh water should be provided.

Nutrition

Horses: Requirements, Functions, and Deficiency Signs of Some Vitamins

Vitamins	Some functions	Some deficiency signs
Vitamin A (2,000 IU/kg)[a]	Growth and development of bone and epithelial cells, vision	Night blindness; poor conception rate, abortion, loss of libido, testicular degeneration; convulsions, elevated cerebrospinal fluid pressure
Vitamin D (250 IU/kg)	Absorption of dietary calcium and phosphorus	Poor mineralization of bone, bone deformities
Vitamin E (15 IU/kg)	Antioxidant in tissues	Decreased serum tocopherol, increased red blood cell fragility; muscular dystrophy
Thiamin (3 mg/kg)	Coenzyme in energy metabolism	Loss of appetite and weight; incoordination, muscular weakness and twitching
Riboflavin (2 mg/kg)	Coenzyme in many enzyme systems	Conjunctivitis, lacrimation, aversion to bright light

[a]Units per kg of air dry feed

Further Reading

Horse Feeding and Nutrition. T.J. Cunha. Academic Press, Inc., Order Department, Orlando, FL 32887-0015. $33.00.

Horse Nutrition: A Practical Guide. H.F. Hintz. Arco Publishing Co., 215 Park Avenue, South, New York, NY 10003. $15.95.

Feeding and Care of the Horse. L.D. Lewis. Lea and Febiger, Merchandising Department, 600 South Washington Square, Philadelphia, Pa. 19106-4198. $16.00.

Nutrient Requirements of Horses. National Research Council Press, 2101 Constitution Avenue, N.W., Washington, DC 20418. $5.95.

Horse Farm Hazards

By Robert H. Singer

There are many potential hazards horses may be exposed to that can cause severe injury or death. They include common materials and chemicals found on most horse farms, electrical outlets and wiring, and conditions predisposing to heat stroke.

Common chemicals present on horse farms and in stables that can be injurious or cause poisoning include disinfectants, cleansers, soaps, detergents, bleaches, tars, rat poisons, organic insecticides, fertilizers, petroleum products, antifreezes and paints.

Many disinfectants contain phenols (carbolic acid), cresols and pine oil, each of which is quite poisonous. They usually are provided as a concentrate to be diluted with water before use. Phenols and

---

Robert H. Singer is a Veterinary Toxicologist in Winchester, Ky.

cresols are very injurious to all tissues and will cause severe burns to the skin as well as linings of the mouth, stomach and intestines.

Phenols and cresols also are quite volatile. Their fumes irritate the eyes and can be absorbed through the skin, causing poisoning. Around animal quarters they should be used only in a diluted form as directed and in well-ventilated areas.

Cleansers, Bleaches

Liquid cleansers vary in composition. Many contain pine oil, organic solvents and petroleum distillates, all of which are poisonous if consumed.

Bleaches contain sodium hypochlorite which yields chlorine in solution and if consumed will cause considerable irritation to the gastrointestinal tract, resulting in abdominal distress or colic. Soaps and detergents also can

Horse Farm Hazards

irritate the gastrointestinal tract, and may cause severe colic if consumed.

The main hazard is permitting buckets or other containers filled with soap suds, cleansing solutions and disinfectant solutions to sit around a stable after use where horses may have access to them or someone inadvertently permits the animal to drink from them. Buckets and containers used for washing and cleansing should be emptied and rinsed well immediately after use to prevent possible accidents of this kind.

Tar Dangers

Various tars contain chemical agents that are quite poisonous if consumed by animals, or in some cases if animals are exposed to heavy concentrations of fumes emitted from them.

Coal, wood and petroleum tars have varying concentrations of different phenols as well as numerous chemical residues. As stated during the discussion of disinfectants, phenols and their fumes are quite poisonous, very injurious to all tissues, cause severe burns, and can be absorbed directly through the skin.

Some tars contain a considerable amount of lead and have been responsible for cases of lead poisoning in horses, as well as other species. They also may have high concentrations of chromium salts which also can cause poisoning.

Coal, wood and petroleum tars often are used on farms and in stables. As wood preservatives they prevent wood rot and insect damage for fencing and wooden structures. Because of their disinfecting and insect-deterring qualities they are used to treat wood on the interior of stables.

Freshly treated fencing and wooden structures are especially hazardous because some animals will lick the wet surfaces, causing severe mouth burns, and possible colic and phenolic poisoning if swallowed. Also, the fresh tar will burn the skin if animals rub against the treated surfaces.

If tars containing phenols are applied on the interior of a stable, even though the area to which the tar has been applied is not accessible to the horses, the fumes can burn them and cause poisoning— especially on hot days and in poorly ventilated barns.

Tars are applied to utility poles of power lines that may pass through fields used to pasture horses. These tars may contain aniline and its derivatives that are also poisonous to horses. Animals should be kept out of the pasture until application of the tar is completed, debris and tar droppings around the poles are cleaned up, and the tar has dried to have a tough skin before permitting animals near them. It is best to place a guard fence around each pole to be sure the horses will not chew the material. A small mouthful can cause severe colic.

Where farm buildings are treated with roofing tar, the tar that often drips from the roof's edge to the ground into the barnlot area has been the source of poisoning in animals, causing severe colic and in some cases death. The same is true of paving tars that are used near barnlots and on entries into paddocks.

Fertilizers

Inorganic fertilizers should be regarded as quite poisonous to horses because of concentrations of various ingredients— such as nitrates, ammonium salts, potash and phosphates— which can cause poisoning. The raw fertilizer in small quantities can cause severe colic.

Freshly fertilized pastures should not be used for grazing until the fertilizer has worked into the ground, or until after the first rain. Also, be sure that small piles of fertilizer are not left exposed in the pasture.

Bags of fertilizer should never be stored in the feed bin, on top of grain or hay. Leakage of the fertilizer onto the feed, grain or hay has led to severe poisoning of animals when fed the contaminated feedstuff.

Miscellaneous Products

Buckets which contain petroleum products such as crankcase oil, gasoline or distillates used for cleaning machine parts should never be permitted where animals can possibly consume them. These products are poisonous if animals drink them. The same is true of antifreeze such as ethylene glycol which has a sweet flavor to it. Many animals, including horses, have died from the poisonous effects of ethylene glycol by drinking it from buckets used to drain auto cooling systems.

Paints in the liquid state are poisonous and should be handled with care around horses and other animals.

Oil base paints contain drying oils and thinners that can severely irritate the gastrointestinal tract and may

USDA-APHIS
Marie T. Sebrechts

A number of chemical products, including disinfectants, pesticides and paints are regularly used on the farm. It's important to use them as directed and to clean up immediately after use. A curious horse could drink sudsy water from a pail, so don't leave it unattended , or nibble on a fence post, so move horses to another pasture when you paint fences or treat posts .

cause systemic poisoning if enough has been consumed. Toxicity of the pigments depends upon the type of pigment.

Lead base paints should never be used on buildings or fences of any animal farm.

When buildings or fences are being painted, animals should be removed from the painting area until the paint has dried, any spillage has been cleaned up, and paint buckets and equipment removed.

Lead base paints are no longer supposed to be available; however, many farm buildings and fences still have such paints on them from past applications. In many areas these buildings and fences never seemed to be a poisoning problem. In other areas horses chewed on them and consumed enough of the lead paint to cause poisoning.

Occasional chewing by an occasional horse is not an uncommon thing; however, excessive chewing by a number of horses indicates they are trying to fulfill a nutritional requirement.

Bedding. Sawdust and wood shavings are being used as bedding for stalls on a number of horse farms. It is essential to know the type of wood from which they are derived.

Severe laminitis (founder) has resulted in horses where black walnut shavings were being used for bedding. Black walnut (*Juglans nigra*) wood contains a number of aromatic chemical agents, some of which are quite toxic to horses. Eating a few of the fresh shavings will cause severe gastrointestinal irritation and severe founder.

Fumes from the shavings in a stall with poor ventilation also may be responsible for the poisoning condition.

Rat and mice poisons are used around many stables. They should never be placed where other animals may consume them, and certainly

never around the hay or in the feed bin. Even the less poisonous coumarin derivatives are poisonous to species other than rats and mice and should never be used in a careless manner.

Insecticides

Organic insecticides have been in wide use for years for control of insects in farm crops and treatment of animals for lice and other ectoparasites. The treatment of horses for lice, mange mites or other ectoparasites with organic insecticides should be conducted under the advice of a veterinarian.

The organic insecticides are classified as organochlorine insecticides, organophosphates, and carbamates. Many of the organochlorine types no longer are available because of governmental restrictions. Some organochlorine insecticides are known under the names of DDT, DDD, Aldrin, Dieldrin, Endrin, Toxaphene, Benzene hexachloride, Lindane and Methoxychlor.

Toxicity of the organochlorine insecticides varies; however, poisoning by them generally causes central nervous system symptoms.

Organophosphate insecticides are known under the names of Parathion, Malathion, Diazinon, Dimethoate, Trichlorfon, Ronnel, Ruelene, Dichlorvos and Coumaphos, to name a few. The insecticides vary considerably in their toxicity and for the most part break down in the animal body or plant material and in the soil into harmless products after a few days.

The organophosphates are referred to as nerve poisons because one of their effects is inhibiting the activity of an enzyme called cholinesterase.

Horses exposed to an organophosphate or organothiophosphate may not show any of the symptoms of cholinesterase inhibition; however, the cholinesterase that has been inhibited is not restored to its normal level for several days. Exposure to the same or any other cholinesterase inhibitor within a few days after the initial exposure may cause severe cholinesterase inhibition, symptoms of poisoning, and possible death. Such exposure must be prevented.

Some worm remedies for horses contain organophosphates, such as Trichlorfon and Dichlorvos, that have the same action and must not be used for some time following the exposure to a cholinesterase inhibitor.

Of the carbamates, carbaryl commonly known as

Sevin is used as an insecticide. A number of other carbamates have insecticidal properties but also are used as fungicides. The carbamates too are cholinesterase inhibitors; however, their toxicity is relatively low in comparison to the organophosphates.

Pasture Use. Many organophosphates and carbamates are used as insecticides and for fungus control on a variety of crops. They also are occasionally used to control insects in pastures. Horses and other animals should not be placed in a pasture treated with an organophosphate or carbamate for at least 10 days, and preferably not until after the pasture has a rainfall.

A number of cases of illness in horses have occurred while being pastured in fields adjacent to crop fields, orchards and citrus groves following the spraying of the crops, orchards and groves with insecticides and carbamate fungicides.

Spray residues from the sprayed fields were carried into the adjoining pasture. In most cases, sufficient residue had not been carried into the pasture with the horses to cause frank poisoning; however, high incidences of severe colic with some deaths were experienced. They were thought to be caused by irritation from some of the residues to the gastrointestinal tract.

Whenever pesticides are being sprayed on crops, orchards and groves adjacent to a pasture, horses and other animals should be removed from the pasture until it is known that the residue has decomposed into harmless products and rain has washed it from the pasture grasses.

Electrical Problems

There are a number of cases of accidental electrocution of horses as well as other species every year. These accidents usually occur as the result of careless installation of electrical wiring in the barn and in the barnyard, in easy reach of the animals where they can chew on the wiring.

Electrocution has occurred around water troughs where the water is pumped to the trough using an improperly grounded electric motor to drive the pump.

In other cases stray electricity from the electrical system of the motor or wiring follows the pipes to the trough. The amount of electric current may be quite small but sensed by the horses, so that they refuse to drink from the trough. If another water supply is not available, they become dehydrated.

Heat stroke is not as common today as it was when horses were used for work before the use of machinery. Yet heat stroke does occur in horses during the hot summer months in the heat of the day. It is caused by overexertion on a hot, humid day; by confinement to a poorly ventilated stall on such a day when the stall temperature may be high; by transportation in vans on hot, humid days; and on exercisers that are not shaded from the hot sun. Most susceptible are horses that have been idle and are not conditioned to the work or the climate. Also, a lack of adequate water can predispose to heat stroke.

Veterinary assistance is required immediately in cases of heatstroke. However, first aid measures should be instituted right away, consisting of ice packs on the head between the ears and cold cloth packs along the spinal column.

If ice packs are not available, cloth sacks saturated with cold water should be directed over the head and down the spinal column. The veterinarian will provide other cooling methods and supportive treatment.

Pediatrics

By H. Steve Conboy

Pediatrics is the branch of equine medicine that deals with health of the foal from birth until weaning. To successfully raise a foal, it is essential to have a basic knowledge of the normal anatomy, physiology and behavior of the foal. It also helps to understand the terminology that describes both normal and abnormal conditions that affect foals. In most cases the diagnosis and treatment of foal diseases is best done by the veterinarian but the horse owner needs to recognize early signs of illness in order to know when to call the vet.

Unlike the newborn human, a foal is born without protective antibodies in its circulation. The foal must acquire passive immunity to disease by absorbing antibodies

---

H. Steve Conboy is Director of Veterinary Services for Castleton Farms, Lexington, Ky.

from the mare's first milk, colostrum, by way of the digestive system. The reason for this is that the equine placenta will not permit the passage of antibodies from the mare's circulation to the fetal circulation.

Passive transfer of antibodies to the foal occurs during the first 24 to 48 hours following the foal's birth. After this time the colostral antibodies diminish significantly, as does the foal's ability to absorb them.

It is easy to understand why it is so important for the newborn to receive the antibody-rich colostrum soon after birth. Veterinarians and horse owners have learned to take advantage of this mechanism of passive transfer by boosting the mare's antibody titers with certain vaccines a month before foaling to provide an adequate supply of antibodies in the mare's colostrum.

Following a foal's birth,

treat the navel stump with an antiseptic (a 50–50 mixture of strong iodine and glycerine is excellent). The stump should be treated by dipping it in this mixture once a day for a minimum of 5 days to prevent infection and to encourage proper drying of the navel cord stump.

The neonate (newborn) foal should be very active shortly after birth and will struggle about the stall before it is able to stand, which usually takes 30 minutes to an hour. After the foal is on its feet, it should begin looking for the mare's udder to nurse. It is not uncommon for the foal to make attempts at nursing the mare's flank or leg before it actually finds the teats. In most cases, the foal will have nursed in 2 to 3 hours after birth.

A veterinarian should examine the newborn foal to check its state of health and recommend any special care or treatment needed.

Abnormalities, Illness
Musculoskeletal abnormalities are very common in newborn foals. Some require immediate therapy, others only need observation as they will correct spontaneously with time. Foals that have severely contracted tendons and scoliosis

(lateral curvature) of the spine—contracted foal syndrome—respond very poorly to therapy and generally require euthanasia. Mildly contracted tendons without skeletal defects respond to casting or splinting. Foals born with very weak tendons that allow hyperextension of the ankle and carpal joints improve dramatically with controlled exercise.

Umbilical and scrotal hernias occur frequently and do not usually require immediate attention. Most of these hernias will disappear as the foal develops. If they persist at weaning age, surgical correction may be required.

As mentioned earlier, it is important to recognize the symptoms of a sick foal so proper therapy can be started. Usually the first sign of any illness in the foal is its failure to nurse, which is indicated by the mare's udder being full and distended. When this is observed, the foal's temperature should be recorded with a rectal thermometer. The foal's normal temperature is 99.4° to 101.5° F.

A foal with a significant fever usually will be depressed and inactive. A healthy foal generally will jump to its feet when approached. The normal foal's

Pediatrics

respiration is usually rhythmic and thoracic. Panting, pumping or breathing abdominally is abnormal unless the foal has been running. Following are brief descriptions of several diseases and conditions that affect foals.

Rhinopneumonitis. Occasionally a foal will be born to a mare that experienced equine herpes virus-I during pregnancy. Usually the fetus will be aborted during the later part of pregnancy but when the fetus is carried to term, it is born very weak and is unable to stand or nurse. Despite the most diligent care, these foals fail to survive more than 24 to 48 hours. There are several vaccines that prevent this disease but they must be given during the mare's pregnancy.

Sleeper or Septic Foal. This condition is seen in the neonate and is caused by a bacterial septicemia. The foal is lethargic, reluctant to nurse, and has a moderate fever. Aggressive antibiotic therapy and intensive nursing care is required in treating this condition. The prognosis is guarded but treatment is often successful.

Neonatal Isoerythrolysis, a condition often referred to as the jaundice foal syndrome, occurs when the mare develops antibodies against the foal's red blood cells (RBC's) and the foal is allowed to nurse the mare's colostrum.

Symptoms include jaundiced (yellow) mucous membranes and sclera (white of the eye), listlessness, yawning, accelerated heart rate and respiration, weakness, and occasional red urine. The primary clinical symptoms are anemia and jaundiced plasma.

In the very acute form, the foal may be found dead several hours after a normal birth. In the less acute form, the physical symptoms usually are noticed during the first 2 to 4 days after birth.

This condition can be prevented by not allowing the foal to nurse the mare's colostrum when it contains RBC antibodies.

There are several ways to identify these antibodies. The most reliable is to blood type the mare and stallion prior to the birth to reveal any potential incompatibility, and then to screen the mare's serum for RBC antibodies shortly before foaling. Another method tests the mare's colostrum with the foal's RBC's to identify the presence of RBC antibodies.

Treatment for this condition often requires a blood transfusion to replace the foal's damaged RBC's.

David F. Berna, USDA-SCS

A foal is born without protective antibodies in its blood. A mare's first milk, colostrum carries with it antibodies which protect the foal by passive immunity to disease before the foal begins producing its own antibodies.

Ruptured urinary bladder is a condition seen on the third to fifth day after birth. The foal usually is colicky and reluctant to nurse. The abdomen generally appears pendulous and distended. The only treatment for this condition is surgical repair of the bladder. When diagnosed early, the prognosis is good for complete recovery.

Meconial Impaction. The neonate frequently is plagued with severe constipation caused by dry fecal balls that become lodged in the rectum and small colon. This condition causes the foal to strain in an effort to defecate, with negative results. As the condition progresses, the foal will show signs of abdominal pain by getting up and down.

Digital palpation of the rectum will usually reveal hard large fecal balls. Treatment consists of soapy water enemas and intestinal lubricants until the fecal balls are softened and passed.

Patent Urachus. The umbilical stump contains the urachus (the urinary canal of the fetus) that was responsible for transferring urine from the fetal bladder to the placenta. Very soon after birth, it seals and is no longer functional. If it fails to seal, urine will continue to leak from the bladder. Usually the condition is corrected by dipping the cord daily in an iodine anti-

Pediatrics

septic. If this therapy fails to seal the canal, the opening can be cauterized with silver nitrate or phenol. It usually is not advisable to clamp or ligate the stump.

Omphalitis. When bacteria invade the umbilical cord, an abscess occasionally develops creating a lemon-size swelling in the umbilical area. This is not to be confused with an umbilical hernia that is soft and easily pushed into the abdomen. Infection of the umbilical cord is very serious and demands antibiotic therapy. Failure to treat this condition properly can lead to more serious systemic infections.

Septic arthritis occurs when bacteria invade a joint and establish infection. Cause of this disease usually is a combination of the foal's failure to receive adequate antibodies from the colostrum and a bacterial invasion via the umbilicus. However, the bacteria can also invade through other routes such as the respiratory system.

Clinical symptoms are a painful, hot, swollen joint. This condition requires immediate veterinary attention that will include culturing of the joint, systemic antibiotic therapy, and lavage of the affected joint. Many cases respond rapidly to this therapy

but others fail to respond and eventually are euthanized. Septic arthritis usually is seen during the first 3 months after birth.

Neonatal Maladjustment Syndrome is a noninfectious condition of foals that is seen shortly after birth. Usually there is a history of a normal delivery and an uneventful first 12 hours, but soon thereafter the foal appears hyperactive, runs about the stall, wants to nurse but cannot, and in the most severe cases develops convulsions. In most cases, respiration is very rapid and there is a moderate to high fever.

This is a stress-related disease caused by edema and hemorrhage of the brain. The syndrome requires intensive medication as well as dedicated nursing care for several days. The prognosis always is guarded but many cases respond to therapy.

Diarrhea

Causes of foal diarrhea are numerous but very seldom is it related to bacterial infection. Therefore it becomes very important to know that antibiotic therapy usually is not indicated in treating diarrhea. In fact, intensive antibiotic therapy frequently causes diarrhea as it destroys the intestinal microflora that aid digestion. In most cases, ensuring that adequate fluids are consumed is all that is necessary.

Commonly the foal stops nursing when diarrhea occurs. This is beneficial in that milk may contribute to diarrhea during intestinal upsets. When this does occur, it may be necessary to force-feed fluids and electrolytes to maintain hydration.

Common causes of foal diarrhea follow:

1) Fetal or neonatal diarrhea. Foals with this condition are born weak and usually have a diarrhea stained placenta. An intrauterine bacterial enteritis is the cause and in this case antibiotics are indicated. The prognosis is guarded when the foal is extremely weak. If the foal is able to stand and nurse, the survival rate is good.

2) Foal heat diarrhea. Most foals experience diarrhea during the mare's first heat period around the 8th to 10th day after birth. Therapy usually is not indicated as the diarrhea generally ceases in 4 to 5 days. The cause for this phenomenon is unknown.

3) Parasitic diarrhea. Several parasites will cause diarrhea. *Strongyloides westeria,*

the "milk worm," passes to the foal via the mare's milk—causing diarrhea during the first month of age. The parasite eggs are easily seen on fecal exam and the parasite responds to most vermifuges.

Heavy infestations of large strongyles (blood worms) cause diarrhea and severe enteritis at about 6 to 8 months of age. Other symptoms are fever, anorexia, depression, and colic. These cases respond to larvacidal (high) doses of thiabendazole or to Ivermectin. Ascarids, the large roundworm, also will cause diarrhea around the third or fourth month. These parasites respond to piperazine.

4) Viral diarrhea. Rotovirus is the most common viral infection causing diarrhea. It occurs in very young (1 week old) to older foals (3 months old). This diarrhea can be mild to very severe. Therapy is limited to fluid replacement and intestinal protectants such as bismuth subsalicylate. Use of antibiotics is not advisable because generally the animal recovers without further treatment.

5) Bacterial diarrhea. The bacteria that cause diarrhea are *E. coli, Klebsiella, Salmonella, clostridium perfringens* and *equi.* These are not com-

monly the cause of diarrhea and require fecal cultures for proper diagnosis. When it has been determined that a bacterial infection is causing the diarrhea, the proper antibiotic should be administered. Fluid therapy and good nursing usually are required.

Gastric and Duodenal Ulcers. This syndrome usually follows a period of stress such as diarrhea or prolonged illness. When the condition occurs suddenly, the foal may be found dead or in deep shock. That occurs when the ulcer has perforated, causing peritonitis. There is no treatment in this case.

When the disease occurs over a short period of time, the foal shows signs of severe abdominal pain by grinding the teeth, rolling on its back, and frequent dipping into the water bucket without drinking. Therapy consists of antiacids, and gastric acid suppressors. The prognosis is guarded in these cases. Successful therapy usually requires at least a month.

Pneumonia is a serious illness in the foal that can be caused by bacterial or viral infection as well as by mechanical agents such as deworming medication, mineral oil, milk or other liquids given orally.

The clinical symptoms include labored breathing, fever, cough, depression, and failure to nurse. Examination and treatment by a veterinarian is indicated when any of these symptoms appear. Antibiotic therapy and good nursing care are essential. The prognosis is guarded to good in most cases.

Shaker Foal Syndrome is thought to be caused by the bacteria *Clostridium botulinum* type B. This syndrome frequently occurs in Central Kentucky but only occasionally is diagnosed in other areas. The symptoms are most commonly seen around 21 days of age. It does, however, occur in older foals.

Typical symptoms include a trembling or shivering convulsion followed by involuntary collapsing to the ground. These convulsions occur at regular intervals with gradually increasing frequency until death occurs in 1 to 2 days.

Therapy includes the use of antitoxin and antibiotics, and intense nursing care. The prognosis is grave but some cases do survive. Use of antitoxin has recently increased the success rate. Vaccination of the pregnant mare appears to prevent this syndrome from occurring in the foal.

X. TABLES AND GLOSSARY

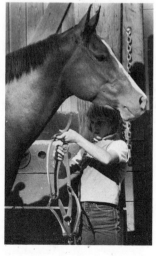

Common Names for Animals

By Larry D. Mark and Edward L. Menning

Would you be startled if you met a clowder of cats? Perhaps apprehensive if you encountered a sleuth of bears? What about a gaggle of geese? And, speaking of geese, if "what's sauce for the goose is sauce for the gander" here in the United States, would you say "what's sauce for the flyer is sauce for the boomer" in Australia?

What do all these strange words mean? Well, "clowder," "sleuth" and "gaggle" each refers to the name used for a group of that kind of animal. And "flyer" and "boomer" are the special names for the female and male kangaroo. All are terms we use for our animals.

Larry D. Mark is Public Affairs Officer, Animal and Plant Health Inspection Service. Edward L. Menning is Executive Vice President, National Association of Federal Veterinarians. They compiled this entire section.

Humans, through the ages, have developed a special bond with their animals. In many instances, particular and separate names have evolved for each sex, the young, and for that most magical time of all—giving birth.

Animal terms and characteristics color our language. He's chicken and she's pigheaded, so where's the beef? She's catty, she's kittenish, she's just a pussycat. He's a bull in a china shop, he's lionhearted, but sometimes a turkey. She's a silly goose and he's a funny bird, but they're making calf eyes at each other, so it must be puppy love. Well, it's a dog's life . . . frankly, we're kind of sheepish about the whole thing.

The tables and glossary are presented with the hope that you may learn something new and interesting, and have in one place some useful information on different kinds of animals and their lives.

Tables and Glossary

Common Names for the Sexes, Young, Groups and Birthing of Various Animals

Animal	Male	Female	Young	Group	Name for giving birth
Antelope	buck	doe	kid	herd	kidding
Bear	boar	sow	cub	sleuth	cubbing
Beaver	boar	sow	pup	colony	—
Bird	cock/stag	hen	fledgling/ nestling	flock	hatch
Bison	bull	cow	calf	herd	calve
Bobcat	tom	lioness/queen	kitten	litter	—
Cat	tom	pussy/queen	kitten	clowder	queening
Cattle	bull	cow/heifer	calf	herd/drove	calve
Chicken	rooster/cock	hen/pullet	chick	flock	hatch
Deer	buck/stag	doe	fawn	herd	—
Dog	dog	bitch	pup/puppy	kennel	whelp
Donkey	jackass	jennet/ jenneyass	colt	herd	foal
Duck	drake	duck	duckling	flock	hatch
Elephant	bull	cow	calf	herd	calve
Fox	reynard	vixen	cub/pup	earth/skulk	pupping
Giraffe	bull	cow	calf	herd	calve
Goat	billy/buck	nanny	kid	trip	kidding
Goose	gander	goose	gosling	gaggle/flock	hatch
Hog	boar	sow/gilt	piglet/shoat	herd/drove	farrow
Horse	stallion/stud	mare/dam	foal colt (male) filly (female)	stable/herd	foal
Kangaroo	buck/boomer	doe/flyer	joey	troop/herd	—
Lion	lion/tom	lioness/she lion	cub	pride/flock	whelp
Ostrich	cock	hen	chick	flock	hatch
Owl	owl	jenny/ howlet	howlet/owlet	flock	—
Ox	steer	cow	stot	herd/drove	calve
Rabbit	buck	doe	kitten	colony	—
Rat	buck	doe	—	colony	—
Seal	bull	cow	pup	herd/harem/ rookery	—
Sheep	buck/ram	ewe/dam	lamb/ lambkin	flock/hurtle	lamb
Swine — see hog					
Turkey	tom	hen	poult	flock	hatch
Walrus	bull	cow	cub	herd	—
Whale	bull	cow	calf/cub/pup	herd/pod	pupping
Wolf	he-wolf	she-wolf	cub/pup	pack	whelp
Zebra	stallion	mare	colt	herd	foal

Table of Norms

Features of the Reproductive Cycle (Pets)*

	Cats	Dogs	Guinea pigs	Hamsters	Mice	Rabbits
Age at puberty	6–15 months	6–12 months**	55–70 days	5–8 weeks	35 days	5½–8½ months
Cycle type	Provoked ovulation, seasonally polyestrous, spring & early fall	Monestrous, all year, but mostly late winter & summer	Polyestrous	Polyestrous	Polyestrous	Polyestrous, induced ovulation
Cycle Length	15–21 days	6–7 months	16 days	4 days	4 days	1 month or more
Duration of heat	9–10 days in absence of male, 4–6 days if mated	4–14 days standing heat	6–11 hours	10–20 hours	9–20 hours	1 month or more
Best time for breeding	Daily from day 2 of heat	On alternate days from day 2 to end of heat	10 hours after start of heat	At start of heat, 8–10 p.m.	At start of heat	Anytime
First heat after birth	4–6 weeks	3–5 months	6–8 hours	1–2 weeks after litter removed	2–4 days after litter removed	Immediate
Number of young	1–10	1–22	1–8	1–12	1–12	3–13

*Adapted from *Merck Veterinary Manual*, 5th edition
** Earlier in smaller breeds, later in larger breeds

Table of Norms
Recorded Lifespan of Various Animal Species

Species	Average years	Maximum years
Livestock		
Cattle	20–25	30
Goats	8–10	18
Horses	20–30	50
Sheep	10–15	20
Swine	16	27
Pets		
Cats	13–17	21
Dogs	13–17	34
Guinea pigs	2 plus	6 plus
Hamsters	1	2–3
Mice	1–2	3 plus
Rabbits	5–6	13
Rats	2–3	4
Monkey (rhesus)	15	29
Poultry		
Chicken	—	30
Geese	—	31
Turkey	—	12½
Pet birds		
Canary	—	24
Lovebirds	—	8 plus
Parrots (various species)	—	30–65
Others		
Snakes (various species)	—	6–20

Table of Norms
Gestation Periods*

Species	Time (days)	Species	Time (days)	(months)
Livestock		**Wild Animals**		
Ass	365	Ape, Barbary	210	
Cattle:		Bear, black		7
Angus	281	Bison		9
Ayrshire	279	Camel	410	
Brown Swiss	290	Coyote	60–64	
Charolais	289	Deer, Virginia	197–220	
Guernsey	283	Elephant		20–22
Hereford	285	Elk, Wapiti		8½
Holstein	279	Giraffe		14–15
Jersey	279	Hare	88	
Red Poll	285	Hippopotamus	225–250	
Shorthorn	282	Kangaroo, red	32–34**	
Simental	289	Leopard	92–95	
Goat	148–156	Lion	108	
Horse, heavy	333–345	Llama		11
Horse, light	330–337	Marmoset	140–150	
Pig	112–115	Monkey, macaque	150–180	
Sheep:		Moose	240–250	
Mutton breeds	144–147	Musk ox		9
Wool breeds	148–151	Opossum	12–13	
Pets		Panther	90–93	
		Porcupine	112	
Cat	59–68	Pronghorn	230–240	
Dog	56–68	Raccoon	63	
Guinea pig	58–75	Reindeer		7–8
Hamster	15–18	Rhinoceros,		
Mouse	19–31	African	530–550	
Rabbit	30–35	Seal		11
Rat	21–30	Shrew	20	
Fur Animals		Skunk	62–65	
Chinchilla	105–115	Squirrel, grey	44	
Ferret	42	Tapir	390–400	
Fisher	338–358	Tiger	105–113	
Fox	49–55	Walrus		12
Marten, European	236–274	Whale, sperm		16
Pine Marten	220–265	Wolf	60–63	
Mink	40–75	Woodchuck	31–32	
Muskrat	28–30			
Nutria (coypu)	120–134			
Otter	270–300			

*Adapted from *Merck Veterinary Manual*, 5th edition
**Delayed development as long as a "joey" is in the pouch

Table of Norms
Features of the Reproductive Cycle (Livestock)*

	Cattle	Goats	Horses	Sheep	Swine
Age at puberty:					
Range	4–18 months	4–8 months	10–24 months	7–12 months	4–9 months
Average	12 months	5 months	18 months	9 months	7 months
Cycle type	Polyestrous, all year	Seasonally polyestrous, early spring to late winter	Seasonally polyestrous, early spring on	Seasonally polyestrous, early fall to winter**	Polyestrous, all year
Cycle length:					
Range	18–24 days	18–21 days	19–26 days	14–20 days	16–24 days
Average	21 days	19 days	21 days***	16½ days	21 days
Duration of heat:					
Range	10–24 hours	2–3 days	2–10 days	24–48 hours	2–3 days
Average	18 hours	—	6 days	—	—
Best time for breeding	From mid-heat until 6 hours after end	Daily during heat	Last few days, should be bred at 2-day intervals	Little significance	Little significance
First heat after birth	Varies, best to breed at 60–90 days	Next fall	4–14 days, 9 days average	Next fall	4–10 days after weaning
Number of young	1	1–2	1	1–2	2–14

*Adapted from *Merck Veterinary Manual*, 5th edition
**Prolonged seasons in Dorsets and Marinos
***Very variable

Table of Norms
Heart Rates (beats/minute)*

Animal	Average	Range
Human	70	58–104
Ass	50	40–56
Bat	750	100–970
Camel	30	25–32
Cat	120	110–140
Cow	–	60–70
Dog	–	100–130
Elephant	35	22–53
Giraffe	66	–
Goat	90	70–135
Guinea pig	280	260–400
Horse	44	23–70
Lion	40	–
Monkey	192	165–240
Mouse	534	324–858
Rabbit	205	123–304
Rat	328	261–600
Sheep	75	60–120
Skunk	166	144–192
Squirrel	249	96–378
Swine	–	58–86
Chicken (adult)	–	250–300
Chicken (baby)	–	350–450

*Adapted from *Merck Veterinary Manual*, 5th edition

Table of Norms
Eruption of the Teeth, Horses & Cattle*

Tooth	Horses	Cattle
Temporary incisor #1	Birth–1 week	Before birth
Temporary incisor #2	4–6 weeks	Before birth
Temporary incisor #3	6–9 months	Birth–week
Permanent incisor #1	2½ years	1½–2 years
Permanent incisor #2	3½ years	2–2½ years
Permanent incisor #3	4½ years	3 years
Temporary canine	Does not erupt	Birth–2 weeks**
Permanent canine	4–5 years	3½–4 years**
Temporary premolar #2	Birth–2 weeks	Birth–3 weeks
Temporary premolar #3	Birth–2 weeks	Birth–3 weeks
Temporary premolar #4	Birth–2 weeks	Birth–3 weeks
Permanent premolar #1	5–6 months (wolf tooth)	None
Permanent premolar #2	2½ years	2–2½ years
Permanent premolar #3	3 years	1½–2½ years
Permanent premolar #4	4 years	2½–3 years
Permanent molar #1	9–12 months	5–6 months
Permanent molar #2	2 years	1–1½ years
Permanent molar #3	3½–4 years	2–2½ years

*Adapted from *Merck Veterinary Manual*, 5th edition
**The canine tooth of domestic ruminants has commonly been accounted a fourth incisor

Table of Norms
Eruption of the Teeth, Sheep, Goats & Swine*

Tooth	Sheep & Goats	Swine
Temporary incisor #1	Birth–1 week	2–4 weeks
Temporary incisor #2	1–2 weeks	6–12 weeks
Temporary incisor #3	2–3 weeks	Before birth
Permanent incisor #1	1–1½ years	1 year
Permanent incisor #2	1½–2 years	16–20 months
Permanent incisor #3	2½–3 years	8–10 months
Temporary canine	3–4 weeks**	Before birth
Permanent canine	3–4 years**	6–10 months
Temporary premolar #2	Birth–4 weeks	5–7 weeks
Temporary premolar #3	Birth–4 weeks	1–4 weeks
Temporary premolar #4	Birth–4 weeks	1–4 weeks
Permanent premolar #1	None	5 months
Permanent premolar #2	1½–2 years	12–15 months
Permanent premolar #3	1½–2 years	12–15 months
Permanent premolar #4	1½–2 years	12–15 months
Permanent molar #1	3–5 months	4–6 months
Permanent molar #2	9–12 months	8–12 months
Permanent molar #3	1½–2 years	18–20 months

*Adapted from *Merck Veterinary Manual,* 5th edition
**The canine tooth of domestic ruminants has commonly been accounted a fourth incisor

Table of Norms
Eruption of the Teeth, Dogs & Cats*

Tooth	Dogs	Cats
Temporary incisor #1	4–5 weeks	2–3 weeks
Temporary incisor #2	4–5 weeks	3–4 weeks
Temporary incisor #3	5–6 weeks	3–4 weeks
Permanent incisor #1	2–5 months	3½–4 months
Permanent incisor #2	2–5 months	3½–4 months
Permanent incisor #3	4–5 months	4–4½ months
Temporary canine	3–4 weeks	3–4 weeks
Permanent canine	5–6 months	5 months
Temporary premolar #2	4–6 weeks	Upper: 2 months Lower: none
Temporary premolar #3	4–6 weeks	4–5 weeks
Temporary premolar #4	6–8 weeks	4–6 weeks
Permanent premolar #1	4–5 months	None
Permanent premolar #2	5–6 months	Upper: 4½–5 months Lower: none
Permanent premolar #3	5–6 months	5–6 months
Permanent premolar #4	4–5 months	5–6 months
Permanent molar #1	5–6 months	4–5 months
Permanent molar #2	6–7 months	None
Permanent molar #3	6–7 months	None

*Adapted from *Merck Veterinary Manual*, 5th edition

Table of Norms
Rectal Temperatures*

Animal	Degrees F. +/− 1 deg.	Degrees C. +/− 0.5 deg.
Human	98.6	37
Cat	101.5	38.5
Cow	101.5	38.5
Dog	102	39
Goat	102	39
Horse	100.5	38
Pig	102	39
Rabbit	102.5	39.3
Sheep	103	39.5

*Adapted from *Merck Veterinary Manual*, 5th edition

Table of Norms
Incubation Periods*

Poultry	Days
Chicken	20–22
Duck	26–28
Muscovy duck	33–35
Goose	30–33
Guinea fowl	26–28
Turkey	26–28
Pet and game birds	
Budgerigar	17–21
Dove	12–19
Finch	11–14
Parrot	17–31
Pheasant	21–28
Pigeon	16–18
Quail	21–28
Swan	21–35

*Adapted from *Merck Veterinary Manual*, 5th edition

Table of Norms
Respiratory Rates (breaths/minute)*

Animal	Rate
Human	12
Cat	26
Cow	30
Dog	22
Guinea pig	90
Hamster	74
Horse	12
Monkey	40
Pig	8–18
Rabbit	39
Rat	97
Sheep	19
Chicken (male)	12–20
Chicken (female)	20–36
Duck (male)	42
Duck (female)	110
Goose (male)	20
Goose (female)	40
Pigeon	25–30
Turkey (male)	28
Turkey (female)	49

*Adapted from *Merck Veterinary Manual*, 5th edition

Diseases Transmitted Between Animals and Humans (Zoonoses)*—1

Disease (& Disease Agent)	Mode of Transmission	Common Animal Hosts	Prevalence in Humans	Seriousness of Infection in Humans
Viral infections				
Contagious ecthyma—orf (poxvirus)	Contact	Sheep	Sporadic	Mild
Cowpox (poxvirus)	Contact	Cattle	Common	Mild
Influenza and parainfluenza (Type A & D influenza virus)	Contact	Swine, fowl, horses	Common	Serious
Lymphocytic choriomeningitis (arenavirus)	Contact	Rodents	Sporadic	Serious
Newcastle disease (paramyxovirus)	Contact	Fowl, wild birds	Sporadic	Mild
Rabies (rabies virus)	Contact	Dogs, cats, wild mammals	Sporadic	Fatal
Vesicular stomatitis (VSV virus)	Contact & vector	Cattle, horses, swine	Sporadic	Usually mild
Catscratch fever (virus or small bacteria)***	Contact	Cats	Common	Mild
Rickettsial infections				
Q fever (Coxiella burnetti)	Vehicle, contact	Sheep, cattle, wild mammals	Common	Serious
Bacterial infections				
Anthrax (Bacillus anthracis)	Contact	Cattle, horses, swine, sheep	Sporadic	High mortality

Zoonoses—2

Disease (& Disease Agent)	Mode of Transmission	Common Animal Hosts	Prevalence in Humans	Seriousness of Infection in Humans
Brucellosis:				
(Brucella abortus)	Vehicle, contact	Cattle, sheep	Sporadic	Serious
(B. melitensis)	Vehicle, contact	Sheep, goats	Sporadic	Serious
(B. suis)	Vehicle, contact	Swine	Sporadic	Serious
Campylobacteriosis (Campylobacter jejuni)	Vehicle	Dogs, swine, cattle & others	Common	Serious
Colibacillosis (Escherichia spp.)	Vehicle	Cattle, swine	Common	Serious
Erysipeloid (Erysipelothrix rhusiopathiae)	Contact	Swine, fowl, fish	Sporadic	Serious
Leptospirosis (Leptospira spp.)	Vehicle, contact	Dogs, cattle, rodents	Sporadic	Serious
Listeriosis (Listeria monocytogenes)	Vehicle, contact	Cattle, sheep, fowl	Sporadic	High mortality
Pasteurellosis (Pasteurella multocida)	Contact	Cattle, horses, sheep, swine, dogs, cats	Sporadic	Serious
Pseudotuberculosis (Pasturella pseudotuberculosis)	Contact	Rodents	Sporadic	Serious
Psittacosis/ornithosis–parrot fever (Chlamydia psittaci)	Contact	Fowl, birds	Sporadic	Sometimes fatal, usually mild

Disease	Transmission	Reservoir	Frequency	Severity
Rat-bite fever (Spirillum minus, Streptobacillus moniliformis)	Contact	Rodents.	Sporadic	Serious
Salmonellosis (Salmonella spp.)	Vehicle	Fowl, rodents, swine, turtles & others	Common	Serious
Staphylococcosis (Staphylococcus spp.)	Vehicle, contact	Dogs, other animals	Common	Serious
Streptococcosis (Streptococcus spp.)	Vehicle, contact	Cattle, dogs	Common	Serious
Tuberculosis:				
(Mycobacterium tuberculosis bovis)	Vehicle, contact	Cattle	Common	Serious
(M.t. hominis)	Vehicle, contact	Cattle, dogs	Common	Serious
(M.t. avium)	Vehicle, contact	Fowl, swine	Sporadic	Serious
Tularemia (Pasteurella tularensis)	Contact	Wild mammals	Sporadic	Serious
Fungal infections				
Ringworm:				
(Microsporum spp.)	Contact	Dogs, cats	Common	Serious
(Trichophyton spp.)	Contact	Cattle, horses	Common	Serious
Protozoal infections				
Amebiasis (Entamoeba histolytica)	Vehicle	Dogs, monkeys	Common	Sometimes serious, usually mild

Animal Diseases in Humans

611

Zoonoses—3

Disease (& Disease Agent)	Mode of Transmission	Common Animal Hosts	Prevalence in Humans	Seriousness of Infection in Humans
Balantidiasis (Balantidium coli)	Vehicle	Swine	Sporadic	Serious
Giardiasis (Giardia lamblia)	Vehicle	Primates, dogs, cats, beavers	Sporadic	Sometimes serious
Toxoplasmosis (Toxoplasma gondii)	Vehicle	Cats, other mammals	Common	Sometimes serious, usually mild
Nematode infections				
Dipylidiasis–dog tapeworm (Dipylidium caninum)	Ingestion of dog flea	Dogs	Sporadic	Mild
Larva migrans–cutaneous (Ancylostoma spp. & other hookworms)	Contacting soil	Dogs, cats, other mammals	Common	Mild
Larva migrans–visceral (Toxocara spp. & other roundworms)	Ingestion of soil	Dogs, cats, other mammals	Common	Serious
Trichinosis (Trichinella spiralis)	Vehicle	Swine, rodents, dogs, foxes, bears & other wild animals	Sporadic	Serious

Arthropod infestations Scabies (Sarcoptes scabei & other mites)	Contact	Horses, dogs, cats	Sporadic	Sometimes serious

*Includes only the most common such diseases in the United States. Does not include diseases that must be transmitted by mosquitoes, fleas, ticks, or other vectors, such as equine encephalitis (sleeping sickness), plague, or Rocky Mountain spotted fever

**Anything that can mechanically carry a disease organism

***Disease agent not known for sure

Pet Animal Control Laws—1

State	Authorized Agency	Rabies Control Law	Rabies Vaccination Required	Dog Minimum Age	Dog Vacc. Interval	Cat Minimum Age	Cat Vacc. Interval	Dog Control Law	Leash Required	Excrement Restricted
AL	Health	yes	yes	3	1	3	1	no	no	no
AK	Health	yes	—	—	—	—	—	no	no	no
AZ	Health	yes	—	—	—	—	—	yes	no	no
AR	Health	yes	—	—	—	—	—	no	no	no
CA	Health	yes	yes	4	2	—	—	no	no	no
CO	Health	yes	no	—	—	—	—	no	no	no
CT	Agric.	yes	—	—	—	—	—	no	no	no
DE	Nat.Res.	no	no	—	—	—	—	yes	yes	no
DC	Health	no	no	—	—	—	—	yes	yes	no
FL	Nat.Res.	no	no	—	—	—	—	yes	no	no
GA	Health	yes	yes	3	1-3	3	1	no	no	no
HI		no	—	—	—	—	—	no	no	no
ID	Agric.	no	no[a]	3	3	—	—	no	no[a]	no
IL	Agric.	yes	yes	4	1-3	—	—	yes	no	no
IN	Health	yes	no[a]	6	1	—	—	no	no	no
IA[a]	Agric.	yes	yes	6	1-3	—	—	no	—	—
KS	Health	no	no	3	1-3	—	—	no	no	no
KY	Health	yes	yes	4	1-3	—	—	yes	yes	yes
LA	Health	yes	yes	3	1-3	—	—	no	no	yes
ME	Agric.	yes	yes	6	2	—	—	yes	yes	no
MD	Health	yes	yes	4	1-3	—	—	no	no	yes
MA	Health	yes	yes	3	1-3	—	—	yes	no[a]	no[a]
MI	Agric.	yes	yes	6	—[b]	—	—	yes	yes	no
MN		no	no	—	—	—	—	no	no	no
MS	Health	yes	yes	3	1	—	3	no	no	no
MO		no	no	—	—	—	—	no	no	no
MT	Agric.	yes	yes	3	1-3	3	1-3	no	no	no
NE	Health	yes		4	1-3	—	—	no	no	
NV	Health	yes	yes	4	2	4	2	yes	yes	no
NH	Agric.	yes	yes	3	1-3	—	—	no	no	
NJ	Health	yes	yes	7	1-3	—	—	yes	yes	yes[a]
NM	Health	yes	yes	3	1	3	1	no	no	yes
NY	Agric.	yes		—	—	—	—	yes	yes	yes[c]
NC[d]	Health	yes	yes	4	3	4	3	no	no	
ND[a]	Health	yes	yes	—	—	—	—	no	no	no

Tables and Glossary

Pet Animal Control Laws—2

State	Authorized Agency	Rabies Control Law	Rabies Vaccination Required	Dog Minimum Age	Dog Vacc. Interval	Cat Minimum Age	Cat Vacc. Interval	Dog Control Law	Leash Required	Excrement Restricted
OH		no	no	—	—	—	—	no	no	no
OK		no	no	—	—	—	—	no	no	no
OR	Health	yes	yes	—	—	—	—	—	—	yes
PA	Agric./ Health	yes	no	—	—	—	—	yes	no	no
RI		no	no	—	—	—	—	no	no	no
SC	Health	yes	yes	—e	1	—e	1	yes	yes	yes
SD		no	no	—	—	—	—	no	no	no
TN	Health	yes	yes	3	1-3	6	1-3	yes	no	no
TX	Health	yes	yes	3	1	3	—	noa	noa	yes
UT	Health/ Agric.	no	yes	4	2	4	1	no	no	no
VT		yes	yes	6	—	—	—	noa	noa	no
VA	Health	yes	yes	6	1	—	—	yes	noa	yes
WA	Health	yes	no	—	—	—	—	no	no	no
WV		no	no	—	—	—	—	no	no	no
WI	Agric.	yes	yes	5	—	—	—	no	no	no
WYa		no	no	3	2	—	—	no	no	no

a. optional
b. vaccination expiration date
c. New York City and Buffalo only
d. 1 year, every 3 years thereafter
e. veterinarian option

Health: Departments or Divisions of Health, Human Resources, etc.
Agric.:   Departments or Divisions of Agriculture, Livestock Sanitary Boards, etc.
Nat.Res.:   Departments or Divisions of Natural Resources, Fish and Game and Wildlife Agencies, etc.

Updated and adapted from charts by John K. Emerson, D.V.M., Colorado Department of Health, Denver

Interstate Shipment Requirements—1
Dogs/Cats

State	Health Certificate (dogs/cats)	Rabies Vaccination (dogs/cats)	Minimum Age–Months (dogs/cats)	Remarks
AL	yes/yes	yes/yes	3/3	
AK	yes/yes	yes/	4/	
AZ	no/no	yes/no	4/	Must be apparently healthy
AR	yes/yes	yes/yes	3/3	
CA	/no	yes/no	4/	
CO	yes/yes	yes/	3/	Approval on dogs and cats for resale
CT	yes/no	yes/no	2/	Cert. exemption— breeding, exhibition, etc.
DE	yes/yes	yes/	4/	
DC				
FL	yes/	yes/	6/	No exposure statement for 100 days
GA	yes/no	yes/no	3/	
HI				120-day quarantine
ID	yes/yes	yes/yes	3/3	No exposure statement for 180 days
IL	yes/	yes/	4/	Cert. exemption— breeding, exhibition, etc.
IN	yes/yes	yes/yes	3/3	
IA	yes/yes	yes/	3/	Cert. exemption— breeding, exhibition, etc.
KS	yes/yes	yes/yes	3/3	
KY	yes/yes	yes/yes	4/4	Cert. exemption— breeding, exhibition, etc.
LA	yes/no	yes/	3/	

Interstate Shipment Requirements—2
Dogs/Cats

State	Health Certificate (dogs/cats)	Rabies Vaccination (dogs/cats)	Minimum Age–Months (dogs/cats)	Remarks
ME	yes/yes	yes/yes	6/6	Distemper—not more than 30 days or less than 7 days.
MD	yes/	yes/	4/	No exposure statement for 100 days
MA	yes/	yes/	2/	Cert. exemption— breeding, exhibition, etc.
MI	yes/yes	yes/	6/	
MN	yes/	yes/	3/	Cert. exemption— exhibition
MS	yes/yes	yes/yes	3/3	
MO	yes/	yes/	4/	Cert. dated within 30 days of entry
MT	yes/	yes/	3/	
NE	yes/yes	yes/	4/	
NV	yes/yes	yes/yes	4/4	
NH	yes/	yes/	3/	
NJ	yes/			No exposure statement for 100 days
NM	yes/yes	yes/yes	3/3	
NY	yes			Cert. dated within 7 days of entry and mailed
NC	yes/	yes/	4/	No exposure statement for 100 days
ND	yes/no	yes/	4/	Cert. exemption— breeding, exhibition, etc.

Interstate Shipment Requirements—3
Dogs/Cats

State	Health Certificate (dogs/cats)	Rabies Vaccination (dogs/cats)	Minimum Age–Months (dogs/cats)	Remarks
OH	yes/	yes/	6/	
OK		yes/yes	4/	Or health certificate
OR	yes/yes	yes/yes	4/4	Special permit for breeding or resale
PA	yes/	yes/	3/	No exposure statement for 100 days
RI	yes/yes	yes/yes	3/3	
SC	yes/yes	yes/yes	3/3	
SD	yes/yes	yes/yes	3/3	
TN	yes/yes	yes/yes	3/6	Cert. exemption over 15 days and on leash
TX	yes/	yes/	4/	
UT	yes/yes	yes/yes	4/4	
VT	yes/yes	yes/yes	6/6	
VA	yes/yes	yes/yes	4/4	Cert. dated 10 days from entry
WA	yes/yes	yes/	4/	
WV	yes/yes	yes/yes	5/	Cert. mailed prior to entry
WI	yes/no	yes/no	6/	
WY	yes/no	yes/no	4/	
CANADA		yes/	3/	

Updated and adapted from charts by John K. Emerson, D.V.M., Colorado Department of Health, Denver.

Tables and Glossary

Exotic Animal Control Laws and/or Regulations—1

REGULATED ANIMALS
Wild and/or Exotic

State	Authorized Agency	Skunks	Raccoons	Felines	Canines	Other	Primates	Turtles	Birds	Poisonous Animals	Wild Animal Law	Easter Chick Law
AL	Nat.Res.	A	A								yes	no
AK	Nat.Res.	A	A			B[1]					yes	no
AZ	Nat.Res.	B	A	B	B	B	A	A	A	B	yes	no
AR	Nat.Res.	B	A	A	A	A	A		A		yes	no
CA	Health/ Nat.Res.	B	A	A			A	B			yes	no
CO	Health	B	B				B	B		B	yes	yes
CT	Agric./ Env.Prot.	C	C	A	A	A		A	A	C	yes	yes
DE	Agric./ Nat.Res.		A		A[2]		A	A			yes	yes
DC	Health				A	A	A	A		A	yes	no
FL	Nat.Res.			C	C	A	C	A	A	C	yes	no
GA	Nat.Res.	A	A	A	A	A	A	A	A	A	yes	no
HI	Agric.	A	A	A	A	A	A	A	A	B	yes	no
ID	Agric./ Nat.Res.	B	B	A	B[2]	A					yes	no
IL	Agric./ Nat.Res.	B	A	A	B[3]	A	A	A	A	B	yes	yes
IN	Nat.Res.	A	A	A	A	A	A	A	A	A	yes	yes
IA	Agric./ Nat.Res.	A	A	A	A						no	no
KS	Health	A	A					A			no	no
KY	Nat.Res.	A	A	A	A						yes	no
LA	Health	A	A	A		A					yes	no
ME	Nat.Res.	A	A	A	A	A	A	A	A	A	yes	yes
MD	Health							A			yes	yes
MA	Nat.Res.										yes	no

Exotic Animal Control Laws and/or Regulations—2

State	Authorized Agency	Skunks	Raccoons	Felines	Canines	Other	Primates	Turtles	Birds	Poisonous Animals	Wild Animal Law	Easter Chick Law
MI	Nat.Res.	B	B								yes	yes[4]
MN	Nat.Res.	C									yes	yes
MS	Nat.Res.	B	B	B	B	B					yes	no
MO											no	no
MT	Agric.	B	B		B						yes	yes
NE	Nat.Res.									yes	no
NV	Agric./ Nat.Res.	A						A			yes	no
NH	Nat.Res.	A	A	A	A	A	A		A	A	yes	no
NJ	Nat.Res.	B	B	B	B	A	B	A	A	B	yes	no
NM	Health	A	A		A		A				yes	no
NY	Nat.Res.	A	A	A	A	A	A	A	A		yes	yes
NC								A			no	yes
ND	Agric.	A							A		yes	yes
OH	Nat.Res.		A						A	A	yes	no
OK	Agric.	A	A	A	A	A	A	A	A	A	yes	no
OR	Agric./ Fish & Game	A	A	A	A		A	A			yes	no
PA	Health/ Agric./ Nat.Res.	A	A	A	A	A		A	A	A	yes	yes
RI	Agric.	B	B	B	B	B	B	B	B	B	yes	yes
SC	Nat.Res.	C	C	C	C	C	A	A	A	A	yes	yes
SD											no	no
TN	Health/ Nat.Res.	B	A	A	A	A		B	A	B	yes	no
TX	Nat.Res.	A	A	A	A	A		A	A	A	yes	no

Exotic Animal Control Laws and/or Regulations—3

State	Authorized Agency	Skunks	Raccoons	Felines	Canines	Other	Primates	Turtles	Birds	Poisonous Animals	Wild Animal Law	Easter Chick Law
UT	Health/ Agric.	A	A	A	A	A	A	A	A	A	yes	no
VT	Nat.Res.	A	A	A	A	A	A	A	A	B	yes	yes
VA	Agric.	A	A	A	A	A	A	A	A	A	yes	yes
WA	Health	A	A		B²						yes	no
WV	Nat.Res.	A	A	A	B	A	A	A	A	A	yes	no
WI	Agric./ Nat.Res.	A		A							yes	yes
WY	Health/ Nat.Res.	B	A			A	A	A	A	A	yes	no

A: Permit required   B:Possession Prohibited   C: Sale prohibited

Health: Departments or Divisions of Health, Human Resources, etc.
Agric.:   Departments or Divisions of Agriculture, Livestock Sanitary Boards, etc.
Nat.Res.:   Departments or Divisions of Natural Resources, Fish and Game and Wildlife Agencies, etc.
Env. Prot.:   Environmental Protection

[1]Ferrets
[2]Fox
[3]Coyotes
[4]Agriculture

Updated and adapted from charts by John K. Emerson, D.V.M., Colorado Department of Health, Denver.

Animal Biological Products*

Disease	Product	Age or other factors	Repeat dose	Comments**
Cattle				
Anaplasmosis	Vaccine	2 years or older	Every 2 years	Restricted use
Blackleg & related diseases	Several combinations	Variable	Variable	—
Brucellosis	Vaccine	Calfhood	None	Restricted use
Diarrheal diseases	Several viral & bacterial products	Variable	Variable	—
Enterotoxemia	Several toxoids	Variable	Variable	Long-term protection
Enterotoxemia	Antitoxins	Any age	Usually none	Short-term protection
Johne's disease (paratuber-culosis)	Bacterin	7–35 days	None	Restricted use
Keratocon-junctivitis (pinkeye)	Bacterin	6–8 weeks before pinkeye season	Twice yearly	—
Respiratory diseases (shipping fever, pneumonia)	Several viral & bacterial products	Variable	Variable	—
Staphylococcal mastitis	Bacterin or bacterin-toxoid	5–6 months	Every 6 months	—
Vibrionic & leptospiral abortions	Several bacterins	Variable	Every year	—
Warts	Vaccine	Any age	3–5 weeks	Prevention only
Horses				
Encephalomyelitis (sleeping sickness)	Several vaccines	Variable	Variable	Some restricted
Influenza	Vaccine	Any age	Yearly or before expected exposure	—
Rhinopneumonitis (viral abortion)	Vaccine	Variable	Variable	—
Strangles (distemper)	Bacterin or bacterial extract	Two doses before exposure, any age	Yearly or before expected exposure	
Sheep				
Blackleg or related diseases	Several combinations	Variable	Variable	—

Tables and Glossary

Disease	Product	Age or other factors	Repeat dose	Comments**
Bluetongue	Vaccines	Before insect vector season	Every year	—
Enterotoxemia (overeating disease)	Several toxoids	Variable	Variable	Long-term protection
Ovine ecthyma (soremouth)	Vaccine	Any age	None	—
Ram epididymitis	Bacterin	Two doses initially	Every year	—
Vibrionic abortion	Bacterin	Two doses before breeding	Every year	—
Swine				
Atrophic rhinitis	Bacterin	Two doses before farrowing & in baby pigs	Every year	—
Diarrheal diseases	Several viral & bacterial products	Variable	Variable	—
Erysipelas	Antiserum	Treatment or short-term protection	Variable	—
Erysipelas	Vaccine or bacterin	Variable	Twice yearly in breeding animals	—
Infectious abortions	Several viral & bacterial products	Variable	Variable	—
Pseudorabies	Vaccines	Before farrowing & in baby pigs	Variable	Some restricted
Respiratory diseases	Several bacterial products	Variable	Variable	—
Poultry				
Avian encephalo-myelitis (epidemic tremors)	Vaccines	Variable	Variable	—
Avian reovirus & tenosynovitis (pale bird syndrome, viral arthritis)	Vaccines	Variable	Variable	Some restricted
Bacterial respiratory diseases	Bacterins & vaccines	Variable	Variable	—

Bronchitis	Vaccines	Variable	Variable	Several serotypes, some restricted
Bursal disease (gumboro)	Vaccines	Variable	Variable	Some restricted
Turkey erysipelas	Bacterin	3 months or older	Every 3 months	—
Fowl cholera	Vaccines & bacterins	6 weeks or older	Variable	—
Fowl laryngotracheitis	Vaccines	Variable	Variable	Some restricted
Fowl pox	Vaccines	Variable	Variable	—
Marek's disease	Vaccines	1 day	None	Some restricted
Newcastle disease	Vaccines	Variable	Variable	Some restricted
Dogs and cats				
Canine distemper	Vaccine	8–12 weeks	Yearly	—
Canine hepatitis	Vaccine	8–12 weeks	Yearly	—
Canine tracheobronchitis (kennel cough)	Vaccines & bacterins	Variable	Variable	—
Canine leptospirosis	Bacterin	8–12 weeks	Yearly	—
Diarrheal diseases	Vaccines & bacterins	Variable	Variable	—
Feline panleukopenia (distemper)	Vaccines	8–16 weeks	Yearly	—
Feline respiratory diseases	Several vaccines	Variable	Variable	—
Fur bearing animals				
Botulism	Toxoid	6–8 weeks	Yearly	—
Fox encephalitis	Vaccine	8–12 weeks	Yearly	—
Mink distemper	Vaccine	8–9 weeks	None	—
Mink enteritis	Vaccine	4–6 weeks	Yearly	—

*In contrast to drugs and medicines, which are manufactured products, animal biological products are produced from micro-organisms, such as bacteria or viruses. They generally work through the animal's own immune mechanism. As natural products, biologics don't constitute a residue problem and disease organisms don't develop a tolerance against them. USDA's Animal and Plant Health Inspection Service regulates all animal biological products imported into the United States or shipped across State lines. (Drugs and medicines are regulated by the Food and Drug Administration.) All licensed animal biological products carry a U.S. veterinary license number on the label. USDA tests each product to make sure it is pure, safe, potent and effective. USDA also reviews each label to make sure it tells what the product is, how long it will last, how to administer it, and what the expected results should be. Observe all directions and cautions on the label. (Table compiled by David F. Long, Animal and Plant Health Inspection Service)

**USDA puts restrictions on the distribution and use of certain products; for instance, some vaccines can be administered only by a veterinarian, others only with permission of State animal health officials

Glossary of Some Commonly Used Veterinary Medical Terms

Abdomen—part of a mammal's body between the thorax and the pelvis. The belly. The cavity of this part of the body.

Abscess—localized collection of pus in a cavity formed by disintegration of tissues.

Acute—having a short and relatively severe course of development. Opposite of chronic.

Adhesion—abnormal union of two adjacent tissues or organs.

Aerobic—requiring air or free oxygen to live and grow.

Alimentary canal—tubular passage functioning in the digestion and absorption of food. In most animals, beginning at the mouth and ending at the anus.

Anaerobic—living or growing best in the absence of free air or oxygen.

Anemia—deficiency of hemoglobin, usually accompanied by reduced number of red blood cells.

Anorexia—lack of or loss of appetite.

Ante mortem—before death.

Anterior—toward the front or head.

Antibiotic—any of a large group of soluble chemical substances produced by various micro-organisms and fungi. Antibiotics inhibit the growth of or destroy bacteria and other micro-organisms.

Antigen—specific biological substance inoculated into an animal to stimulate resistance or immunity to a specific disease.

Antibody—the very specific biological substance that the body itself manufactures to combat specific diseases following a vaccination or following an attack of a disease.

Antiseptic—an agent that destroys or severely inhibits micro-organisms that cause disease, decomposition or fermentation.

Antiserum—serum from blood containing one or more specific antibodies. It is injected into animals to give immediate though very short term protection.

Antitoxin—antibody that neutralizes toxin of a bacteria.

Aqueous—watery, or prepared with water.

Artery—vessel through which blood passes from the heart to various organs or parts of the body.

Arthritis—inflammation of a joint and its adjacent tissues.

Aseptic—free from micro-organisms that cause disease, fermentation or putrefaction.

Ataxia—failure or irregularity of muscular action producing a stumbling or staggering gait.

Atrophy—shrinking or wasting away of a tissue or organ.

Attenuated—weakening of viruses in a laboratory so they will not produce disease, but will still produce antibody production when used as a vaccine.

Autoimmunity—production

by an animal of an allergic reaction to its own tissues which may produce clinical disease.

Bactericidal—having properties that destroy or kill bacteria.

Bacterin—killed or inactivated bacteria used as vaccines.

Bacteriostatic—inhibiting or retarding bacterial growth.

Bacterium, bacteria—single-celled organism that multiplies by simple division. Can be either spherical, rod-shaped or spiral. Some are beneficial and others cause disease.

Benign—not malignant, not likely to recur or metastasize.

Bladder—stretchable membrane sac that temporarily stores urine secreted by the kidneys.

Cancer—malignant types of tumors that have a tendency to spread to other tissues or organs (metastasize).

Capillary—smallest vessel of the circulatory system. Capillaries connect the smallest arteries (arterioles) and the smallest veins (venules). Walls of the capillaries are in direct contact with individual cells of the tissues.

Carcinoma—malignant type of cancer composed of epithelial or gland cells that have a tendency to spread (metastasize) quickly.

Carrier—infected animal (or person) that harbors a specific infectious agent in the absence of discernible clinical disease and serves as a potential source of infection for other animals.

Cartilage—a specialized fibrous, elastic or hyaline connective tissue found in many locations in the body. Cartilage may form the shape of a part, such as on the ear and the tip of the nose, or may serve as a soft, somewhat flexible end of a long bone, such as on the distal end of the ribs.

Caudal—of, toward, attached to or near the tail.

Cecum, ceca—blind pouches at the junction of small and large intestines. Poultry have two ceca.

Cellulitis—inflammation of cellular tissue, especially purulent (consisting of pus) inflammation of the loose subcutaneous tissue.

Celsius—name of a Swedish astronomer who calibrated a thermometer to indicate the freezing point of water at 0° and the boiling point at 100°. Also called centigrade, because of the 100 degrees between these two points.

Cervical—of or pertaining to the neck. Also of or pertaining to the cervix.

Chronic—persisting or continuing over a long period of time. The opposite of acute.

Cirrhosis—disease characterized by degeneration of liver tissue with a replacement by hard though fibrous, connective tissue. Hardening or fibrosis of any tissue or organ, but especially the liver.

Clinical—based on actual observation of signs or symptoms.

Cloaca—portion of the lower end of the avian digestive tract that provides a passageway for products of the urinary, digestive and reproductive systems.

Coccidiostat—any of a group of chemical agents mixed in feed or drinking water to control coccidiosis.

Coccygeal—of, or pertaining to, vertebrae of the tail.

Comatose—state of unconsciousness from which a subject cannot be aroused, even by powerful stimulations.

Communicable disease—illness due to a specific infectious agent or its toxic products arising through transmission of that agent or its products from a reservoir to a susceptible host.

Congestion—presence of abnormally increased amounts of blood in an organ or tissue.

Conjunctiva—mucous membrane that lines inner surface of the eyelids.

Conjunctivitis—inflammation of the conjunctiva.

Connective tissue—tough fibrous tissue that supports and connects other tissues of an animal body.

Contagious—capable of spreading from one animal to another.

Cranial—of, toward, attached to or near the head.

Cyanosis—bluish discoloration of tissues due to reduced oxygen in the blood.

Cyanotic—adjective of above.

Cyst—any sac or bag-like structure, normal or abnormal, especially one that contains a liquid or semi-solid material.

Dewclaws—hard horny structures above the hoof on the rear surface of the legs of cattle, swine and sheep. Rudimentary or vestigial toes also on dogs, etc.

Disinfection—killing infectious agents outside the body by chemical or physical means, directly applied.

Distal—farthest away or most distantly removed from the center or point of attachment.

Dorsal—upper surface.

Edema—accumulation of serous fluid in intercellular spaces of a tissue.

Emaciation—wasted condition of a body characterized by slimy degeneration of fatty tissues and serous infiltration of the muscles.

Embryo—in livestock, very earliest stage of individual development within the uterus. The embryo grows and develops into a fetus. In poultry, developing of the individual within the eggshell.

Emphysema—swelling or inflation due to presence of air in the interstitial connective tissue framework of the lung.

Encephalitis—an inflammation of the brain.

Endemic—constant presence of a disease or infectious agent within a given geographic area; may also refer to usual prevalence of a given disease within such area.

Endocarditis—inflammation of the endocardium, the tissue that lines interior chambers of the heart.

Enteritis—inflammation of the intestine, especially the small intestine.

Enterotoxin—toxin that is specific for the cell of the intestinal mucosa.

Enzyme—any of a series of complex organic catalysts produced by living cells that initiate, sustain or accelerate biological chemical reaction, especially the chemical reactions of digestion.

Epidemic—occurrence in a community or region of cases of a human illness (or an outbreak) clearly in excess of normal expectancy and derived from a common or a propagated source.

Epidemiology—science or study of the causes and control of epidemics.

Epizootic—any widely diffused and rapidly spreading disease of animals. (Epidemic for humans).

Esophagus—tubular structure, which extends from the pharynx to the stomach, through which food passes as it is swallowed.

Estrus—periodic sexual excitement of most female mammals during which there is a time that the female will accept mating. Same as heat.

Feces—bowel movements, excrement from the intestinal tract.

Fetus—later stage of individual development within the uterus. Generally, the new individual is regarded as an embryo during the first half of pregnancy, and as a fetus during the last half.

Fistula—abnormal passageway or tube extending between two organs or draining an internal organ to outside surface of the body.

Flaccid—flabby, limp, relaxed, without firm shape or consistency.

Fluke—trematode flatworm parasite of humans, animals and birds. A common parasite of domestic livestock is the liver fluke Fasciola hepatica. Different species of flukes may live in the bloodstream, intestine or lung.

Fungus—any of a large group of microscopic or larger plants that do not contain chlorophyll and that reproduce by forming spores. Examples include mildews, molds and mushrooms.

Gastritis—inflammation of the stomach.

Gestation—state, process or period of intrauterine development from conception to birth.

Heat—see estrus.

Helminth—category of worms.

Hepatic—of or pertaining to the liver.

Hepatitis—inflammation of the liver.

Hormone—chemical substance, produced in the body, that has a specific effect on the activity or function of a certain organ.

Host—human or other living animal, including birds and arthropods, that affords food or a home to an infectious agent under natural conditions.

Hypertrophy—morbid enlargement or overgrowth of an organ or part due to increase in size of its constituent cells.

Icterus—abnormal accumulation of greenish and yellowish bile pigments in tissues.

Immunity—active immunity is when an individual has manufactured its own antibodies to combat a disease either from having the disease or from being vaccinated. Passive immunity is when an individual acquires the antibodies produced by another individual—such as from the mother's milk, when in the uterus, or from an injection of antiserum.

Inapparent infection—presence of infection in a host without occurrence of recognizable clinical signs or symptoms. Inapparent infections are only identifiable by laboratory means. Synonym: Subclinical infection.

Inbreeding—breeding of closely related animals. Usually done to bring out specifically wanted traits.

Incidence—number of cases of a disease diagnosed during a specific time frame.

Incubation period—time interval between exposure to an infectious agent and appearance of the first sign or symptom of the disease in question. Also, the time elapsed between a bird's laying an egg until it hatches.

Infection—entry and development or multiplication of an infectious agent in the body of humans or animals.

Infectious—capable of invading and growing in living tissues. Used to describe various pathogenic micro-organisms such

as viruses, bacteria, protozoa and fungi.

Infectious agent—an organism, chiefly a micro-organism but including worms, that is capable of producing infection or infectious disease.

Inflammation—reaction of a tissue to irritation or injury. Inflammation is characterized by pain, redness, heat (fever), swelling and loss of function.

Ingest—anything taken into the stomach.

Inhibitor—agent that slows or prevents a chemical reaction.

Jaundice—see icterus.

Laceration—jagged tear or wound.

Lactation—secretion of milk by a mammary gland.

Lesion—internal visible morbid change in the structure, color or size of an organ or part of the body. It may be microscopic in size.

Leukosis—serious disease of the blood-forming organs, characterized by marked increase in number of white blood cells in the circulating blood, together with enlargement and quick growth of lymphoid tissue of the spleen, lymph glands and bone marrow.

Lymph—clear yellowish, slightly alkaline fluid contained in lymphatic vessels.

Lymph node—any of many gland-like structures located along the course of the lymph vessels. The nodes produce lymphocytes and function as a filter for the fluid lymph.

Malignant—tending to become progressively worse, recurring or spreading. Opposite of benign.

Mammary gland—gland that secretes milk.

Mange—communicable dermatitis of humans and animals caused by minute mites that burrow into the skin to feed, live and reproduce.

Mastitis—inflammation of a mammary gland.

Melanin—dark (black or brown) pigment found in the skin, hair, certain parts of the eye and brain, and in certain of the darker (melanotic) tumors.

Melanosis—condition characterized by deposition or accumulation of abnormally large amounts of pigment melanin.

Metabolism—sum of all physical and chemical processes by which living organized substance is produced and maintained, and also the transformation by which energy is made available for use by the organism.

Metastasis—transfer of disease from one organ to another not directly connected with it. It may occur as a result of transfer of pathogenic organisms as in tuberculosis, or as a result of cells, as in cancer.

Milk fever—see parturient paresis.

Mites—very small (in many cases microscopic) jointed-legged creatures very similar to ticks. Mites are found everywhere, and infest both animals and plants. Mites that burrow into the skin of animals cause mange.

Morbid—affected by, caused by, causing or characteristic of disease.

Morbidity rate—number of individuals in a group that become ill during a specified time.

Moribund—in dying state, near death.

Mortality rate—number of individuals that die from a disease during a specified time, usually one year.

Mucosa or mucous membranes—membranes that line cavities of the body that are exposed to air, and lining of the intestinal tract.

Mucus—slimy exudate of the mucous membranes.

Myocardium—heart muscle; the middle and thickest layer of the heart wall, composed of cardiac muscle.

Mycosis—any disease caused by a fungus.

Nares—external openings of the nasal passages.

Necrosis—death of a tissue, usually as individual cells, groups of cells or in small localized areas.

Nematode—class of roundworms or threadworms, such as hookworms, ascarids.

Neoplasm—new growth of different or abnormal tissue; a tumor.

Nephritis—inflammation of the kidney.

Noxious—unpleasant, disagreeable.

Organoleptic—making an impression on, or stimulating, any of the special senses: sight, smell, taste and touch.

Tables and Glossary

Osteopetrosis—abnormal condition of the bone characterized by increased size, density and brittleness.

Osteoporosis—abnormal rarefaction or thinning of the bone, making it weaker.

Oviduct—tubes through which the egg passes from the ovary to the uterus or cloaca. In poultry, the shell is built around the egg in the cloaca.

Palpation—examining a tissue or organ by the sense of touch.

Parasite—plant or animal that lives on or within another organism from which it derives sustenance or protection without compensation.

Paresis—partial or incomplete paralysis.

Parturient paresis—partial paralysis that occurs at or near time of giving birth to young and beginning lactation. The mother mobilizes large amounts of calcium to produce milk to feed newborn, and blood calcium levels drop below the point necessary for impulse transmission along the nerve trucks. Commonly called "milk fever."

Parturition—act of giving birth or delivering the young.

Pasteurization—process of heating a food material, usually a liquid, to a specific temperature for a specific length of time. This heating process destroys some pathogenic bacteria and significantly delays development of others. Pasteurizing temperatures are not high enough to coagulate

protein or caramelize sugar components of the liquid.

Pathogen—disease agent.

Pathogenic—capable of producing disease or developing pathology.

Pericarditis—inflammation of the sac surrounding the heart and the roots of the great blood vessels of the heart.

Pericardium—thin tough connective tissue membrane that encloses the heart in a sac-like or bag-like structure.

Peritoneum—thin serous membrane located in the abdominal cavity. Parietal peritoneum lines walls of the cavity. Visceral peritoneum covers outer surfaces of abdominal viscera and organs.

Peritonitis—inflammation of the peritoneum (see above).

Phlebitis—inflammation of the veins.

pH number—number that indicates acidity or alkalinity of a solution. Number 7 indicates a neutral (non-reactive) solution. Numbers above 7 indicate an alkaline solution, and numbers below 7 indicate an acid solution.

Physiological—of or relating to normal body, organ or tissue function.

Pleura—thin serous membrane located in the thoracic cavity. Parietal pleura lines inside surface of the rib cage. Visceral pleura covers outer surfaces of the lungs.

Pleuritis—inflammation of the pleura. "Pleurisy" is an old name for this condition.

Pneumonia—inflammation

of the lungs, usually involving one or more lobes, that causes consolidation of lung tissue and usually a generalized toxemia.

Pneumonitis—condition of localized acute inflammation of the lung without gross or generalized toxemia.

Post mortem—of, pertaining to or occurring in the time following death.

Potable—fit or suitable for drinking. This term is used to describe water supplies that have been tested and determined to meet or exceed the appropriate health authority standards for drinking water.

Prevalence—number of cases of disease in a specific group at a particular time.

Protozoa—single-celled microscopic animal living chiefly in water. Can be parasitic or beneficial. The common amoeba is an example.

Protein—any of a group of complex organic nitrogenous compounds, usually composed of alpha-amino acids, that form the principal constituents of cell protoplasm in animal and plant tissues.

Proteolytic—used to describe substances, usually enzymes, that attack or digest complex proteins, resulting in simpler proteins or amino acids.

Proventriculus—true or glandular stomach of poultry, lying between the ingluvies (crop) and the ventriculus (gizzard).

Purulent—full of, containing, forming or discharging pus.

Pus—liquid product of in-

flammation composed of dead white blood cells (leukocytes) and cellular fluids.

Raptors—birds of prey, such as eagles, falcons, hawks, owls.

Reactor—animal that has reacted positively to a test for an infectious disease, such as tuberculosis or brucellosis.

Renal—of, pertaining to or located near the kidney.

Reservoir of infectious agents—any humans, animals, arthropods, plants, soil or inanimate matter in which an infectious agent normally lives and multiplies, and on which it depends primarily for survival and reproduces itself in such a manner that it can be transmitted to a susceptible host.

Resistance—sum total of body mechanisms that interpose barriers to the progress of invasion or multiplication of infectious agents or to damage by their toxic products.

Rhinitis—inflammation of the mucous membranes lining the nasal passages.

Riger mortis—stiffness or rigidity that occurs soon after death as a result of coagulation of cell protoplasm proteins.

Ruminant—animal that has four-compartment stomach and chews a cud of food. Cattle, sheep, goats, deer and elk are ruminants.

Salpingitis—imflammation of the oviduct.

Scrotum—pendulous skin sac that encloses and contains the testicles.

Semi-comatose—state of very low consciousness, approaching total unconsciousness or coma.

Septic—of or resulting from absorption of poisonous putrefactive material.

Septicemia—pathogenic organisms, their toxic product and poisonous putrefactive material absorbed into and distributed throughout the body by the circulatory system.

Serological, serologically—pertains to blood serums (sera) with regard to tests for antibodies against specific diseases.

Serosa (serous membrane)—thin membrane that lines most of the closed cavities of the body and covers the outer surface of the viscera. The pleura and peritoneum are serous membranes.

Serotype—classification of a micro-organism as determined by kinds of antigens it contains.

Serous—resembling or composed of blood serum.

Serum—clear liquid portion of the blood.

Sign—any objective evidence of a disease.

Sinus—cavity or hollow space

Sinusitis—inflammation of a sinus cavity. Dehorning cattle often produces a frontal sinusitis.

Spastic—pertaining to or affected by spasm or sudden uncontrollable muscular contractions.

Spinal canal—canal or tube formed by vertebral arches containing the spinal nerve cord.

Spinal cord—thick trunk of nerve tissue that extends down spinal canal from base of the brain to pelvic region.

Spleen—large, highly vascular, ductless visceral organ in upper left abdomen, laying near or across surface of the stomach. The spleen has a complex function in modifying and regulating cellular components of the blood.

Spore—seed of microscopic plants, such as fungi. Also, inactive or resting form of certain bacteria.

Sterile—completely free of living organisms.

Sternum—thin structure of bone and cartilage that forms ventral surface rib cage and serves as an attachment for distal ends of the ribs. Commonly called keel or breastbone when referring to poultry.

Stifle—joint between the hip and the hock. Corresponds to knee of humans.

Subclinical—see inapparent infection.

Subcutaneous—located or attached beneath the skin.

Suppuration—formation or discharge of pus.

Systemic—of, or involving, the entire body.

Tendon—tough, fibrous connective tissue at ends of muscle bundles that attach muscle to bones or cartilage structures.

Thorax—cavity enclosed by the rib cage and the diaphragm. The chest.

Toxemia—generalized poisoning due to absorption and circulation of bacterial products (toxins) formed at a localized source.

Toxin—a poison. Frequently used to refer specifically to a protein or conjugated protein substance produced by plants, certain animals and pathogenic bacteria that is highly toxic for other living organisms.

Toxoid—a portion of bacterial toxin that has no toxicity but still retains ability to stimulate production of antitoxin when injected.

Trauma—wound or injury that injures and destroys tissue.

Trematode—see fluke.

Tumor—mass of new tissue that persists and grows independently of its surrounding structures and has no physiologic function. A neoplasm. Tumors may be classed as benign or malignant.

Udder—mammary glands of cattle and certain other animals. The bovine udder consists of four mammary glands. The equine, ovine and caprine udders consist of two mammary glands. May be called "bag" or "dug."

Ulcer—a loss of substance on a cutaneous or mucous surface with an erosion, disintegration and necrosis of the tissues.

Uremia—an intoxication (poisoning) caused by accumulation in the blood of waste materials normally eliminated in urine. Uremia is a result of inadequate function of the kidneys.

Uterus—hollow muscular abdominal organ of female animals in which the fertilized ovum is implanted and the embryo and fetus are protected and developed. The womb.

Vaccines—products containing high numbers of weakened or killed organisms known to cause a particular disease. They are specific in that a separate vaccine must be used for immunization against each disease.

Vector—carrier. A term applied to flies, mosquitoes, ticks, etc., that are capable of transmitting a disease.

Vehicle—anything that can mechanically carry disease organisms from one source animal to another, such as clothing, food, water, dust.

Vein—vessel through which blood passes from various organs or parts back to the heart.

Ventral—on, or located toward, the lower or bottom surface.

Vertebrae—bones that make up the spinal column, extending from the head to the tail.

Vesicle—small bladder or sac containing liquid. A blister.

Vesicular disease—a disease that includes development of fluid-filled vesicles or blisters in outer layers of the skin or mucous membranes. Vesicles break, leaving raw erosions or ulcers. Vesicular diseases of animals include foot-and-mouth disease, vesicular stomatitis, swine vesicular disease, and vesicular exanthema.

Vestigial—of, or pertaining to, a mark, trace or visible evidence of something no longer present or in existence.

Virus—ultra-microscopic bundle of genetic material capable of multiplying only in living cells. Viruses cause a wide range of disease in plants, animals and humans, such as rabies and measles.

Viscera—internal organs and glands contained in the thoracic and abdominal cavities.

Viscous—sticky, thick, syrupy.

Zoonosis—infection or infectious disease transmissible under natural conditions from vertebrate animals to humans. May be enzootic or epizootic (see endemic and epidemic).

Credits

My special thanks to Kevin Shields who, with typical enthusiasm and high energy, shared with us his photo journalism expertise during the critical weeks before printing deadline researching mountainous files, setting up assignments and editing countless photos that were submitted by cooperators.

Kevin and I want to thank the many persons who contributed photographs. Their submissions arrived on our desks from all over the United States, packaged with generous portions of genuine interest, expert advice and very useful suggestions.

Between the click of the camera and the finished photos that illustrate the Yearbook is the indispensable magic performed by the photo laboratory. The editors thank the many talented people at the USDA Photography Division and at commercial laboratories for the highly professional attention they gave to assure quality photo processing. Special thanks go to USDA's Robert Overby and Charles Flory, who coordinated the processing.

Credit for each photograph is given when the source is known. Prints or duplicate slides of photographs taken for or by USDA are available for a nominal charge from the Photography Division, Office of Information, Room 4407-So., U.S. Department of Agriculture, Washington, D.C. 20250.

Marie T. Sebrechts
Photo Coordinator

Design, Printing, Editing

Art Direction:
George Baka, Design Division, Office of Information

Design and Production:
William J. Kircher & Associates, Inc.

Printing Coordinator:
Warren Bell, Publishing Division, Office of Information

Editor:
Jack Hayes, Publishing Division, Assistant, Mocile C. Trotter

Publishing Division Proofreaders:
Earthaline Harried, Delores Harris, Elizabeth Mitchell

Photo Credits—Color Section
Gene Alexander: ii bottom left, xxv middle
John E. Bowen: ii bottom right, xi mid right, xxxi top left, xxxii top right
J.L. Carlson: iii top left, xxxii bottom
William E. Carnahan: iii mid right, xvii top left
R. Elliott: iii middle left, vi top, xx bottom, xxviii mid left & right
Charles Ford: x bottom left
John Kucharski: xxv bottom
Llewellyn: xxiv top
Tim McCabe: xiii top and bottom, xiv top & bottom, xxvii bottom, xxviii top
Charles O'Rear: xxvi bottom
Karen Rusinski: vii top, ix top, xxi top right & bottom
Marie Sebrechts: ii top left, iii top right & bottom, iv, v bottom, vi bottom, viii, x bottom right, xi top left & bottom, xii, xiii mid left, xiv mid left, xvi bottom left & right, xvii top right & bottom, xviii bottom, xix top left & bottom, xxi top left, xxv top, xxvi top, xxvii top, xxix top left & right, xxx top & bottom, xxxii middle left
Kevin Shields: ii top right, vii bottom left & mid right, xiv mid right, xv top, xviii top, xix top right, xxiv mid left & mid right & bottom right, xxxi top right & bottom

Index

Index

Scientific Names

Index   645

LC 84-601135

☆ U.S. Government Printing Office: 1984-451-784